Middle School 2-1

기말고사 완벽대비

KB084535

적중100

영어 기출 문제집

중**2**

시사 | 송미정

Best Collection

구성과 특징

교과서의 주요 학습 내용을 중심으로 학습 영역별 특성에 맞춰 단계별로 다양한 학습 기회를 제공하여 단원별 학습능력 평가는 물론 중간 및 기말고사 시험 등에 완벽하게 대비할 수 있도록 내용을 구성

Words & Expressions

Step1 Key Words 단원별 핵심 단어 설명 및 풀이
Key Expression 단원별 핵심 숙어 및 관용어 설명
Word Power 반대 또는 비슷한 뜻 단어 배우기
English Dictionary 영어로 배우는 영어 단어

Step2 실력평가 단원별 수시평가 대비 주관식, 객관식 문제풀이

Step3 서술형 대비 학업성취도 및 수행능력평가 대비 서술형 문제풀이

Conversation

Step1 핵심 의사소통 의사소통에 필요한 주요 표현 방법 요약
핵심 Check 기본적인 표현 방법 및 활용능력 확인

Step2 대화문 익히기 상황에 따른 대화문 활용 및 연습

Step3 기본평가 시험대비 기초 학습 능력 평가

Step4 실력평가 단원별 수시평가 대비 주관식, 객관식 문제풀이

Step5 서술형 대비 학업성취도 및 수행능력평가 대비 서술형 문제풀이

Grammar

Step1 주요 문법 단원별 주요 문법 사항과 예문을 알기 쉽게 설명
핵심 Check 기본 문법사항에 대한 이해 여부 확인

Step2 기본평가 시험대비 기초 학습 능력 평가

Step3 실력평가 단원별 수시평가 대비 주관식, 객관식 문제풀이

Step4 서술형 대비 학업성취도 및 수행능력평가 대비 서술형 문제풀이

Reading

Step1 구문 분석 단원별로 제시된 문장에 대한 구문별 분석과 내용 설명
확인문제 문장에 대한 기본적인 이해와 인지능력 확인

Step2 확인학습A 빈칸 채우기를 통한 문장 완성 능력 확인

Step3 확인학습B 제시된 우리말을 영어로 완성하여 작문 능력 키우기

Step4 실력평가 단원별 수시평가 대비 주관식, 객관식 문제풀이

Step5 서술형 대비 학업성취도 및 수행능력평가 대비 서술형 문제풀이
교과서 구석구석 교과서에 나오는 기타 문장까지 완벽 학습

Composition

|영역별 핵심문제|
단어 및 어휘, 대화문, 문법, 독해 등 각 영역별 기출문제의 출제 유형을 분석하여 실전에 대비하고 연습할 수 있도록 문제를 배열

|서술형 실전 및 창의사고력 문제|
학교 시험에서 점차 늘어나는 서술형 시험에 집중 대비하고 고득점을 취득하는데 만전을 기하기 위한 학습 코너

|단원별 예상문제|
기출문제를 분석한 후 새로운 시험 출제 경향을 더하여 새롭게 출제될 수 있는 문제를 포함하여 시험에 완벽하게 대비할 수 있도록 준비

|단원별 모의고사|
영역별, 단계별 학습을 모두 마친 후 실전 연습을 위한 모의고사

INSIGHT on the textbook

교과서 파헤치기

- 단어Test1~2 영어 단어 우리말 쓰기와 우리말을 영어 단어로 쓰기
- 대화문Test1~2 대화문 빈칸 완성 및 전체 대화문 쓰기
- 본문Test1~5 빈칸 완성, 우리말 쓰기, 문장 배열연습, 영어 작문하기 복습 등 단계별 반복 학습을 통해 교과서 지문에 대한 완벽한 습득
- 구석구석지문Test1~2 지문 빈칸 완성 및 전문 영어로 쓰기

Contents

Lesson 3

The School Club Activity Day

 의사소통 기능

- 능력 여부 묻기
  A: I don't know how to swim. Do you know how to?
  B: Yes, I can teach you.
- 좋아하는 것 표현하기
  A: What do you enjoy doing when you have free time?
  B: I enjoy painting pictures of people in the park.

 언어 형식

- 의문사 + to부정사
  We also teach children **how to play** musical
  instruments as a service to our community.

- 주격 관계대명사
  Anyone **who** likes to paint can join.

교과서

Words & Expressions

Key Words

- **activity** [æktívəti] 명 활동
- **actually** [ǽktʃuəli] 부 실제로, 사실은
- **bake** [beik] 동 (빵 등을) 굽다
- **bit** [bit] 명 조금, 한 조각[가지], 부분 *beat 때리다,치다*
- **bright** [brait] 형 밝은, 똑똑한
- **clothes** [klouz] 명 옷, 의상
- **club** [klʌb] 명 동아리, 클럽
- **concert** [ka:nsərt] 명 연주회
- **cook** [kuk] 동 요리하다 명 요리사
- **cooking** [kúkiŋ] 명 요리, 음식
- **dolphin** [dálfin] 명 돌고래
- **doughnut** [dóunət] 명 도넛
- **drone** [droun] 명 무인 비행기
- **easy** [í:zi] 형 쉬운
- **elementary school** 초등학교
- **experience** [ikspíəriəns] 명 경험, 경력
- **fly** [flai] 동 (항공기, 우주선, 인공위성 등을) 조종하다, 날게 하다
- **free time** 여가 시간
- **garden** [gá:rdn] 명 정원
- **get** [get] 동 사다, 획득하다
- **grow** [grou] 동 (동식물을) 기르다, 자라다
- **hold** [hould] 동 (모임, 식 등을) 개최하다 *잡다*
- **however** [hauévər] 부 그러나, 하지만

- **interest** [íntərəst] 명 관심 동 ~의 관심[흥미]을 끌다
- **introduce** [ìntrədjú:s] 동 소개하다
- **join** [dʒɔin] 동 참여하다, 가입하다
- **leader** [lí:dər] 명 지도자, 대표
- **library** [láibrèri] 도서관
- **main gate** 명 정문
- **musical instrument** 악기
- **neighbor** [néibər] 명 이웃
- **neighborhood** [néibərhùd] 명 동네, (도시 내의 한 단위) 지역 *동네*
- **note** [nout] 명 음, 음표
- **opportunity** [àpərtjú:nəti] 명 기회
- **orchestra** [ɔ́:rkəstrə] 명 오케스트라, 교향악단
- **own** [oun] 형 (소유격 다음에서 강조어로 쓰여) 자기 자신의
- **practice** [prǽktis] 명 연습 동 연습하다
- **present** [préznt] 명 선물 형 참석한
- **project** [prádʒekt] 명 사업, 계획
- **service** [sə́:rvis] 명 봉사, 유익한[전문적인] 활동
- **several** [sévərəl] 형 몇몇의
- **Spanish** [spǽniʃ] 명 스페인어 형 스페인의
- **vegetable** [védʒətəbl] 명 채소
- **volunteer** [vàləntíər] 동 봉사하다
- **walk** [wɔ:k] 동 (사람·동물을) 걷게 하다

Key Expressions

- **a bit**: 조금
- **a little bit**: 아주 조금
- **as a result**: 결과적으로
- **ask for help**: 도움을 청하다
- **at first**: 처음에
- **at night**: 밤에
- **be good at**: ~을 잘하다 *-ing를자격씀*
- **change into**: ~로 변화시키다[바꾸다]
- **enjoy+-ing**: ~하는 것을 즐기다
- **fall into**: ~에 빠지다

- **get better**: (병·상황 등이) 나아지다
- **have a great time**: 좋은 시간을 보내다
- **how to**+동사원형: ~하는 방법
- **let**+목적어+동사원형: …가 ~하게 하다 *have, make 사역동사*
- **look at**: ~을 보다
- **look for**: ~을 찾다
- **participate in**: ~에 참여하다
- **thank for**: ~에 대해 감사하다
- **watch out (for)**: (~에 대해서) 조심하다
- **would like to** +동사원형: ~하고 싶다

Word Power

※ 서로 반대되는 뜻을 가진 단어
- **bright**(밝은) ↔ **dark**(어두운)
- **easy**(쉬운) ↔ **difficult**(어려운)

※ 서로 비슷한 뜻을 가진 단어
- **actually**(실제로, 사실은) : **really** (정말로, 실제로)
- **bright**(총명한) : **clever**(영리한)
- **get**(사다, 획득하다) : **obtain**(획득하다), **gain**(얻다, 입수하다)
- **grow**((식물을) 재배하다) : **farm**(경작하다)
- **leader**(지도자, 대표) : **chief**(장, 우두머리)
- **practice**(연습) : **training**(훈련), **exercise**(연습)
- **project**(사업, 계획) : **plan**(계획)
- **several**(몇몇의) : **a few**(약간의), **some**(조금의) *a few/거의 없는*
- **foolish**(어리석은) : **stupid**(어리석은)
- **join**(참여하다, 가입하다) : **enter**(~에 들어가다)
- **opportunity**(기회) : **chance**(기회)
- **present**(선물) : **gift**(선물)

English Dictionary

- **a bit** 조금, 약간
  → slightly or to a small degree(= a little)
  약간, 적은 정도로
- **bake** (빵 등을) 굽다
  → to cook something using dry heat, in an oven
  오븐 안에서 건조한 열을 사용하여 무언가를 요리하는 것
- **bright** 밝은
  → strong and easy to see
  강렬하며 쉽게 보이는
- **club** 동아리
  → organization for people who share a particular interest or enjoy similar activities, or a group of people who meet together to do something they are interested in
  특정한 흥미를 공유하거나 비슷한 활동을 즐기는 사람들을 위한 단체 또는 그들이 관심 있는 무언가를 위해서 같이 만나는 사람들의 모임
- **drone** 무인 비행기
  → aircraft that does not have a pilot, but is operated by radio
  조종사가 없지만 무선으로 작동되는 비행기
- **garden** 정원
  → a part of the area next to a house, which has plants and flowers in it
  집 옆에 식물과 꽃이 있는 지역의 일부
- **grow** 자라다
  → to develop or increase in size or length
  크기나 길이가 발달하거나 증가하다
- **hold** (모임·식 등을) 개최하다
  → to have a meeting, party, election etc in a particular place or at a particular time
  회의, 파티, 선거 등을 특정한 장소 또는 특정한 시간에 가지다
- **join** 참여하다, 가입하다
  → 1. to become a member of an organization, society, or group
  조직, 사회 또는 그룹의 구성원이 되다
  2. to begin to take part in an activity that other people are involved in
  다른 사람들이 관련된 활동에 참여하기 시작하다
- **leader** 지도자, 대표
  → the person who directs or controls a group, organization, country, etc.
  그룹, 조직, 국가 등을 총괄하거나 통제하는 사람
- **musical instrument** 악기
  → something that you use for playing music, such as a piano or guitar
  피아노나 기타와 같은 음악을 연주하기 위해 사용하는 어떤 것
- **neighbor** 이웃
  → someone who lives next to you or near you
  당신의 옆이나 근처에 사는 어떤 사람
- **neighborhood** 인근, 이웃 사람들, 동네
  → the area around you or around a particular place, or the people who live there
  당신 또는 특정한 장소 주변의 지역 또는 거기에 사는 사람들
- **opportunity** 기회
  → a chance to do something or an occasion when it is easy for you to do something
  무엇인가를 할 기회 또는 당신이 무엇인가 하는 것이 쉬운 때
- **orchestra** 오케스트라, 교향악단
  → a large group of musicians playing many different kinds of instruments and led by a conductor
  많은 여러 종류의 악기를 연주하는 음악가들과 지휘자에 의해 지휘되는 큰 규모의 집단
- **practice** 연습하다
  → to do something regularly in order to do it better
  어떤 것을 더 잘하기 위해서 규칙적으로 그것을 하다
- **walk** [동물을] 걷게 하다
  → to take a dog for a walk for exercise
  개를 운동시키기 위해 산책시키다

01 다음 짝지어진 두 단어의 관계가 같도록 빈칸에 알맞은 단어를 쓰시오.

> increase : decrease – difficult : _____

① easy ② hard ③ different
④ bright ⑤ early

[02~03] 다음 빈칸에 들어갈 말로 적절한 것은?

02

> I'm _____ some bread in an oven.

① baking ② eating ③ biting
④ breaking ⑤ buying

03

> They use organic methods of _____ vegetables.

① growing ② flying
③ forgetting ④ repairing
⑤ falling

04 다음 밑줄 친 부분과 의미가 가장 가까운 것을 고르시오.

> It was a valuable opportunity to see how rich people lived.

① chance ② experience ③ effort
④ effect ⑤ situation

서답형
05 다음 영영 풀이에 해당하는 단어를 주어진 철자로 시작하여 쓰시오.

> someone who lives next to you or near you

➡ n_____

서답형
06 다음 괄호 안의 단어를 문맥에 맞게 알맞은 형태로 고쳐 쓰시오.

> She is the _____ of the most powerful country in Europe. (lead)

07 다음 대화의 빈칸에 들어갈 말로 적절한 것은?

> A: What festival is the most famous in New York?
> B: It is Halloween festival. New York City _____ the largest Halloween parade in the U.S. every year.

① grows ② finds ③ falls
④ takes ⑤ holds

08 다음 중 밑줄 친 부분의 뜻풀이가 바르지 않은 것은?

① What's the most popular free time activity for teenagers? (활동)
② I really miss your cooking. (요리)
③ She doesn't like bright colors. (밝은)
④ He plays the piano perfectly even though he cannot read a single note. (메모)
⑤ Korea has already won several medals. (몇 개의)

서답형
09 다음 우리말에 맞게 빈칸에 알맞은 말을 쓰시오.

> Anyone _____ loves books _____ _____ our event! (책을 좋아하는 사람은 누구라도 우리의 행사에 참여할 수 있어요!)

01 다음 〈보기〉와 같은 관계가 되도록 빈칸에 주어진 철자로 알맞은 말을 쓰시오.

┌─ 보기 ┤
happy – pleased
└─────────

(1) gain – g_____
(2) gift – p_____

[02~03] 다음 빈칸에 공통으로 들어갈 말을 쓰시오. (대·소문자 무시)

02
• The more you _____, the more you want.
• _____ a great time before the new semester begins!

03
• _____ can I join this club?
• I want to learn _____ to do that.

04 다음 빈칸에 알맞은 어구를 〈보기〉에서 골라 쓰시오. (형태 변화 가능)

┌─ 보기 ┤
introduce / concert / doughnut / dolphin
└─────────

(1) Let me _____ my friend Caden to you.
(2) I saw many _____ swimming in the sea.
(3) You should fry a _____ for 1 or 2 minutes.
(4) The orchestra held a _____ at Seoul Arts Center to help children in North Korea.

05 다음 괄호 안의 단어를 문맥에 맞게 알맞은 형태로 고쳐 쓰시오.

(1) What kind of club _____ do you like? (act)
(2) This _____ is great for shopping. (neighbor)

06 다음 주어진 우리말에 맞게 빈칸을 채우시오. (철자가 주어진 것도 있음)

(1) 나는 항상 싼 옷을 산다.
➡ I always buy cheap c_____.
(2) 어떻게 하면 우리의 제품을 많은 사람들에게 소개할 수 있을까요?
➡ How can we _____ our products to a lot of people?
(3) 나는 당신의 기사를 많은 흥미를 가지고 읽었다.
➡ I read your article with great _____.
(4) 너는 많은 신선한 과일과 야채를 먹어야 한다.
➡ You must eat a lot of fresh fruit and _____.

07 다음 우리말과 같은 뜻이 되도록 주어진 단어를 알맞은 순서로 배열하시오.

┌─────────
│ 내가 이 동아리에 가입한다면, 나는 매우 열심히 연습할 것이다. (if, club, very, join, I, I, this, practice, will, hard)
└─────────

➡ _____

Conversation

1 능력 여부 묻기

> **A** I don't know how to swim. Do you know how to? 나는 수영하는 법을 알지 못해. 너는 방법을 알고 있니?
> **B** Yes, I can teach you. 응, 내가 가르쳐 줄 수 있어.

■ 'how to+동사원형'은 '~하는 방법, 어떻게 ~하는지'의 의미로, 'Do you know how to + 동사원형 ~?' 을 이용해 상대방의 능력이나 무언가를 하는 방법에 대해 물을 수 있다.

능력 여부 묻기

- Do you know how to + 동사원형 ~?
- Can you + 동사원형 ~?

능력 여부 대답하기

- 긍정: Yes, I do[can]./ Of course I do[can].
- 부정: No, I don't./ No, I can't.

■ '의문사+to부정사'는 명사구로 문장에서 주어, 목적어, 보어로 쓰일 수 있다. 여기에 사용될 수 있는 의 문사는 what, when, where, how, which, whom 등이 있다.

의문사+to부정사

- what to부정사: 무엇을 ~할지
- where to부정사: 어디에서 ~할지
- how to부정사: 어떻게 ~할지, ~하는 방법
- when to부정사: 언제 ~할지
- which to부정사: 어느 것을 ~할지
- whom to부정사: 누구를 ~할지

■ '의문사+to부정사'는 '의문사+주어+should 동사원형'으로 바꾸어 쓸 수 있다.
Tell me how to do it. (내가 그것을 어떻게 해야 할지 말해 주세요.)
= Tell me how I should do it.

핵심 Check

1. 우리말과 일치하도록 빈칸에 알맞은 말을 쓰시오.

   He taught me _____ _____ _____ my new cellphone.

   (그는 나에게 새 휴대 전화를 사용하는 법을 가르쳐 주었다.)

2. 우리말과 일치하도록 주어진 단어를 배열하여 문장을 완성하시오.

   _____ (learn, pictures, I, to, good, want,

   how, take, to) (나는 좋은 사진을 찍는 법을 배우고 싶다.)

2 좋아하는 것 표현하기

> **A** What do you enjoy doing when you have free time? 너는 여가 시간에 뭐 하는 것을 즐기니?
>
> **B** I enjoy painting pictures of people in the park. 나는 공원에서 사람들을 그리는 것을 즐겨.

■ 'I enjoy 동명사'는 '나는 ~하는 것을 즐긴다.'는 의미로 자신이 좋아하는 것을 나타내는 표현이다. 주로 취미 등을 묻는 'What do you enjoy doing when you have free time?', 'What do you usually do in your free time?' 등에 대한 응답으로 쓰인다.

좋아하는 것 표현하기

- I enjoy 동명사 ~.
- I like 동명사/to부정사 ~.
- I love 동명사/to부정사 ~.

■ 동사를 주어, 목적어, 보어의 자리에 쓰기 위해서 동명사 또는 to부정사를 사용할 수 있다. 하지만, 특정한 동사의 목적어로 동명사나 to부정사가 사용될 때는 그 동사의 종류에 따라 동명사를 사용할지, 아니면 to부정사를 사용할지 잘 선택해야 한다.

■ enjoy는 동명사를 목적어로 사용할 수 있고, want는 to부정사를 목적어로 사용한다. like와 love는 동명사와 to부정사 둘 다 목적어로 사용할 수 있다.

핵심 Check

3. 다음 대화의 우리말과 일치하도록 빈칸에 알맞은 말을 쓰시오.

A: _____ enjoy _____ when you have _____ ?
(너는 여가 시간에 뭐 하는 것을 즐기니?)

B: _____. (나는 음악을 듣는 것을 즐겨.)

4. 다음 그림을 보고, 주어진 단어를 사용하여 빈칸을 완성하시오.

A: What do you like to do on weekends?

B: _____. (enjoy)

Listen & Speak 1 A

G: ❶Do you know ❷how to make a paper cat?

B: Of course. ❸It's easy.

G: 종이 고양이 만드는 법을 알고 있니?
B: 물론이지. 그건 쉬워.

❶ 'Do you know ∼?'는 어떤 것을 아는지 질문할 때 사용한다. 비슷한 의미로 'Can you tell me ∼?'를 대신 사용할 수 있다.

❷ how to부정사: 어떻게 ∼할지, ∼하는 방법   ❸ 인칭대명사 It은 how to make a paper cat을 가리킨다.

Check(√) True or False

(1) The boy knows how to make a paper cat.　　　　　　　　　　T ☐ F ☐

(2) The way to make a paper cat is not difficult.　　　　　　　　T ☐ F ☐

Listen & Speak 1 B-1

G: I heard ❶you went to Yuna's violin concert yesterday. ❷How was it?

B: It was great. ❸I hope I can play the violin ❹like her someday.

G: I didn't know ❺you knew how to play the violin.

B: I can, but ❻I'm not good at it yet.

G: 어제 유나의 바이올린 콘서트에 갔다고 들었어. 어땠니?
B: 좋았어. 나도 언젠가 그녀처럼 바이올린을 연주할 수 있기를 바라.
G: 나는 네가 바이올린 연주하는 법을 아는지 몰랐어.
B: 할 수 있어, 그러나 아직 잘하지는 못해.

❶ heard와 you 사이에 명사절을 이끄는 접속사 that이 생략되어 있다. 'you went to Yuna's violin concert yesterday'는 heard의 목적어로 사용되었다.

❷ 과거의 경험에 대해 묻고자 할 때 'How was ∼?' 표현을 사용한다. 과거의 경험에 대한 답변이 되어야 하므로 대답의 동사도 과거형을 사용한다. 여기서 it은 Yuna's violin concert를 가리킨다.

❸ 'I hope I can 동사원형 ∼.'은 자신이 어떤 것을 할 수 있기를 희망하거나 기대를 한다는 표현이다.

❹ like: (전치사) ∼처럼, ∼와 같이

❺ know와 you 사이에 명사절을 이끄는 접속사 that이 생략되어 있다. how to부정사: 어떻게 ∼할지, ∼하는 방법

❻ be good at: ∼을 잘하다

Check(√) True or False

(3) Yuna is good at playing the violin.　　　　　　　　　　　T ☐ F ☐

(4) The girl knew that the boy knew how to play the violin.　　　T ☐ F ☐

Listen & Speak 1 B-2

G: ❶Look at these pictures. I ❷grew these vegetablcs ❸myself. I have my ❹own garden.

B: Cool! Do you know how to cook the vegetables you grow, too?

G: Yes, my grandmother ❺taught me.

G: 이 사진들 좀 봐. 나는 이 채소들을 직접 길렀어. 나는 내 정원이 있어.
B: 멋지다! 네가 재배한 채소로 요리하는 법도 아니?
G: 응, 할머니께서 내게 가르쳐 주셨어.

❶ look at: ∼을 보다 pictures가 복수형이므로, this가 아닌 these를 사용한다.

❷ grew는 grow의 과거형이다. grow: [식물을] 재배하다

❸ 재귀대명사의 강조 용법으로 주어 'I'를 강조하고 있다.

❹ own은 소유격 다음에서 강조어로 사용한다. own: 자기 자신의, 직접 ∼한

❺ taught는 teach의 과거형 동사이다.

Check(√) True or False

(5) In the pictures, there are vegetables.　　　　　　　　　　T ☐ F ☐

(6) The girl doesn't know how to cook the vegetables.　　　　　T ☐ F ☐

Listen & Speak 2 A

A: Do you enjoy ❶looking at the stars at night?
G: Yes, I ❷love doing that.

❶ enjoy는 동명사를 목적어로 취하는 동사이다. look at: ~을 보다 at night: 밤에
❷ love는 목적어로 동명사와 to부정사를 취할 수 있다. love doing it = love to do it / doing that=looking at the stars

Listen & Speak 2 B-1

B: Do you ❶enjoy reading books, Yumi?
G: Yes, I love reading science books. ❷How about you?
B: I love reading books, too.
G: Then, ❸let's go to the library ❹after school today.

❶ enjoy(~을 즐기다)를 사용해서 좋아하는 것을 말할 수 있다. enjoy는 목적어로 동명사를 취하는 동사로 reading을 사용해야 한다.
❷ 'How about you?'는 '너는 어때?'라고 묻는 내용이다. 'What about you?'로 바꿔 쓸 수 있다.
❸ 'Let's+동사원형'은 '~하자'라는 의미로, 제안하는 말을 할 때 쓴다. go to 장소: ~에 가다
❹ after school: 방과 후에

Listen & Speak 2 B-2

G: ❶What did you do on the weekend, Minsu?
B: ❷I made breakfast ❸for my family.
G: Do you enjoy cooking?
B: Yes, I'm a good ❹cook! My family loves my ❺cooking.

❶ 과거에 무엇을 했는지 묻고 싶을 때에는 What did you do?라고 묻는다. 특정한 때를 넣어 어떤 날에 무엇을 했냐고 물을 수도 있다.
❷ 과거에 무엇을 했는지 묻는 질문에 대한 대답이므로, 과거형 동사를 사용해야 한다.
❸ make는 간접목적어를 직접목적어 뒤로 보낼 때 for를 붙인다.
❹ cook: (동) 요리하다 (명) 요리사 / 이 문장에서는 명사로 썼다.
❺ cooking: 요리, 음식

Listen & Speak 2 B-3

B: Jiyun, that's a pretty backpack! Where did you ❶get it?
G: My sister made ❷it for me.
B: Wow! She's a really good designer.
G: Yes, she is. And she enjoys making ❸clothes, too.

❶ get: 얻다, 사다
❷ it은 앞에 나온 a backpack을 가리킨다.
❸ clothes: 옷, 의상 cloth: 천, 옷감 cloths: 옷감들

Real-Life Zone A

B: Hello, Kate. I'm Hamin, the ❶leader of the Nanum Orchestra. ❷Thank you for your interest in our club.
G: Hi. Nice to meet you.
B: You play the violin? ❸When did you start playing the violin?
G: I started learning ❹how to play the violin when I was ten.
B: ❺Do you have any experience playing in a group?
G: Yes. Actually, I was a member of an orchestra ❻when I was in elementary school.
B: Great. We also ❼volunteer to teach children. Do you enjoy teaching others?
G: I have no experience teaching others. But I enjoy working with people, so ❽I'd like to try.
B: Good. I think we'll have a great time playing together. Welcome to the Nanum Orchestra.

❶ leader: 지도자, 대표
❷ 'Thank you for ~.'는 감사를 표현하는 말로 for 다음에 감사의 이유나 원인이 나온다. interest: 관심
❸ 'When did you 동사원형 ~?'은 '너 언제 ~했니?'의 의미로, 과거에 언제 어떠한 일을 했는지 묻는 질문이다.
❹ how to부정사: 어떻게 ~할지, ~하는 방법
❺ Do you have any experience~?는 어떤 일을 한 경험이 있는지 물을 때 쓰인다.
❻ when: (접) ~할 때
❼ volunteer: 자원봉사하다
❽ 'I'd'는 'I would'를 줄여서 표현한 것이다. would like to 동사원형: ~하고 싶다

● 다음 우리말과 일치하도록 빈칸에 알맞은 말을 쓰시오.

Listen & Speak 1 A

A: Do you _____ _____ _____ make a paper cat?

B: Of course. It's easy.

Listen & Speak 1 B

1. G: I _____ _____ _____ _____ Yuna's violin concert yesterday. _____ was it?

   B: It was great. _____ _____ _____ _____ _____ the violin like her someday.

   G: I didn't know you _____ _____ _____ _____ _____ _____ .

   B: I can, but I'm not _____ _____ it yet.

2. G: Look _____ these pictures. I ____ these vegetables _____ . I have my _____ garden.

   B: Cool! Do you know _____ _____ _____ the vegetables you grow, too?

   G: Yes, my grandmother _____ me.

Listen & Speak 2 A

A: Do you enjoy _____ _____ the stars _____ _____ ?

G: Yes, I love doing that.

Listen & Speak 2 B

1. B: _____ _____ _____ reading books, Yumi?

   G: Yes, I _____ _____ science books. How _____ you?

   B: I love _____ books, too.

   G: Then, let's _____ to _____ _____ after school today.

2. G: _____ _____ _____ _____ on the weekend, Minsu?

   B: I _____ breakfast for my family.

   G: _____ _____ _____ _____ ?

   B: Yes, I'm a good _____ ! My family loves my _____ .

해석

G: 종이 고양이 만드는 법을 알고 있니?
B: 물론이지. 그건 쉬워.

1. G: 어제 유나의 바이올린 콘서트에 갔다고 들었어. 어땠니?
   B: 좋았어. 나도 언젠가 그녀처럼 바이올린을 연주할 수 있기를 바라.
   G: 나는 네가 바이올린 연주하는 법을 아는지 몰랐어.
   B: 할 수 있어. 그러나 아직 잘하지는 못해.
2. G: 이 사진들 좀 봐. 나는 이 채소를 직접 길렀어. 나는 내 자신의 정원이 있어.
   B: 멋지다! 네가 기르는 채소로 요리하는 법도 아니?
   G: 응, 할머니께서 내게 가르쳐 주셨어.

B: 너는 밤에 별을 보는 것을 즐기니?
G: 응, 나는 별을 보는 것을 아주 좋아해.

1. B: 유미야, 너는 책 읽는 것을 즐기니?
   G: 응, 나는 과학 책을 읽는 것을 좋아해. 너는 어때?
   B: 나도 책 읽는 것을 좋아해.
   G: 그럼 오늘 방과 후에 도서관 가자.
2. G: 민수야, 주말에 뭐 했니?
   B: 가족을 위해 아침을 만들었어.
   G: 너는 요리를 즐기니?
   B: 응, 나는 훌륭한 요리사야! 우리 가족은 내 요리를 좋아해.

3. **B:** Jiyun, that's a pretty backpack! _____ did you _____ it?

   G: My sister _____ _____ _____ _____ .

   B: Wow! She's a really good _____ .

   G: Yes, she is. And she _____ _____ _____ , too.

Real-Life Zone A

B: Hello, Kate. I'm Hamin, _____ _____ of the Nanum Orchestra. Thank you for your _____ in our club.

G: Hi. Nice to meet you.

B: You play the violin? _____ _____ _____ _____ _____ the violin?

G: I started learning _____ _____ _____ _____ _____ _____ I was ten.

B: Do you have any _____ _____ in a group?

G: Yes. Actually, I was a member of _____ _____ _____ I was in _____ school.

B: Great. We also _____ _____ _____ children. _____ _____ _____ _____ others?

G: I have no _____ teaching others. But I _____ _____ _____ people, so I'd like to try.

B: Good. I think we'll _____ a great time playing together. Welcome to the Nanum Orchestra.

Wrap Up

B: These cookies _____ so _____ . Did you make them?

G: Yes. I _____ _____ _____ yesterday. I enjoy _____ . I'm _____ _____ make doughnuts this Saturday.

B: Oh, I _____ _____ _____ _____ _____ _____ doughnuts. Is it difficult?

G: Not _____ all. You can come to my house and join me if you want.

B: Thanks, Bora. What _____ should I come?

G: At 2:00.

B: _____ good. _____ you then.

해석

3. B: 지윤아, 그거 예쁜 배낭이네! 어디서 샀어?
   G: 언니가 내게 만들어 준 거야.
   B: 와! 그녀는 정말 훌륭한 디자이너구나.
   G: 응, 그래. 그리고 그녀는 옷 만드는 것도 즐겨.

B: 안녕, 케이트. 나는 나눔 오케스트라의 대표 하민이야. 우리 동아리에 관심을 가져줘서 고마워.
G: 안녕. 만나서 반가워.
B: 너는 바이올린을 연주하니? 언제 바이올린 연주를 시작했니?
G: 10살 때 바이올린을 연주하는 법을 배우기 시작했어.
B: 그룹에서 연주해 본 경험이 있니?
G: 응. 사실 나는 초등학교 때 오케스트라 단원이었어.
B: 좋아. 우리는 자원봉사로 아이들도 가르쳐. 다른 사람들을 가르치는 것을 즐기니?
G: 나는 다른 사람들을 가르친 경험이 없어. 그러나 나는 사람들과 일하는 것을 즐겨, 그래서 나는 해보고 싶어.
B: 좋아. 나는 우리가 함께 연주하며 좋은 시간을 보낼 것이라고 생각해. 나눔 오케스트라에 온 걸 환영해.

B: 이 쿠키들은 정말 맛있어 보여. 네가 만들었니?
G: 응. 어제 내가 직접 만들었어. 나는 제빵을 즐겨. 이번 주 토요일에 도넛을 만들 예정이야.
B: 오, 나는 도넛 만드는 법을 배우고 싶어. 그건 어렵니?
G: 전혀 아니야. 네가 원한다면 우리 집에 와서 같이 해도 돼.
B: 고마워, 보라야. 내가 몇 시에 가야 해?
G: 2시에.
B: 좋아. 그때 보자.

[01~02] 다음 대화의 빈칸에 알맞은 말은?

01

A: What do you enjoy doing when you have free time?

B: _____

① I went shopping.

② I want to have free time.

③ I will go to the movie with my friends.

④ I enjoy painting pictures of people in the park.

⑤ I don't like to play computer games.

02

A: Do you know _____?

B: Of course. It's easy.

① how to make a paper cat

② what to make a paper cat

③ making a paper cat

④ how making a paper cat

⑤ that I can make a paper cat

03 다음 주어진 문장과 의미하는 것이 같은 문장을 고르시오.

Do you know how to make doughnuts?

① Do you want to make doughnuts?

② Are you practicing making doughnuts?

③ Do you mind making doughnuts?

④ Can you make doughnuts?

⑤ Why don't you make doughnuts?

04 다음 문장의 빈칸에 알맞은 것을 모두 고르시오.

G: Look at these pictures. I grew these vegetables myself. I have my own garden.

B: Cool! Do you know how to cook the vegetables you grow, too?

G: (A)_____, my grandmother taught me.

① Yes, I do　　② No, I can't　　③ Of course

④ Not at all　　⑤ Yes, I am

[01~03] 다음 대화를 읽고 물음에 답하시오.

G: I heard you went to Yuna's violin concert yesterday. (①)

B: It was great. (②) I hope I can play the violin (A)like her someday. (③)

G: I didn't know you knew how to play the violin. (④)

B: I can, but I'm not good at it yet. (⑤)

01 위 대화의 ①~⑤ 중 다음 주어진 말이 들어갈 알맞은 곳은?

How was it?

① ② ③ ④ ⑤

 밑줄 친 (A)like와 같은 의미로 쓴 문장을 고르시오.

① I don't know why he doesn't like me.

② I don't like to study English.

③ I could dance like that!

④ Why do you like to climb the mountain?

⑤ She likes to watch TV all day.

03 위 대화의 내용과 일치하지 <u>않는</u> 것은?

① The boy thinks that Yuna's violin concert was great.

② The boy thinks he is good at playing the violin.

③ The boy went to Yuna's violin concert.

④ Yuna's violin concert was held yesterday.

⑤ The boy knows how to play the violin.

04 다음 대화의 빈칸에 알맞은 말은?

A: I don't know how to speak Spanish.

_____

B: Yes, I can teach you.

① Do you know how to?

② Why don't we learn to speak Spanish?

③ What are you going to speak?

④ How do you say this in Spanish?

⑤ What are you good at?

05 다음 중 짝지어진 대화가 <u>어색한</u> 것은?

① A: Do you know how to use the washing machine?

B: Yes. I do.

② A: Do you know how to play the guitar?

B: No, I don't.

③ A: What do you do after school?

B: I enjoy drawing cartoons.

④ A: What do you like to do in your free time?

B: I enjoy reading books. How about you?

⑤ A: Do you know how to take pictures?

B: Of course I am.

서답형
06 (A)와 (B)에 주어진 단어를 이용해 빈칸에 들어갈 수 있는 말을 쓰시오.

A: Do you enjoy (A)_____(look) at the stars at night?

G: Yes, I love (B)_____(do) that.

[07~09] 다음 대화를 읽고 물음에 답하시오.

B: Jiyun, that's a pretty backpack! (①)
G: (②) My sister made it for me. (③)
B: Wow! She's a really good designer. (④)
G: (A)_____ (⑤) And she enjoys making clothes, too.

07 위 대화의 ①~⑤ 중 다음 주어진 말이 들어갈 알맞은 곳은?

> Where did you get it?

① ② ③ ④ ⑤

08 빈칸 (A)에 알맞은 말을 고르시오.

① Yes, she does. ② Yes, she can.
③ No, she isn't. ④ No, she doesn't.
⑤ Yes, she is.

09 위 대화의 내용과 일치하지 <u>않는</u> 것은?

① Jiyun's sister made her a backpack.
② Jiyun knows how to make a backpack.
③ Jiyun's sister is a good designer.
④ Jiyun's sister enjoys making clothes.
⑤ Jiyun has a sister.

[10~13] 다음 대화를 읽고 물음에 답하시오.

B: Hello, Kate. I'm Hamin, the leader of the Nanum Orchestra. Thank you for your interest in our club.
G: Hi. Nice to meet you.
B: You play the violin? When did you start playing the violin? (①)
G: (the, I, I, ten, started, when, how, learning, was, play, violin, to)

B: Do you have any experience playing (A) [alone / in a group]? (②)
G: Yes. Actually, I was a member of an orchestra when I was in elementary school.
B: Great. (③) Do you enjoy teaching others?
G: I have (B)[no experience / many experiences] teaching others. (④) But I enjoy working with people, so I'd like to try.
B: (⑤) Good. I think we'll have a great time playing together. Welcome to the Nanum Orchestra.

10 위 대화의 ①~⑤ 중 다음 주어진 말이 들어갈 알맞은 곳은?

> We also volunteer to teach children.

① ② ③ ④ ⑤

서답형

11 (A)~(B)에 들어갈 말로 적절한 것을 고르시오.

➡ (A) _____ (B) _____

서답형

12 괄호 안에 주어진 어휘를 바르게 배열하여 문장을 완성하시오. (I로 시작할 것)

➡ _____

13 위 대화의 내용과 일치하지 <u>않는</u> 것을 고르시오.

① Kate will join the Nanum Orchestra after this conversation.
② Kate is a member of an orchestra now.
③ Kate knows how to play the violin.
④ Hamin is the leader of the Nanum Orchestra.
⑤ Kate and Hamin meet for the first time.

[01~02] 주어진 문장 다음에 이어질 대화의 순서를 바르게 배열하시오.

01

> Mina, do you enjoy cooking?

> (A) Then why don't you join the cooking club?
> (B) Hmm, let me think about it.
> (C) Sometimes. I know how to make a pizza.

➡ _____

02

> Did you buy that drone?

> (A) No, I got it as a present from my parents, but I don't know how to use it. Do you know how to?
> (B) Then, I will ask her for help.
> (C) No, maybe Jina knows how to do it. She enjoys flying drones.

➡ _____

[03~05] 다음 대화를 읽고 물음에 답하시오.

> G: Look __(A)__ these pictures. (B)I grew these vegetables me. I have my own garden.
> B: Cool! (C)네가 기르는 채소를 요리하는 법을 아니, too?
> G: Yes, my grandmother taught me.

03 빈칸 (A)에 알맞는 전치사를 쓰시오.

➡ _____

04 밑줄 친 (B)에서 어색한 것을 찾아 고치시오.

➡ _____

05 (C)의 밑줄 친 우리말을 주어진 단어를 이용해 영작하시오.

➡ _____
(how, vegetables)

06 밑줄 친 부분에서 어색한 것을 찾아 고치시오. (2개)

> A: Do you enjoy looking at the stars at night?
> B: Yes, I enjoyed do that.

➡ _____

[07~08] 다음 대화를 읽고 물음에 답하시오.

> G: I heard you went to Yuna's violin concert yesterday. How was it?
> B: It was great. I hope I can play the violin like her someday.
> G: (A)나는 네가 바이올린 연주하는 법을 아는지 몰랐어.
> B: I can, but (B)(not, at, yet, I'm, good, it).

07 (A)에 주어진 우리말을 영작하시오. (10 단어)

➡ _____

08 괄호 (B) 안에 주어진 어휘를 알맞게 배열하여 문장을 완성하시오.

➡ _____

Grammar

1 의문사 + to부정사

> We also teach children **how to play** musical instruments as a service to our community. 우리는 지역 사회를 위한 봉사로 아이들에게 악기를 연주하는 법도 가르칩니다.
> I don't know **what to do**. 나는 무엇을 해야 할지 모르겠어.

■ '의문사+to부정사'는 문장 속에서 주어, 목적어, 보어 역할을 하는 명사구로 사용되어 '~해야 할지, ~ 하는 것이 좋을지'라는 뜻을 나타낸다.

• Please tell me **when to go**. (언제 가야 할지 나에게 말해 줘.)

■ what, which, who, whom, how, when, where 등의 의문사가 사용되지만 why는 쓰지 않는다는 점에 주의한다.

형태	의미	예문
how + to부정사	어떻게 ~할지	He doesn't know how to talk politely.
what + to부정사	무엇을 ~할지	Please tell me what to do next.
when + to부정사	언제 ~할지	I also don't know when to ask him.
where + to부정사	어디에 ~할지	I am not sure where to put the key.

■ '의문사+to부정사'는 '의문사+주어+should/can+동사원형'으로 바꾸어 쓸 수 있다.

• She asked me **whom to meet**. (그녀는 내게 누구를 만나야 할지 물었다.)
  = She asked me whom she should meet.

■ 의문사가 의문형용사로 쓰여 to부정사와의 사이에 명사가 올 수 있다.

• The host usually tells the guests **what time to leave**. (주인은 대개 손님들에게 몇 시에 떠나야 하는지를 말해 준다.)

핵심 Check

1. 다음 우리말과 일치하도록 빈칸에 알맞은 말을 쓰시오.

 (1) 나는 그녀에게 무슨 말을 해야 할지 모르겠어.

 ➡ I don't know _____ _____ say to her.

  = I don't know _____ _____ _____ say to her.

 (2) 이번 주말에 그를 어디서 만날지 내게 말해줘.

 ➡ Tell me _____ _____ _____ him this weekend.

  = Tell me _____ _____ _____ _____ him this weekend.

② 주격 관계대명사

> Anyone **who** likes to paint can join. 그림 그리는 것을 좋아하는 사람은 누구나 가입할 수 있습니다.
> She has a cat **which** has brown hair. 그녀는 갈색 털을 가진 고양이를 갖고 있다.

■ 관계대명사는 접속사와 대명사의 역할을 한다. 관계대명사절은 명사를 수식해 주는 절의 한 종류로 관계대명사절이 꾸며 주는 말을 선행사라고 하고 관계대명사는 앞의 선행사와 같은 대상을 가리킨다. 관계대명사절이 되기 전의 문장에서 주어로 쓰였으면 주격 관계대명사로, 소유격으로 쓰였으면 소유격 관계대명사로, 목적격으로 쓰였으면 목적격 관계대명사가 된다. 주격 관계대명사는 관계대명사절에서 주어 역할을 하므로 그 다음에는 동사가 온다.

· Mr. Kim is a farmer. He(=Mr. Kim) grows apples.
  = Mr. Kim is a farmer **who**[**that**] grows apples. (주격)

· This is the smartphone. She bought it(=the smartphone) at the shop.
  = This is the smartphone **which**[**that**] she bought at the shop. (목적격)

· This is the dress. Its color is blue.
  = This is the dress **whose** color is blue. (소유격)

■ 관계대명사는 선행사에 따라 다음과 같이 사용되며, 목적격 관계대명사는 생략할 수 있다.

	주격	소유격	목적격
사람	who/that	whose	whom[who]/that
동물, 사물	which/that	whose/of which	which/that

■ 주격 관계대명사절의 동사는 선행사의 인칭과 수에 일치시킨다.

· I have a friend **who**[**that**] helps me a lot. (나는 나를 많이 도와주는 친구가 있다.)

■ 관계대명사 that은 who, whom과 which 대신 사용할 수 있으며 소유격은 없다. 또한 선행사가 '사람+동물[사물]'인 경우에는 반드시 that을 써야 한다.

· There are a boy and his dog **that** are running in the park. 공원에서 뛰고 있는 소년과 그의 개가 있다.

■ '주격 관계대명사 + be동사'는 생략이 가능하다.

· The boy (**who is**) singing on the stage is my brother. (무대에서 노래하고 있는 소년은 내 동생이다.)

핵심 Check

2. 다음 우리말과 일치하도록 빈칸에 알맞은 말을 쓰시오.

(1) 나는 서울에 살고 있는 친구가 있다.
➡ I have a friend _____ lives in Seoul.

(2) 매우 멋있어 보이는 저 옷 좀 봐.
➡ Look at that dress _____ looks very nice.

01 다음 문장에서 어법상 <u>어색한</u> 부분을 바르게 고쳐 쓰시오.

(1) I can't decide what eating.

_____ ➡ _____

(2) Do you know when go?

_____ ➡ _____

(3) There is a man which is waiting for his bag.

_____ ➡ _____

(4) This is the movie who made me laugh a lot.

_____ ➡ _____

02 다음 중 어법상 <u>어색한</u> 문장을 <u>모두</u> 고르시오.

① Marie Curie is the person who first found radium.

② I lost the watch which my father had given to me.

③ I want to show you some pictures who I took a few days ago.

④ Please show me how do it.

⑤ Will you tell me where to stay in Seoul?

03 다음 우리말에 맞게 주어진 단어를 바르게 배열하시오. (필요하면 어형을 바꿀 것)

(1) 그녀는 내게 무엇을 해야 할지 묻지 않았다.

(she / me / what / do / ask / didn't / to)

➡ _____

(2) Mariel은 어디로 가야 할지 몰랐다.

(where / Mariel / go / know / didn't / to)

➡ _____

(3) Degas는 춤추고 있는 무용수를 그리는 것을 좋아했다.

(Degas / dancers / who / liked / dancing / paint / were / to)

➡ _____

(4) 그는 어제 그 소녀에게 짖은 개를 갖고 있다.

(he / that / dog / girl / yesterday / the / the / barked / has / at)

➡ _____

01 다음 빈칸에 알맞은 것은?

> I don't know _____ to do it.

① how   ② what
③ that   ④ whom
⑤ why

02 다음 문장의 빈칸에 들어갈 알맞은 것은?

> Look at the boy _____ is dancing.

① which   ② who
③ whose   ④ whom
⑤ what

03 다음 빈칸에 알맞은 말이 바르게 짝지어진 것은?

> • She knows _____ to solve the problem.
> • Molly is reading the message from Kate _____ arrived yesterday.

① what – which   ② what – who
③ how – which   ④ how – who
⑤ that – that

04 서답형 다음 문장에서 어법상 <u>틀린</u> 부분을 찾아 바르게 고쳐 쓰시오.

> The painting is about a party who took place in a small town.

05 중요 다음 중 어법상 <u>어색한</u> 것은?

① I don't know how to make a paper doll.
② Can you tell me whom to wait for here?
③ We asked him when to start.
④ Morri told us where to go after we finished the work.
⑤ I wanted to know what to do it.

06 다음 중 어법상 올바른 것은?

① This is the book who has many exciting stories.
② Anyone which loves books can join our event!
③ I saw a tree who looked like a big elephant.
④ He is the man that lived next door five years ago.
⑤ Amy likes movies who have sad endings.

07 다음 중 어법상 올바른 것은?

① They went to the restaurant who was famous for its traditional Korean food.
② I know a girl who name is Karen.
③ Please let me know how way I should go.
④ Tom has a painting who was drawn by a famous artist.
⑤ The two brothers always argue about how to share their presents.

서답형

08 괄호 안에서 알맞은 것을 고르시오.

(1) This is a sea horse (which / who) lives in the sea.

(2) There lived a girl and her dog (that / which) would play on the grass together.

(3) They enjoyed samgyupsal (that / who) tasted yummy last night.

(4) Let's look at some paintings that (was / were) painted by my aunt.

(5) He is a great novelist (who / which) writes many interesting novels.

(6) This is the boy (who / whom) helped me yesterday.

(7) Paul gave her a bag (which / which was) made in Korea.

서답형

09 다음 우리말을 두 가지로 영작하시오.

> 나는 무엇을 입을지 결정하지 못하겠어.

➡ _____

➡ _____

서답형

10 다음 중 관계대명사가 들어갈 곳을 고르고 알맞게 쓰시오.

(1) I can't ① remember ② the lady ③ visited ④ me ⑤ last night.

(2) There ① was ② a big house ③ has ④ a beautiful garden ⑤ over there.

➡ (1) _____ (2) _____

서답형

11 괄호 안에서 알맞은 것을 고르시오.

(1) Let me tell you (how / what) to use the machine.

(2) I don't know where (spending / to spend) the holidays.

(3) Jennifer didn't know (what / why) to do, so she just waited for him.

(4) I'm not sure what (I should / I) do after graduation.

(5) At first, he did not know (how he read / how to read) a note.

중요

12 다음 〈보기〉의 밑줄 친 부분과 쓰임이 같은 것은?

> ┤ 보기 ├
> These are the animals which live both on the land and in the water.

① Which do you like better, this one or that one?

② That is the dog which barked at me the other day.

③ Can you tell me which one will be good for Harry?

④ The scarf which she is wearing around her neck looks beautiful.

⑤ Let's decide which way to take.

13 다음 빈칸에 적절하지 않은 것을 모두 고르시오.

> He didn't tell us _____ to go.

① what   ② where   ③ when

④ how   ⑤ why

14 다음 중 주어진 문장의 밑줄 친 that과 용법이 같은 것은?

> The girl that is talking to Jack over there is very kind.

① Yuna has a cat that likes to hide in boxes.
② Don't forget that small efforts can make big differences.
③ I didn't know that.
④ Look at that big bird.
⑤ I can't understand you when you speak that fast.

15 두 문장의 의미가 같아지도록 빈칸에 알맞은 말을 쓰시오.

(1) We are going to teach them how to do magic.
= We are going to teach them _____ _____ _____ _____ magic.

(2) I can't decide where to put this computer.
= I can't decide _____ _____ _____ _____ this computer.

(3) Please inform me what to do next.
= Please inform me _____ _____ _____ _____ next.

16 다음 빈칸에 공통으로 알맞은 말은?

> • The boy _____ gave me a present is my boyfriend.
> • She has a dog _____ has a short tail.

① who
② whose
③ whom
④ which
⑤ that

[17~18] 다음 우리말에 맞게 영작한 것을 고르시오.

17
> 아버지는 그 기계를 어떻게 사용해야 하는지 배우셨다.

① My father learned when to use the machine.
② My father learned where to use the machine.
③ My father learned how to use the machine.
④ My father learned what to use the machine.
⑤ My father learned that to use the machine.

18
> 기린은 긴 목을 가진 동물이다.

① A giraffe is an animal who has a long neck.
② A giraffe is an animal whose has a long neck.
③ A giraffe is an animal whom has a long neck.
④ A giraffe is an animal which has a long neck.
⑤ A giraffe is an animal that it has a long neck.

19 우리말과 일치하도록 주어진 어휘를 이용하여 빈칸에 알맞은 말을 쓰시오.

(1) 그는 그것을 어디서 살지 모른다. (buy)
➡ He doesn't know _____ _____ _____ it.

(2) 나는 사진이 많이 들어간 여행 책을 좋아한다. (have)
➡ I like travel books _____ _____ lots of pictures.

Grammar **25**

01 다음 글에서 어법상 잘못 쓰인 것을 찾아 알맞게 고치시오.
(3개)

> I volunteered at a computer school for old people. I met several old people which want to know about computers. I helped the teacher taught them how using a computer.

➡ _____

02 다음 중 어법상 어색한 것을 바르게 고치시오.

(1) I want to have a toy who can speak.

_____ ➡ _____

(2) The dog is running after the girl has long ears.

_____ ➡ _____

(3) Angie likes to take pictures of old ladies whom were working.

_____ ➡ _____

(4) Look at the people who is standing in line.

_____ ➡ _____

(5) She is the teacher who she teaches us English.

_____ ➡ _____

03 다음 빈칸에 알맞은 것을 쓰시오.

(1) Do you know how to swim?
= Do you know _____ _____ _____ _____?

(2) Which movie to watch is hard for us to decide.
= _____ _____ _____ _____ _____ is hard for us to decide.

(3) I did not know whom to thank for the gift.
= I did not know _____ _____ _____ _____ for the gift.

04 주어진 두 문장을 한 문장으로 바꿔 쓰시오.

(1) • Here are two club leaders.
    • They want students to join their clubs.

➡ _____
  _____

(2) • This is the tea.
    • It is good for your health.

➡ _____

(3) • The movie was interesting.
    • It was directed by James Cameron.

➡ _____
  _____

(4) • There are a boy and his dog.
    • They are running at the playground.

➡ _____
  _____

(5) • Do you know the girl?
    • She is dancing on the stage.

➡ _____

05 다음 중 어법상 <u>잘못된</u> 것을 고쳐 문장을 다시 쓰시오.

(1) You need to know how play an instrument to join our club.

➡ _____

_____

(2) The old man didn't know what to use the smartphone.

➡ _____

(3) When I to visit London has to be decided.

➡ _____

(4) I don't know why to go there.

➡ _____

06 다음 중 생략할 수 있는 것을 찾아 쓰시오.

(1) The man who is dancing lives next door.

➡ _____

(2) These are the pictures which were taken at our field trip in spring.

➡ _____

07 주어진 어구와 to부정사를 이용하여 자신의 문장을 쓰시오.

(1) how, speak

➡ _____

(2) what, say to

➡ _____

(3) where, park

➡ _____

[08~09] 다음 그림을 보고 주어진 어휘를 이용하여 빈칸에 알맞은 말을 쓰시오.

08
A: Do you know the girl _____ _____? (be, read)

B: Oh, she is Sumi.

09
A: Does Minsu know _____ the piano? (play)

B: Of course. He plays the piano very well.

10 다음 우리말을 괄호 안에 주어진 어구를 이용하여 영작하시오.

(1) 어떻게 영어로 이메일을 쓸 수 있는지 나에게 말해 줄 수 있니? (tell, write, an email, in English, 12 단어)

➡ _____

(2) 나는 무엇을 먼저 해야 할지 모르겠어. (know, do, first, 8 단어)

➡ _____

(3) 너는 강을 따라 뛰고 있는 저 남자를 알고 있니? (that, run, along the river, 11 단어)

➡ _____

_____

Reading

Why Don't You Join Our Club? 그래지 않을래?

Participating in club activities is a great way to enjoy your school
life. How about joining a club? Here are two club leaders who want
students to join their clubs. Let's listen to what they say.

The Picasso Art Club

   Hi! I am Sora Kang from the Picasso Art Club. As you can guess
from the name of our club, we paint. We also do volunteer work from
time to time. Last summer, our club members participated in the
"Change Our Neighborhood" project. On the dirty old walls of the
buildings in our neighborhood, we painted birds flying high in the sky
and dolphins jumping over blue waves.
As a result, the old neighborhood changed into a bright and beautiful
place. The neighbors were happy to see our work and thanked us. You
don't have to be a good painter. Anyone who likes to paint can join.
Come and be a member of the Picasso Art Club.

join 가입하다
club 동아리
participate in ~에 참여하다
leader 대표, 회장
volunteer 자원봉사자
neighborhood 동네, 이웃
dolphin 돌고래
bright 밝은
as a result 결과적으로

확인문제

● 다음 문장이 본문의 내용과 일치하면 T, 일치하지 않으면 F를 쓰시오.

1 The Picasso Art Club is a painting club. ☐

2 The Picasso Art Club has no interest in volunteer work. ☐

3 This summer, the club members of the Picasso Art Club joined the "Change Our
   Neighborhood" project. ☐

4 The old neighborhood changed into a bright and beautiful place. ☐

5 If you aren't a skillful painter, you can't join the Picasso Art Club. ☐

6 If you like to paint, you can join the Picasso Art Club. ☐

The Boram Orchestra

Hi! I am Minsu Jang, the leader of the Boram Orchestra. Did you see
　　　　　　　　　　　　　　　　　　　　　　　　　　　관현악단

several students playing music at the main gate when you came to
몇몇의　　　　　주격관계대명사 which[that] + be동사 생략　　시간의 접속사 '~할 때'

school today? We were those students. We play music for our friends

every morning. You need to know how to play an instrument a little
　　　　　　　　'~할 필요가 있다'　　how to부정사 '연주하는 방법'　　　　　조금, 약간

bit to join our club. But don't worry if you don't play well. We will
　　　　　　　　　　　　　　　　　조건의 접속사 '만약 ~한다면'

practice hard and get better together. We also teach children how to
연습하다　　　　　　　good의 비교급　　　　　　　　　　　　how to부정사 '연주하는 방법'

play musical instruments as a service to our community. I am teaching
　　　악기　　　　　전치사 '~로(서)'　　　　지역 사회　現재진행형 be동사의 현재형 + ~ing

an eleven-year-old boy to play the violin. At first, he did not know
　　years(x)　　　= how to play　　　'처음에'

how to read a note. Now he can play a simple song. Hearing him play
읽는 법　　음, 악보　　　　　　　　　간단한　　지각동사+목적어+목적격보어(동사원형)

the violin makes me very happy. By joining our club, you can have an
　　　　　　　　　　　　　　　　　'~함으로써'

opportunity to help others. Come and join our club. We are waiting for
기회　　　to부정사의　　= other people
　　　　　형용사적 용법

you.

orchestra 관현악단, 오케스트라
several 몇몇의
a littel bit 조금, 약간
service 서비스, 봉사
practice 연습하다
community 지역 사회
note 음표
opportunity 기회
wait for ~을 기다리다

 확인문제

● 다음 문장이 본문의 내용과 일치하면 T, 일치하지 않으면 F를 쓰시오.

1　Minsu Jang is the leader of the Boram Orchestra. ☐

2　The members of the Boram Orchestra play music for their friends after school. ☐

3　If you can't play an instrument, you can't join the Boram Orchestra. ☐

4　The members of the Boram Orchestra teach children how to play musical

　instruments. ☐

5　Minsu is teaching an eleven-year-old boy to play the violin. ☐

6　Hearing the boy play the violin makes Minsu very upset. ☐

● 우리말을 참고하여 빈칸에 알맞은 말을 쓰시오.

1 _____ _____ _____ Join Our Club?

2 _____ _____ club activities is a great way _____ _____ your school life.

3 _____ _____ joining a club?

4 Here are two club leaders _____ _____ students _____ _____ their clubs.

5 Let's listen to _____ they say.

6 The Picasso _____ _____

7 Hi! I am Sora Kang _____ the Picasso Art Club.

8 _____ you can _____ _____ the name of our club, we paint.

9 We also _____ _____ _____ from time to time.

10 Last summer, our club members _____ _____ the "Change Our Neighborhood" project.

11 _____ _____ _____ _____ _____ of the buildings in our neighborhood, we painted birds _____ high in the sky and dolphins _____ over blue waves.

12 _____ _____ _____, the old neighborhood changed _____ a bright and beautiful place.

13 The neighbors were happy _____ _____ our work and _____ us.

14 You _____ _____ _____ be a good painter.

15 _____ _____ likes to paint can join.

1	우리 동아리에 가입하는 게 어때?
2	동아리 활동에 참여하는 것은 학교생활을 즐기는 좋은 방법이에요.
3	동아리에 가입하는 게 어떤가요?
4	여기 학생들이 그들의 동아리에 가입하기를 원하는 두 명의 동아리 대표가 있어요.
5	그들이 하는 말을 들어 봅시다.
6	피카소 미술 동아리
7	안녕하세요! 저는 피카소 미술 동아리의 강소라입니다.
8	우리 동아리의 이름에서 추측할 수 있듯이, 우리는 그림을 그립니다.
9	우리는 가끔 자원봉사도 합니다.
10	지난여름, 우리 동아리 회원들은 "우리 마을 바꾸기" 프로젝트에 참여했습니다.
11	우리 마을에 있는 건물의 더럽고 오래된 벽에 하늘 높이 나는 새들과 푸른 파도 위로 점프하는 돌고래들을 그렸습니다.
12	결과적으로, 오래된 마을은 밝고 아름다운 곳으로 바뀌었습니다.
13	이웃들은 우리의 작품을 보고 행복해 했고 고마워했습니다.
14	여러분은 그림을 잘 그릴 필요는 없습니다.
15	그림 그리는 것을 좋아하는 사람은 누구나 가입할 수 있습니다.

16 _____ _____ _____ a member of the Picasso Art Club.

17 The Boram _____

18 Hi! I am Minsu Jang, _____ _____ of the Boram Orchestra.

19 Did you see several students _____ _____ at the main gate when you _____ _____ _____ today?

20 We were _____ students.

21 We _____ _____ _____ our friends every morning.

22 You need to know _____ _____ _____ an instrument _____ _____ _____ to join our club.

23 But _____ _____ if you don't play well.

24 We will _____ _____ and _____ _____ together.

25 We _____ _____ children how to play musical instruments _____ _____ _____ _____ our community.

26 I am teaching _____ _____ _____ to play the violin.

27 _____ _____, he did not know how to _____ _____ _____.

28 Now he can play _____ _____ _____.

29 _____ _____ _____ the violin _____ me very happy.

30 _____ _____ our club, you can _____ _____ to help others.

31 _____ _____ _____ our club.

32 We are waiting _____ you.

16 와서 피카소 미술 동아리의 회원이 되세요.

17 보람 오케스트라

18 안녕하세요! 저는 보람 오케스트라의 회장 장민수입니다.

19 오늘 학교에 왔을 때 정문에서 음악을 연주하는 몇 명의 학생들을 보았습니까?

20 우리가 그 학생들이었습니다.

21 우리는 매일 아침 친구들을 위해 음악을 연주합니다.

22 우리 동아리에 가입하기 위해서는 악기 연주하는 법을 조금 알아야 합니다.

23 그러나 여러분이 연주를 잘 못한다고 해서 걱정하지 마세요.

24 우리는 열심히 연습하고 함께 좋아질 것입니다.

25 우리는 지역 사회에 대한 봉사로 아이들에게 악기를 연주하는 법도 가르칩니다.

26 저는 열한 살 소년에게 바이올린을 가르치고 있습니다.

27 처음에 그는 음표를 읽는 법을 알지 못했습니다.

28 이제는 간단한 노래도 연주할 수 있습니다.

29 그가 바이올린을 연주하는 걸 듣는 것은 저를 매우 행복하게 합니다.

30 우리 동아리에 가입함으로써, 여러분은 다른 사람들을 도울 수 있는 기회를 가질 수 있습니다.

31 와서 우리 동아리에 가입하세요.

32 우리는 여러분을 기다리고 있습니다.

• 우리말을 참고하여 본문을 영작하시오.

1 우리 동아리에 가입하는 게 어때?

➡ _____

2 동아리 활동에 참여하는 것은 학교생활을 즐기는 좋은 방법이에요.

➡ _____

3 동아리에 가입하는 게 어떤가요?

➡ _____

4 여기 학생들이 그들의 동아리에 가입하기를 원하는 두 명의 동아리 대표가 있어요.

➡ _____

5 그들이 하는 말을 들어 봅시다.

➡ _____

6 피카소 미술 동아리

➡ _____

7 안녕하세요! 저는 피카소 미술 동아리의 강소라입니다.

➡ _____

8 우리 동아리의 이름에서 추측할 수 있듯이, 우리는 그림을 그립니다.

➡ _____

9 우리는 가끔 자원봉사도 합니다.

➡ _____

10 지난여름, 우리 동아리 회원들은 "우리 마을 바꾸기" 프로젝트에 참여했습니다.

➡ _____

11 우리 마을에 있는 건물의 더럽고 오래된 벽에 하늘 높이 나는 새들과 푸른 파도 위로 점프하는 돌고래들을 그렸습니다.

➡ _____

_____

12 결과적으로, 오래된 마을은 밝고 아름다운 곳으로 바뀌었습니다.

➡ _____

13 이웃들은 우리의 작품을 보고 행복해 했고 고마워했습니다.

➡ _____

14 여러분은 그림을 잘 그릴 필요는 없습니다.

➡ _____

15 그림 그리는 것을 좋아하는 사람은 누구나 가입할 수 있습니다.

➡ _____

16 와서 피카소 미술 동아리의 회원이 되세요.

➡ _____

17 보람 오케스트라

➡ _____

18 안녕하세요! 저는 보람 오케스트라의 회장 장민수입니다.

➡ _____

19 오늘 학교에 왔을 때 정문에서 음악을 연주하는 몇 명의 학생들을 보았습니까?

➡ _____

20 우리가 그 학생들이었습니다.

➡ _____

21 우리는 매일 아침 친구들을 위해 음악을 연주합니다.

➡ _____

22 우리 동아리에 가입하기 위해서는 악기 연주하는 법을 조금 알아야 합니다.

➡ _____

23 그러나 여러분이 연주를 잘 못한다고 해서 걱정하지 마세요.

➡ _____

24 우리는 열심히 연습하고 함께 좋아질 것입니다.

➡ _____

25 우리는 지역 사회에 대한 봉사로 아이들에게 악기를 연주하는 법도 가르칩니다.

➡ _____

26 저는 열한 살 소년에게 바이올린을 가르치고 있습니다.

➡ _____

27 처음에 그는 음표를 읽는 법을 알지 못했습니다.

➡ _____

28 이제는 간단한 노래도 연주할 수 있습니다.

➡ _____

29 그가 바이올린을 연주하는 걸 듣는 것은 저를 매우 행복하게 합니다.

➡ _____

30 우리 동아리에 가입함으로써, 여러분은 다른 사람들을 도울 수 있는 기회를 가질 수 있습니다.

➡ _____

31 와서 우리 동아리에 가입하세요.

➡ _____

32 우리는 여러분을 기다리고 있습니다.

➡ _____

[01~03] 다음 글을 읽고 물음에 답하시오.

Participating in club activities (A)[is / are] a great way to enjoy your school life. ⓐ How about joining a club? Here are two club leaders who (B)[want / wants] students (C)[joining / to join] their clubs. Let's listen to what ⓑthey say.

서답형
01 위 글의 괄호 (A)~(C)에서 어법상 알맞은 것을 골라 쓰시오.

➡ (A)_____ (B)_____ (C)_____

중요
02 위 글의 밑줄 친 ⓐHow about joining과 바꿔 쓸 수 있는 말을 <u>모두</u> 고르시오.

① What about joining
② How do you join
③ Why don't you join
④ Which about joining
⑤ Why do you join

서답형
03 위 글의 밑줄 친 ⓑthey가 가리키는 것을 본문에서 찾아 쓰시오.

➡ _____

[04~06] 다음 글을 읽고 물음에 답하시오.

The Picasso Art Club
Hi! I am Sora Kang from the Picasso Art Club. ⓐAs you can guess from the name of our club, we paint. We also do volunteer work from time to time. (①) Last summer, our club members participated in the "Change Our Neighborhood" project. (②) On the dirty old walls of the buildings in our

neighborhood, we painted birds flying high in the sky and dolphins jumping over blue waves. (③) The neighbors were happy to see our work and thanked us. (④) You don't have to be a good painter. (⑤) Anyone who likes to paint can join. Come and be a member of the Picasso Art Club.

04 위 글의 흐름으로 보아, 주어진 문장이 들어가기에 가장 적절한 곳은?

As a result, the old neighborhood changed into a bright and beautiful place.

①　　　②　　　③　　　④　　　⑤

중요
05 위 글의 밑줄 친 ⓐAs와 같은 의미로 쓰인 것을 고르시오.

① As he often lies, I don't like him.
② As she grew older, she became wiser.
③ She respects him as a mentor.
④ As you know, Julia is leaving soon.
⑤ He told it to me as we went along.

06 위 글의 피카소 미술 동아리에 대한 설명으로 옳지 <u>않은</u> 것은?

① 그림 동아리이다.
② 가끔 자원봉사도 한다.
③ 지난여름, 동아리 회원들은 "우리 마을 바꾸기" 프로젝트에 참여했다.
④ 이웃 마을에 있는 건물의 더럽고 오래된 벽에 그림을 그렸다.
⑤ 동아리 회원이 되려면 그림을 잘 그려야 한다.

[07~09] 다음 글을 읽고 물음에 답하시오.

The Boram Orchestra
Hi! I am Minsu Jang, the leader of the Boram

Orchestra. ⓐ<u>Did you see several students to play music at the main gate when you came to school today?</u> We were those students. We play music for our friends every morning. You need to know ⓑ to play an instrument a little bit to join our club. But don't worry if you don't play well. We will practice hard and get better together. We also teach children how to play musical instruments as a service to our community. I am teaching an eleven-year-old boy to play the violin. At first, he did not know how to read a note. Now he can play a simple song. Hearing him play the violin makes me very happy. By joining our club, you can have an opportunity to help others. Come and join our club. We are waiting for you.

서답형

07 위 글의 밑줄 친 ⓐ에서 어법상 틀린 부분을 찾아 고치시오.

➡ _____

08 위 글의 빈칸 ⓑ에 들어갈 알맞은 말을 고르시오.

① what ② whom ③ how
④ when ⑤ whether

서답형

09 다음 중 보람 오케스트라 동아리에 가입할 수 있는 사람을 고르시오.

> 지혜: I'm interested in doing volunteer work.
> 보람: I don't know how to play an instrument at all, but I like music.
> 선미: I like painting pictures and helping others.
> 준호: I'm not a skillful pianist, but I practice playing the piano hard.
> 혜영: I know how to read a note, but I can't play any instrument.

➡ _____

[10~12] 다음 글을 읽고 물음에 답하시오.

Boram Middle School
Club Membership Form
• **Name of Club**: FC Boram
• **Student Name**: Sunho Park
• **Why You Want to Join the Club**: I love soccer and would like to join FC Boram. I am good at passing the ball and running fast. ⓐ , I don't know how to head the ball, so I want to learn how to do that. I want to become a soccer player who can make wonderful heading goals.
• **Your Goals**: ⓑ<u>If I will join this club, I will practice very hard and become a good team player!</u>

10 위 글의 빈칸 ⓐ에 들어갈 알맞은 말을 고르시오.

① Moreover ② However
③ Therefore ④ Similarly
⑤ For instance

서답형

11 위 글을 읽고 순호가 잘하는 것과 못하는 것을 우리말로 쓰시오.

➡ 잘하는 것: _____
➡ 못하는 것: _____

서답형

12 위 글의 밑줄 친 ⓑ에서 어법상 틀린 부분을 찾아 고치시오.

➡ _____

[13~15] 다음 글을 읽고 물음에 답하시오.

Participating in club activities is a great way ⓐto enjoy your school life. How about ⓑ joining a club? Here are two club leaders ⓒ want students to join their clubs. Let's listen to what they say.

13 위 글의 밑줄 친 ⓐto enjoy와 to부정사의 용법이 다른 것을 <u>모두</u> 고르시오.

① I have much work to do today.

② He is rich enough to buy the car.

③ I have nothing particular to do today.

④ I don't know what to do next.

⑤ Give me a chair to sit on.

서답형

14 위 글의 밑줄 친 ⓑjoining과 바꿔 쓸 수 있는 말을 본문에서 찾아 쓰시오.

➡ _____

서답형

15 위 글의 빈칸 ⓒ에 들어갈 알맞은 말을 쓰시오.

➡ _____

[16~18] 다음 글을 읽고 물음에 답하시오.

The Picasso Art Club

Hi! I am Sora Kang from the Picasso Art Club. As you can guess ⓐ the name of our club, we paint. We also do volunteer work from time to time. Last summer, our club members participated in the "Change Our Neighborhood" project. On the dirty old walls of the buildings in our neighborhood, we painted birds flying high in the sky and dolphins jumping over blue waves. ⓑ , the old neighborhood changed ⓒ a bright and beautiful place. The neighbors were happy ⓓto see our work and thanked us. You don't have to be a good painter. Anyone who likes to paint can join. Come and be a member of the Picasso Art Club.

16 위 글의 빈칸 ⓐ와 ⓒ에 들어갈 전치사가 바르게 짝지어진 것은?

① from – into   ② by – for

③ in – from   ④ from – on

⑤ for – into

17 위 글의 빈칸 ⓑ에 들어갈 알맞은 말을 고르시오.

① However   ② In addition

③ For example   ④ As a result

⑤ In other words

18 아래 보기에서 위 글의 밑줄 친 ⓓto see와 to부정사의 용법이 같은 것의 개수를 고르시오.

─┤ 보기 ├─

① He promised not to do it.

② English is difficult to learn.

③ She has many children to take care of.

④ What a fool he is to say such a thing!

⑤ She worked hard to pass the exam.

① 1개   ② 2개   ③ 3개   ④ 4개   ⑤ 5개

[19~21] 다음 글을 읽고 물음에 답하시오.

The Boram Orchestra

Hi! I am Minsu Jang, the leader of the Boram Orchestra. Did you see several students playing music at the main gate when you came to school today? We were those students. We play music for our friends every morning. You need to know how to play an instrument a little bit to join our club. But don't worry if you don't play well. We will practice hard and get better together. We also teach children ⓐ musical instruments as a service to our community. I am teaching an eleven-year-old boy to play the violin. At first, he did not know how to read a ⓑnote. Now he can play a simple song. Hearing him play the violin makes me very happy. By joining our club, you can have an opportunity to help others. Come and join our club. We are waiting for you.

서답형

19 위 글의 빈칸 ⓐ에 play를 알맞은 형태로 쓰시오.

➡ _____

20 위 글의 밑줄 친 ⓑnote와 같은 의미로 쓰인 것을 고르시오.

① Please make a <u>note</u> of what I'm saying.

② He is striking a <u>note</u> on a piano.

③ She left a <u>note</u> for Ben on the table.

④ Can I borrow your lecture <u>note</u>?

⑤ You must <u>note</u> that this is essential.

서답형

21 위 글을 읽고 보람 오케스트라 동아리의 활동 두 가지를 우리말로 쓰시오.

➡ (1) _____

(2) _____

[22~24] 다음 글을 읽고 물음에 답하시오.

Boram Middle School
Club Membership Form

• **Name of Club**: FC Boram

• **Student Name**: Sunho Park

• **Why You Want to Join the Club**: I love soccer and would like ①joining FC Boram. I am good at ②passing the ball and ③running fast. However, I don't know ④how to head the ball, so I want to learn how to do that. I want to become a soccer player ⑤who can make wonderful heading ⓐgoals.

• **Your ⓑGoals**: If I join this club, I will practice very hard and become a good team player!

서답형

22 위 글의 밑줄 친 ①~⑤ 중 어법상 틀린 것을 찾아 고치시오.

➡ _____

23 위 글의 박 순호에 대한 설명으로 옳지 <u>않은</u> 것은?

① FC Boram에 가입하고 싶어 한다.

② 공을 패스하는 것을 잘한다.

③ 빨리 달린다.

④ 공을 헤딩하는 것을 잘한다.

⑤ 멋진 헤딩 골을 만들 수 있는 축구 선수가 되기를 원한다.

서답형

24 위 글의 밑줄 친 ⓐgoals와 ⓑGoals의 뜻을 쓰시오.

➡ ⓐ _____ , ⓑ _____

[25~27] 다음 글을 읽고 물음에 답하시오.

Looking For Volunteers

We will ⓐ a book fair at Nanum Middle School on May 5. We are looking for volunteers who can introduce and sell books to people. Anyone who loves books can join our event! If you are interested, please let us know!

25 위 글의 빈칸 ⓐ에 들어갈 알맞은 말을 고르시오.

① take   ② turn

③ hold   ④ bring

⑤ grow

서답형

26 다음 질문에 대한 알맞은 대답을 영어로 쓰시오. (8 단어)

Q: What will volunteers do at the event?

A: _____

27 위 글을 읽고 전시회에 대해 알 수 <u>없는</u> 것을 고르시오.

① 전시회의 종류   ② 개최 장소

③ 전시회의 규모   ④ 개최일

⑤ 전시회 참가 자격

[01~03] 다음 글을 읽고 물음에 답하시오.

The Picasso Art Club

Hi! I am Sora Kang from the Picasso Art Club. As you can guess from the name of our club, we paint. We also do volunteer work from time to time. Last summer, our club members participated in the "Change Our Neighborhood" project. On the dirty old walls of the buildings in our neighborhood, we painted birds ⓐ high in the sky and dolphins ⓑ over blue waves. As a result, the old neighborhood changed into a bright and beautiful place. The neighbors were happy to see our work and thanked us. You ©don't have to be a good painter. Anyone who likes to paint can join. Come and be a member of the Picasso Art Club.

01 다음 빈칸 (A)~(C)에 알맞은 단어를 넣어 Picasso Art Club 에 대한 소개를 완성하시오. 단, (B)와 (C)에는 같은 단어를 쓰시오.

> The Picasso Art Club is an art club and sometimes does (A)_____ _____, too. Anyone who likes (B)_____ can join it and don't have to be good at (C)_____.

02 위 글의 빈칸 ⓐ와 ⓑ에 fly와 jump를 각각 알맞은 형태로 쓰시오.

➡ ⓐ_____, ⓑ_____

03 위 글의 밑줄 친 ©don't have to와 바꿔 쓸 수 있는 어구를 쓰시오.

➡ _____

[04~06] 다음 글을 읽고 물음에 답하시오.

The Boram Orchestra

Hi! I am Minsu Jang, the leader of the Boram Orchestra. Did you see several students playing music at the main gate when you came to school today? We were those students. We play music for our friends every morning. You need to know how to play an instrument (A)[a few / a little] bit to join our club. But don't worry ⓐif you don't play well. We will practice hard and get better together. ⓑ우리는 지역 사회에 대한 봉사로 아이들에게 악기를 연주하는 법도 가르칩니다(musical instruments / teach / a service / children / to our community / we / how to play / also). I am teaching an (B)[eleven-year-old / eleven-years-old] boy to play the violin. At first, he did not know how to read a note. Now he can play a simple song. Hearing him play the violin makes me very (C)[happy / happily]. By joining our club, you can have an opportunity to help others. Come and join our club. We are waiting for you.

04 위 글의 괄호 (A)~(C)에서 어법상 알맞은 것을 골라 쓰시오.

➡ (A)_____ (B)_____ (C)_____

05 위 글의 밑줄 친 ⓐ를 다음과 같이 바꿔 쓸 때 빈칸에 들어갈 알맞은 말을 쓰시오.

➡ _____ you play well

06 위 글의 밑줄 친 ⓑ의 우리말에 맞게 한 단어를 보충하여, 괄호 안에 주어진 어휘를 알맞게 배열하시오.

➡ _____

[07~09] 다음 글을 읽고 물음에 답하시오.

The Picasso Art Club

Hi! I am Sora Kang from the Picasso Art Club. As you can guess from the name of our club, we paint. We also do volunteer work from time to time. Last summer, our club members participated in the "Change Our Neighborhood" project. On the dirty old walls of the buildings in our neighborhood, we painted birds flying high in the sky and dolphins jumping over blue waves. As a result, the old neighborhood changed into a bright and beautiful place. The neighbors were happy to see our work and thanked us. ⓐYou must not be a good painter. ⓑ그림 그리는 것을 좋아하는 사람은 누구나 가입할 수 있습니다. Come and be a member of the Picasso Art Club.

07 다음 질문에 대한 알맞은 대답을 영어로 쓰시오.

Q: How did Sora Kang's neighborhood change after the "Change Our Neighborhood" project?

A: _____

08 위 글의 밑줄 친 ⓐ에서 흐름상 어색한 부분을 찾아 고치시오.

➡ _____

09 위 글의 밑줄 친 ⓑ의 우리말에 맞게 주어진 어휘를 이용하여 7 단어로 영작하시오.

anyone

➡ _____

[10~12] 다음 글을 읽고 물음에 답하시오.

The Boram Orchestra

Hi! I am Minsu Jang, the leader of the Boram Orchestra. Did you see several students playing music at the main gate when you came to school today? We were those students. We play music for our friends every morning. You need to know how to play an instrument a little bit to join our club. But don't worry if you don't play well. We will practice hard and get better together. We also teach children how to play musical instruments as a service to our community. I am teaching an eleven-year-old boy to play the violin. At first, he did not know how to read a note. Now he can play a simple song. ⓐHearing him play the violin make me very happy. By joining our club, you can have an opportunity to help others. Come and join our club. We are waiting for you.

10 위 글을 읽고 보람 오케스트라 동아리의 가입 자격을 우리말로 쓰시오.

➡ _____

11 본문의 내용과 일치하도록 다음 빈칸 (A)와 (B)에 들어갈 알맞은 단어를 본문에서 찾아 쓰시오.

Minsu tells the students not to (A)_____ even though they don't play a musical instrument well because they will practice hard and (B)_____ _____ together.

12 위 글의 밑줄 친 ⓐ에서 어법상 틀린 부분을 찾아 고치시오.

➡ _____

After You Read

April 30

Today, Minsu, the leader of the Boram Orchestra, came to community center.
Minsu와 the leader of the Boram Orchestra는 동격이다.

He started teaching me how to play the violin last month. At first, I didn't
start는 동명사와 to부정사를 목적어로 취한다.   how to+동사원형: ~하는 방법   처음에는

know how to read a note.
음, 음표

I hope to join the Boram Orchestra and play the violin at the main gate when I
hope는 to부정사를 목적어로 취한다. join: 가입하다   (접) ~할 때

become a middle school student.

구문해설 • commnunity: 지역 사회 • the main gate: 정문

오늘, 보람 오케스트라의 대표인 민수가 지역 주민 회관에 왔다. 그는 지난달에 바이올린을 연주하는 법을 나에게 가르쳐 주기 시작했다. 처음에는 나는 하나의 음표도 읽는 법을 알지 못했다. 나는 보람 오케스트라에 가입하여, 내가 중학생이 될 때 정문에서 바이올린을 연주하기를 희망한다.

Writing Workshop

Boram Middle School
Club Membership Form

• Name of Club: FC Boram

• Student Name: Sunho Park

• Why You Want to Join the Club: I love soccer and would like to join FC
  = The reason   ~하고 싶다, ~하는 것을 바라다

Boram. I am good at passing the ball and running fast. However, I don't know
be good at: ~을 잘하다, 동명사   동명사

how to head the ball, so I want to learn how to do that. I want to become a
= how I should head   그래서   =head the ball

soccer player who can make wonderful heading goals.
주격 관계대명사(= that)

• Your Goals: If I join this club, I will practice very hard and become a good
조건의 부사절에서 현재시제가 미래시제를 대신함.   열심히

team player!

구문해설 • be good at: ~을 잘하다, • however: 그러나, • wonderful: 아주 멋진, • goal: 득점, 목표, • practice: 연습하다

보람중학교 동아리 지원서

동아리 이름: FC Boram

학생 이름: 박순호

가입을 원하는 이유: 나는 축구를 사랑하고 FC Boram에 가입하고 싶다. 나는 공을 패스하는 것을 잘하고 빨리 달린다. 그러나, 나는 공을 헤딩하는 법을 모르기 때문에 그것을 하는 법을 배우고 싶다. 나는 멋진 헤딩 골을 만들 수 있는 축구 선수가 되기를 원한다.

당신의 목표: 만약 내가 이 동아리에 가입하면, 나는 매우 열심히 연습해서 좋은 팀 플레이어가 될 것이다.

Real Life Zone

I would like to introduce our new orchestra member, Kate. She knows how
= want to   동격(쉼표로 연결)

to play the violin. She also has lots of experience playing in a group. And she
의문사+to부정사: ~하는 법   = much(양과 수 모두에 쓰임)   동명사(앞에 전치사 in이 생략된 것으로 볼 수 있음)

said she enjoys working with people.
enjoys의 목적어로 쓰인 동명사

Let's all welcome her to the Nanum Orchestra.
모두   = Kate

구문해설 • introduce: 소개하다, experience: 경험

나는 우리의 새로운 오케스트라 회원인 케이트를 소개하고 싶어. 그녀는 바이올린을 연주하는 법을 알아. 그녀는 또한 그룹에서 연주해 본 경험이 많아. 그리고 그녀는 사람들과 일하는 것을 즐긴다고 말했어. 모두 그녀가 나눔 오케스트라에 온 걸 환영하자.

Words & Expressions

01 다음 짝지어진 낱말의 관계가 나머지 넷과 다른 것은?

① gift – present ② dark – bright
③ activity – action ④ actually – really
⑤ enter – join

02 다음 빈칸에 알맞은 말이 순서대로 바르게 나열된 것은?

• Are you pretty _____ at using computers?
• We are _____ for volunteers who can introduce books to people.
• I will _____ in the event next time!

① well – starting – participate
② well – looking – enter
③ good – looking – participate
④ good – starting – enter
⑤ good – looking – enter

03 밑줄 친 단어와 의미가 같은 단어를 고르시오.

What should I get them for their wedding gift?

① keep ② bring ③ carry
④ buy ⑤ find

04 다음 빈칸에 공통으로 들어갈 말을 쓰시오.

• You can ask _____ help when you need it.
• Thank you _____ showing your interest.

05 다음 우리말에 맞게 빈칸을 완성하시오. (철자가 주어진 경우, 그 철자로 시작할 것)

(1) 사실 오늘 밤에 나는 나가고 싶지 않다.
➡ A_____, I don't think I want to go out tonight.

(2) 너는 어디서 요리하는 것을 배웠니?
➡ _____ did you learn _____ _____?

(3) 이것은 돈을 절약할 기회이다.
➡ This is an o_____ to save money.

Conversation

[06~07] 다음 대화를 읽고 물음에 답하시오.

B: Do you enjoy ⓐto read books, Yumi?
G: Yes, I love ⓑreading science books. ⓒWhat about you?
B: I love ⓓto read books, too.
G: Then, let's ⓔto go to the library after school today.

06 위 대화의 밑줄 친 ⓐ~ⓔ 중 어법상 틀린 개수를 고르시오.

① 1개 ② 2개 ③ 3개 ④ 4개 ⑤ 5개

07 위 대화를 읽고 답할 수 없는 질문을 고르시오.

① What is the boy's hobby?
② What kinds of books does Yumi love reading?
③ Where are they going to go after school?
④ Does Yumi love reading?
⑤ Does the boy love reading?

[08~09] 다음 대화를 읽고 물음에 답하시오.

> G: (A)_____, Minsu?
> B: I made breakfast for my family.
> G: Do you enjoy ⓐ_____?
> B: Yes, I'm a good ⓑ_____! My family loves my ⓒ_____.

08 빈칸 (A)에 들어갈 알맞은 말을 고르시오.

① Where did you go on the weekend
② Where did you get it
③ What are you going to do on the weekend
④ What are you making for your family
⑤ What did you do on the weekend

09 빈칸 ⓐ~ⓒ에 들어갈 알맞은 말을 보기에서 골라 쓰시오.

┌─── 보기 ───────────────────────┐
│ cook   cooking   to cook   cooked │
└───────────────────────────────┘

➡ ⓐ_____ ⓑ_____ ⓒ_____

[10~12] 다음 대화를 읽고 물음에 답하시오.

> B: Hello, Kate. I'm Hamin, the leader of the Nanum Orchestra. Thank you for your (A)_____ in our club. (①)
> G: Hi. Nice to meet you.
> B: You play ⓐthe violin? ⓑWhen did you start playing the violin?
> G: I started learning how to play the violin ⓒthat I was ten. (②)
> B: Do you have any experience playing in a group?
> G: Yes. Actually, I was a member of an orchestra ⓓwhen I was in elementary school. (③)
> B: Great. We also volunteer ⓔto teach children. Do you enjoy teaching others? (④)
> G: I have no experience teaching others. (⑤)
> B: Good. I think we'll have a great time playing together. Welcome to the Nanum Orchestra.

10 위 대화의 ①~⑤ 중 다음 주어진 말이 들어갈 알맞은 곳은?

> But I enjoy working with people, so I'd like to try.

①   ②   ③   ④   ⑤

11 빈칸 (A)에 들어갈 알맞은 말을 고르시오.

① interest   ② surprise   ③ event
④ attention   ⑤ effort

12 위 글의 밑줄 친 ⓐ~ⓔ 중 어법상 틀린 것을 고르시오.

① ⓐ   ② ⓑ   ③ ⓒ   ④ ⓓ   ⑤ ⓔ

[13~14] 다음 대화를 읽고 물음에 답하시오.

> A: Do you enioy ⓐlook at the stars at night?
> B: Yes, I love ⓑdoing that.

13 위 대화의 밑줄 친 ⓐ를 알맞은 형으로 고치시오.

➡ _____

14 위 대화의 밑줄 친 ⓑ가 가리키는 것을 영어로 쓰시오.

➡ _____

Grammar

15 다음 빈칸에 알맞은 것을 모두 고르시오.

> Jin is a girl _____ likes to play the piano.

① who   ② whose   ③ whom
④ which   ⑤ that

16 다음 주어진 단어를 이용하여 빈칸에 알맞은 말을 쓰시오.

> 지수는 엄마에게 어디에 가방을 둬야 할지 물어
> 봤다.
> = Jisu asked her mother _____
> the bag. (put)

17 밑줄 친 that의 쓰임이 나머지 넷과 다른 것은?

① A baker is a person that bakes bread.

② She told me that I should be more careful.

③ I walked to my school that is three stops away.

④ I know the very person that will do the job quickly.

⑤ The girl that is talking on the phone is my sister, Susan.

18 다음 괄호 안에 주어진 단어를 어법에 맞게 빈칸에 쓰시오.

(1) Do you know how _____ _____ _____ to the National Museum? (get)

(2) I don't know where _____ _____ the bus. (take)

(3) I told him who _____ _____ for. (look)

(4) You should choose _____ dress _____ _____ to the party. (wear)

19 빈칸에 알맞은 말을 어법에 맞게 쓰시오. (that은 쓰지 말 것)

> (1) People look at the boy _____ is playing the piano on the street.
> (2) The coat _____ is black is mine.

20 다음 중 어법상 어색한 문장은?

① I want to become a soccer player who can make wonderful heading goals.

② Would you tell me where to park the car?

③ I have a smartphone that was made in Korea.

④ Her mother taught her how to make delicious spaghetti.

⑤ The writer couldn't decide what to write the story.

21 다음은 두 문장을 관계대명사를 사용하여 한 문장으로 쓴 것이다. 빈칸에 다른 한 문장을 쓰시오.

(1) • _____
  • They can introduce and sell books to people.
  → We are looking for volunteers who[that] can introduce and sell books to people.

(2) • My class has some students.
  • _____
  → My class has some students who[that] are good at English.

(3) • I have a friend.
  • _____
  → I have a friend who[that] lives in New Zealand.

(4) • Angelina loved the present.
  • _____
  → Angelina loved the present that[which] Chuck gave to her on her birthday.

22 다음 밑줄 친 부분의 쓰임이 나머지 넷과 다른 것은?

① I want to learn how <u>to do</u> that.
② Do you know when <u>to start</u> the performance?
③ He couldn't decide what <u>to do</u>.
④ Julia bought a book <u>to read</u> on the train.
⑤ She asked me where <u>to find</u> the ladies' room.

23 두 문장을 관계 대명사를 사용하여 한 문장으로 쓰시오.
(that은 사용하지 말 것)

(1) • She wants to see a movie.
   • The movie is interesting.
   ➡ _____

(2) • Rose is Jake's best friend.
   • She works for a bank.
   ➡ _____

(3) • James bought a new computer.
   • The computer is really nice
   ➡ _____

Reading

[24~26] 다음 글을 읽고 물음에 답하시오.

The Boram Orchestra
Hi! I am Minsu Jang, the leader of the Boram Orchestra. Did you see several students playing music at the main gate when you came to school today? We were ⓐ<u>those students</u>. We play music for our friends every morning. You need to know how to play an instrument a little bit to join our club. But don't worry if you don't play well. We will practice hard and get better together. We also teach children how to play musical instruments as a service to our community. I am teaching an eleven-year-old boy to play the violin. At first, he did not know how to read a note. Now he can play a simple song. ⓑ<u>Hearing</u> him play the violin

makes me very happy. By joining our club, you can have an opportunity to help others. Come and join our club. We are waiting for you.

24 위 글의 밑줄 친 ⓐ<u>those students</u>가 가리키는 것을 본문에서 찾아 쓰시오.

➡ _____
_____

25 위 글의 밑줄 친 ⓑ<u>Hearing</u>과 문법적 쓰임이 다른 것을 모두 고르시오.

① Look at the man <u>hearing</u> the lecture.
② He is interested in <u>hearing</u> the lecture.
③ My dream is <u>hearing</u> the lecture.
④ Are they <u>hearing</u> the lecture now?
⑤ I enjoyed <u>hearing</u> the lecture.

26 위 글의 내용과 일치하지 <u>않는</u> 것은?

① 민수는 매일 방과 후에 친구들을 위해 음악을 연주한다.
② 보람 오케스트라 동아리에 가입하려면 악기를 연주하는 법을 조금 알아야 한다.
③ 보람 오케스트라 동아리는 아이들에게 악기를 연주하는 법도 가르친다.
④ 민수는 열한 살 난 소년에게 바이올린을 가르치고 있다.
⑤ 보람 오케스트라 동아리에 가입함으로써 다른 사람들을 도울 수 있는 기회를 가질 수 있다.

[27~29] 다음 글을 읽고 물음에 답하시오.

The Picasso Art Club
Hi! I am Sora Kang from the Picasso Art Club. As you can guess from the name of our club, we paint. We also do volunteer work ⓐ<u>from time to time</u>. (A)[Last summer / In last summer], our club members participated

in the "Change Our Neighborhood" project. On the dirty old walls of the buildings in our neighborhood, we painted birds flying (B)[high / highly] in the sky and dolphins jumping over blue waves. As a result, the old neighborhood changed into a bright and beautiful place. The neighbors were happy to see our work and (C)[to thank / thanked] us. You don't have to be a good painter. Anyone who likes ⓑ_____ can join. Come and be a member of the Picasso Art Club.

27 위 글의 밑줄 친 ⓐfrom time to time과 의미가 다른 것을 모두 고르시오.

① once in a while　② always
③ now and then　④ sometimes
⑤ rarely

28 위 글의 괄호 (A)~(C)에서 문맥이나 어법상 알맞은 낱말을 골라 쓰시오.

➡ (A)_____　(B)_____　(C)_____

29 위 글의 빈칸 ⓑ에 들어갈 알맞은 말을 고르시오.

① to change the neighborhood
② to play music
③ to paint
④ to help others
⑤ to play sports

[30~31] 다음 글을 읽고 물음에 답하시오.

Hello, everyone. I'm Jason, the leader of the Abracadabra Club. On May 5, our club members will go to Hanguk Hospital to visit sick children. We are going to show them magic and teach ⓐthem how to do magic.

30 위 글의 밑줄 친 ⓐthem이 가리키는 것을 본문에서 찾아 쓰시오.

➡ _____

31 Abracadabra 동아리에 대한 소개를 완성하도록 다음 빈칸에 공통으로 들어갈 단어를 쓰시오.

The Abracadabra Club is a _____ club. On May 5, its members will go to Hanguk Hospital and show _____ to sick children and teach them how to do _____.

[32~33] 다음 글을 읽고 물음에 답하시오.

We will hold a book ⓐfair at Nanum Middle School on May 5. We are looking ⓑ_____ volunteers who can introduce and sell books ⓒ_____ people. Anyone who loves books can join our event! If you are interested, please let us know!

32 위 글의 밑줄 친 ⓐfair와 같은 의미로 쓰인 것을 고르시오.

① We have to be fair to both players.
② Let's take the kids to the fair.
③ She has long fair hair.
④ A fair number of people came along.
⑤ It was a fair and breezy day.

33 위 글의 빈칸 ⓑ와 ⓒ에 들어갈 전치사가 바르게 짝지어진 것은?

① at – to　　② for – of
③ in – on　　④ at – or
⑤ for – to

출제율 85%

01 다음 짝지어진 두 단어의 관계가 같도록 주어진 철자로 시작해 빈칸에 쓰시오.

chief : leader – training : p_____

출제율 95%

02 다음 〈보기〉의 단어를 사용하여 자연스러운 문장을 만들 수 없는 것은?

보기
drone   garden   interest   leader

① He is the _____ of the music club.
② Do you have any _____ in the opera?
③ The house has a _____ with trees and flowers.
④ You can come a little _____ later.
⑤ A _____ is a small remote-controlled helicopter.

[03~06] 다음 대화를 읽고 물음에 답하시오.

B: ⓐThese cookies look so delicious. Did you make ⓑthem?

G: Yes. I made ⓒthem myself yesterday. I enjoy baking. I'm going to make doughnuts this Saturday.

B: Oh, I want to learn how to make ⓓthem. Is it difficult?

G: Not at all. You can come to my house and join me if you want.

B: Thanks, Bora. (A)_____ should I come?

G: At 2:00.

B: Sounds good. See you then.

출제율 90%

03 밑줄 친 ⓐ~ⓓ 중 가리키는 것이 같은 것끼리 짝지어진 것을 고르시오.

① ⓐ, ⓓ
② ⓑ, ⓓ
③ ⓒ, ⓓ
④ ⓐ, ⓑ, ⓒ
⑤ ⓐ, ⓑ, ⓒ, ⓓ

출제율 95%

04 빈칸 (A)에 들어갈 말을 쓰시오. (2 단어)

➡ _____

출제율 90%

05 다음 영영풀이에 해당하는 단어를 대화에서 찾아 쓰시오.

1. to become a member of an organization, society, or group
2. to begin to take part in an activity that other people are involved in

➡ _____

출제율 100%

06 대화를 읽고 답할 수 없는 질문을 고르시오.

① Who made the cookies?
② Where are they going to meet this Saturday?
③ What kinds of food does the boy know how to make?
④ When did the girl make the cookies?
⑤ What will the girl make this Saturday?

07 다음 빈칸에 공통으로 들어갈 말을 쓰시오.

- I'd like _____ _____ soccer.
- I don't know how _____ _____ the piano or violin.

08 다음 우리말 해석에 맞게 빈칸을 완성하시오.

(1) _____ _____ _____, my team lost. (결과적으로, 우리 팀은 졌다.)

(2) _____ _____, I was very _____ in acting. (처음에, 나는 연기에 아주 관심이 많았다.)

(3) It can _____ _____ different types of chair. (그것은 다른 종류들의 의자로 변할 수 있다.)

(4) P l e a s e _____ _____ _____ _____ _____ do it. (그것을 어떻게 해야 하는지 우리에게 알려주세요.)

[09~10] 주어진 문장 다음에 이어질 대화의 순서를 바르게 배열하시오.

09

What did you do on the weekend, Minsu?

(A) Yes, I'm a good cook! My family loves my cooking.
(B) I made breakfast for my family.
(C) Do you enjoy cooking?

➡ _____

10

Jiyun, that's a pretty backpack! Where did you get it?

(A) Wow! She's a really good designer.
(B) My sister made it for me.
(C) Yes, she is. And she enjoys making clothes, too.

➡ _____

11 대화의 밑줄 친 우리말을 주어진 단어를 이용해 영작하시오.

A: 너는 여가 시간에 뭐 하는 것을 즐기니?
B: I enjoy taking pictures of people in the park.

➡ _____

(free, enjoy, have, when)

12 다음 우리말을 주어진 어휘를 이용하여 영작하시오.

(1) Jisu는 그녀의 엄마에게 어디에 가방을 둬야 할지 물어봤다. (where, the bag, put, to)
➡ _____

(2) 너는 다음에 우리가 무엇을 해야 할지 아니? (what, should, next)
➡ _____

(3) 나는 무엇을 요리할지 결정할 수 없었다. (decide, cook, to)
➡ _____

(4) 운동장에서 농구를 하고 있는 소녀들이 몇 명 있다. (there, a few girls, playing, the playground.)
➡ _____

(5) Janet은 재미있는 그림이 많은 책을 아주 좋아한다. (pictures, funny, have, love, many)
➡ _____

(6) 길을 건너던 Linda와 그녀의 개가 부상을 입었다. (crossing the street, injured)

➡ _____

_____

출제율 100%

13 다음 중 어법상 올바른 문장은?

① I know a girl which is good at English.

② I want to buy a bag who is expensive.

③ When to use the model has to be decided.

④ I asked her where putting the baggage.

⑤ We also teach children how play musical instruments as a service to our community.

출제율 90%

14 다음 중 어법상 잘못된 것을 바르게 고치시오.

(1) Can you tell me how get to the subway station?

➡ _____

(2) There are some tips for what to lose weight.

➡ _____

(3) What he to eat is important to him.

➡ _____

(4) I have a friend which likes soccer.

➡ _____

(5) The girl is standing under the tree is waiting for you.

➡ _____

(6) Christel sent a letter to her mom whom missed her a lot.

➡ _____

(7) Mike is wearing shoes that is too small for him.

➡ _____

(8) Peter Pan was a boy who he liked to fly.

➡ _____

[15~16] 다음 글을 읽고 물음에 답하시오.

ⓐParticipating in club activities is a great way to enjoy your school life. How about joining a club? Here are two club leaders who want students ⓑ their clubs. Let's listen to what they say.

출제율 95%

15 위 글의 밑줄 친 ⓐParticipating과 문법적 쓰임이 같은 것을 모두 고르시오.

① She isn't playing tennis.

② My hobby is taking pictures.

③ I saw him walking with his friends.

④ Look at the man sitting on the bench.

⑤ He is proud of being Korean.

출제율 85%

16 위 글의 빈칸 ⓑ에 join을 알맞은 형태로 쓰시오.

➡ _____

[17~19] 다음 글을 읽고 물음에 답하시오.

The Picasso Art Club

Hi! I am Sora Kang from the Picasso Art Club. As you can guess from the name of our club, we paint. We also do ⓐ work from time to time. Last summer, our club members participated in the "Change Our Neighborhood" project. On the dirty old walls of the buildings in our neighborhood, ⓑ하늘 높이 나는 새들과 푸른 파도 위로 점프하는 돌고래들을 그렸습니다. As a result, the old neighborhood changed into a bright and beautiful place. The neighbors were happy to see our work and thanked us. You don't have to be a good painter. ⓒAnyone who likes to paint can join. Come and be a member of the Picasso Art Club.

17 주어진 영영풀이를 참고하여 빈칸 ⓐ에 철자 v로 시작하는 단어를 쓰시오.

출제율 90%

> someone who does work without being paid for it, because they want to do it

➡ _____

18 위 글의 밑줄 친 ⓑ의 우리말에 맞게 한 단어를 보충하여, 주어진 어휘를 알맞게 배열하시오.

출제율 90%

> dolphins / in the sky / and / painted / over blue waves / birds / jumping / flying / we

➡ _____

_____

19 위 글의 밑줄 친 ⓒAnyone who와 바꿔 쓸 수 있는 말을 고르시오.

출제율 95%

① Whoever ② Whichever
③ Whatever ④ However
⑤ Whomever

[20~22] 다음 글을 읽고 물음에 답하시오.

The Boram Orchestra

Hi! I am Minsu Jang, the leader of the Boram Orchestra. (①) Did you see several students playing music at the main gate when you came to school today? (②) We play music for our friends every morning. (③) You need to know how to play an instrument a little bit to join our club. (④) But don't worry if you don't play well. (⑤) We will practice hard and get better together. We also teach children how to play musical instruments ⓐas a service to our community. I am teaching an eleven-year-old

boy to play the violin. ⓑ , he did not know how to read a note. Now he can play a simple song. Hearing him play the violin makes me very happy. By joining our club, you can have an opportunity to help others. Come and join our club. We are waiting for you.

20 위 글의 흐름으로 보아, 주어진 문장이 들어가기에 가장 적절한 곳은?

출제율 90%

> We were those students.

① ② ③ ④ ⑤

21 위 글의 밑줄 친 ⓐas와 같은 의미로 쓰인 것을 고르시오.

출제율 100%

① As she was tired, she soon fell asleep.
② Do as you like.
③ I love you as much as I love her.
④ This box can be used as a chair.
⑤ Her anger grew as she talked.

22 위 글의 빈칸 ⓑ에 들어갈 알맞은 말을 고르시오.

출제율 90%

① Finally ② At first
③ At last ④ Therefore
⑤ As a result

01 다음 대화의 순서를 바르게 배열하시오.

> (A) Yes, I love reading science books. How about you?
> (B) I love reading books, too.
> (C) Then, let's go to the library after school today.
> (D) Do you enjoy reading books, Yumi?

➡ _____

02 다음 대화의 밑줄 친 부분과 의미가 같도록 조동사를 이용하여 영작하시오.

> A: Do you know how to make a paper cat?
> B: Of course. It's easy.

➡ _____

[03~04] 다음 대화를 읽고 물음에 답하시오.

> G: Did you buy that drone?
> B: No, I got it as a present from my parents, but I don't know how to use it. 어떻게 하는지 아니?
> G: No, maybe Jina knows how to do it. She enjoys flying drones.
> B: Then, (ask, help, will, I, her, for)

03 괄호 안의 단어를 이용하여 밑줄 친 우리말을 바르게 영작하시오. (5 단어)

➡ _____ (how)

04 괄호 안의 단어를 배열하여 문장을 만드시오.

➡ _____

05 다음 두 문장의 의미가 같도록 빈칸을 완성하시오.

(1) Do you know how I can get to the National Museum?
= Do you know _____ _____ _____ to the National Museum?

(2) Brigette taught us how we should make a paper cat.
= Brigette taught us _____ _____ _____ a paper cat.

(3) Tell me when I should wake you up.
= Tell me _____ _____ you up.

(4) Tell the driver where he should stop.
= Tell the driver _____ _____.

(5) I do not know what I should do.
= I do not know _____ _____.

(6) Whom I should meet became the most important to me.
= _____ _____ _____ became the most important to me.

06 두 문장을 관계대명사를 사용하여 한 문장으로 쓰시오. (that은 사용하지 말 것)

(1) • Kay lives in a house.
• The house has a beautiful garden.
➡ _____

(2) • Naomi is standing over there.
• She is very beautiful.
➡ _____

[07~09] 다음 글을 읽고 물음에 답하시오.

The Picasso Art Club

Hi! I am Sora Kang from the Picasso Art Club. As you can guess from the name of our club, we paint. We also do volunteer work from time to time. Last summer, our club members participated in the "Change Our Neighborhood" project. On the dirty old walls of the buildings in our neighborhood, we painted birds flying high in the sky and dolphins jumping over blue waves. ⓐ a result, the old neighborhood changed into a bright and beautiful place. The neighbors were happy to see our work and thanked us. You don't have to be a good painter. Anyone ⓑwho likes to paint can join. Come and be a member of the Picasso Art Club.

07 다음 질문에 대한 알맞은 대답을 영어로 쓰시오. (8 단어)

Q: What did the members of the Picasso Art Club do last summer?

A: _____

08 위 글의 빈칸 ⓐ에 알맞는 단어를 쓰시오.

➡ _____

09 위 글의 밑줄 친 ⓑwho와 바꿔 쓸 수 있는 단어를 쓰시오.

➡ _____

[10~12] 다음 글을 읽고 물음에 답하시오.

The Boram Orchestra

Hi! I am Minsu Jang, the leader of the Boram Orchestra. Did you see several students playing music at the main gate when you came to school today? We were (A)[that / those] students. We play music for our friends every morning. You need to know how to play an instrument a little bit to join our club. But don't worry if you don't play well. We will practice (B)[hard / hardly] and get better together. We also teach children ⓐhow to play musical instruments as a service to our community. I am teaching an eleven-year-old boy to play the violin. At first, he did not know how to read a note. Now he can play a simple song. Hearing him (C)[play / to play] the violin makes me very happy. By joining our club, you can have an opportunity to help others. Come and join our club. We are waiting for you.

10 위 글의 괄호 (A)~(C)에서 문맥이나 어법상 알맞은 낱말을 골라 쓰시오.

➡ (A)_____ (B)_____ (C)_____

11 위 글의 밑줄 친 ⓐ를 다음과 같이 바꿔 쓸 때 빈칸에 들어갈 알맞은 말을 쓰시오.

➡ how _____ _____ play

12 위 글의 내용을 다음과 같이 정리하고자 한다. 빈칸 (A)와 (B)에 들어갈 알맞은 단어를 본문에서 찾아 쓰시오.

Minsu Jang is the (A)_____ of the Boram Orchestra and he introduces the activities of his club and tells students to (B)_____ his club.

01 다음 그림을 보고 주어진 〈조건〉에 맞게 문장을 완성하시오.

> 주어진 단어를 사용하고 필요하면 단어의 형태를 변화시킬 것

(1)

➡ I _____ (enjoy, fly)

(2)

➡ We _____ (a pizza, make, want)

02 다음 가입하고 싶은 동아리와 그 이유를 바탕으로 동아리 지원서를 작성하시오.

Club   FC Boram
What I Am Good at   • pass the ball
                             • run fast
What I Want to Learn   • head the ball
My Goals   • practice hard
                             • become a good team player

Boram Middle School
Club Membership Form
• (A)_____ of Club: FC Boram
• Student Name: Sunho Park
• Why You Want to Join the Club: I love soccer and would like to join (B)_____. I am
  good at (C)_____ the ball and (D)_____ fast. However, I don't
  know how to head the ball, so I want to learn how to do that. I want to become a soccer player
  who can make wonderful (E)_____ goals.
• Your Goals: If I join this club, I will practice very hard and become (F)_____!

03 주어진 어휘와 표현을 이용하여 3 문장 이상을 쓰시오.

what	how	when	where	whom
go	start	play	find	say

(1) _____

(2) _____

(3) _____

(4) _____

(5) _____

단원별 모의고사

[01~02] 다음 대화의 빈칸에 알맞은 단어를 고르시오.

01

A: What do you enjoy doing when you have free time?
B: I enjoy _____ my dog in the park.

① making　② getting　③ walking
④ climbing　⑤ knowing

02

B: Jiyun, that's a pretty backpack! Where did you _____ it?
G: My sister made it for me.

① get　② see　③ bake
④ grow　⑤ join

03 다음 빈칸에 들어갈 말을 <보기>에서 찾아 쓰시오. (형태 변화 가능)

┌─ 보기 ─┐
join　own　neighbor　interest

(1) Ben shows a(n) _____ in learning French.
(2) I decided to _____ the army.
(3) One of the _____ complained about the noise from the party.
(4) Bring your _____ book.

04 다음 영영풀이에 해당하는 단어를 주어진 철자로 시작하여 쓰고, (1), (2), (3)에 알맞은 단어를 쓰시오. (형태 변화 가능)

• p_____ : to do something regularly in order to do it better
• h_____ : to have a meeting, party, election etc in a particular place or at a particular time
• n_____ : the area around you or around a particular place, or the people who live there

(1) The meeting will be _____ at this hotel.
(2) Is there a good Chinese restaurant in the _____?
(3) I need to _____ playing the guitar.

[05~07] 다음 대화를 읽고 물음에 답하시오.

B: These cookies look so delicious. Did you make (A)[it / them]? (①)
G: Yes. I made them myself yesterday. (②) I enjoy baking. (B)[I went / I'm going] to make doughnuts this Saturday.
B: Oh, I want to learn how to make doughnuts. (③) Is it difficult?
G: Not at all. (④)
B: Thanks, Bora. (⑤) What time should I (C)[come / to come]?
G: At 2:00.
B: Sounds good. See you then.

05 위 대화의 ①~⑤ 중 다음 주어진 말이 들어갈 알맞은 곳은?

You can come to my house and join me if you want.

①　②　③　④　⑤

06 (A), (B), (C)에 적절한 말을 골라 쓰시오.

➡ (A)_____ (B)_____ (C)_____

07 위 대화의 내용과 일치하지 않는 것을 모두 고르시오.

① The boy wants to learn how to make doughnuts.

② The boy went to her house at 2:00.

③ The girl thinks that making doughnuts is not difficult.

④ The boy wants to go to the girl's house to learn how to make cookies.

⑤ The girl enjoys baking.

[08~10] 다음 대화를 읽고 물음에 답하시오.

> G: Did you buy that drone? (①)
>
> B: No, I got it as a present from my parents, but I don't know (A)_____ use it. (②) Do you know how to? (③)
>
> G: (④) No, maybe Jina knows (B)_____ do it. (⑤)
>
> B: Then, I will ask her for help.

08 위 대화의 ①~⑤ 중 다음 주어진 말이 들어갈 알맞은 곳은?

> She enjoys flying drones.

①   ②   ③   ④   ⑤

09 다음 영영풀이에 해당하는 단어를 대화에서 찾아 쓰시오.

> an aircraft that does not have a pilot, but is operated by radio

➡ _____

10 (A)와 (B)에 공통으로 들어갈 말을 대화에서 찾아 쓰시오.

➡ _____

11 다음 대화에서 어색한 부분을 찾아 고치시오.

> A: ①Do you know ②how to ③make a paper cat?
>
> B: ④Of course not. ⑤It's easy.

➡ _____

[12~14] 다음 대화를 읽고 물음에 답하시오.

> B: Hello, Kate. I'm Hamin, the leader of the Nanum Orchestra. 우리 동아리에 관심을 가져줘서 고마워.
>
> G: Hi. Nice to meet you.
>
> B: You play the violin? (A)_____?
>
> G: I started learning how to play the violin when I was ten.
>
> B: (B)_____?
>
> G: Yes. Actually, I was a member of an orchestra when I was in elementary school.
>
> B: Great. We also volunteer to teach children. (C)_____?
>
> G: I have no experience teaching others. But I enjoy working with people, so I'd like to try.
>
> B: Good. I think we'll have a great time playing together. Welcome to the Nanum Orchestra.

12 다음 영영풀이에 해당하는 단어를 대화에서 찾아 쓰시오.

(1)

> the person who directs or controls a group, organization, country, etc.

➡ _____

(2)

> a large group of musicians playing many different kinds of instruments and led by a conductor

➡ _____

13 밑줄 친 우리말과 의미가 같도록 주어진 단어를 이용해 문장을 완성하시오.

➡ _____

(in, you, your, our)

14 (A)~(C)에 알맞은 질문을 〈보기〉에서 골라 쓰시오.

┤ 보기 ├
- Do you know how to play the violin?
- Do you enjoy teaching others?
- What do you enjoy doing when you have free time?
- When did you start playing the violin?
- Do you have any experience playing in a group?

➡ (A) _____
(B) _____
(C) _____

15 다음 빈칸에 들어갈 말로 알맞지 않은 것은? (2개)

He let me know _____ to do it.

① what   ② how   ③ when
④ why   ⑤ where

16 다음 중 어법상 어색한 것을 고르시오.

① I don't know when to start.
② Where are the pictures that it was taken by Gibson?
③ Can you teach me how to play the guitar?
④ Anyone who likes to paint can join our club.
⑤ This is the key which was lost yesterday.

17 다음 중 어법상 어색한 것을 바르게 고쳐 다시 쓰시오.

(1) Tell me how use this computer.

➡ _____

(2) He didn't know what to go.

➡ _____

(3) Do you know how should I to swim?

➡ _____

(4) The doctors are working in this hospital are very kind.

➡ _____
_____

(5) Did you meet the girl that she is wearing sunglasses?

➡ _____

(6) Mary has a cousin which live in Seoul.

➡ _____

(7) Melina took some pictures of her friends whom were on a hiking trip.

➡ _____
_____

[18~20] 다음 글을 읽고 물음에 답하시오.

The Picasso Art Club
Hi! I am Sora Kang from the Picasso Art Club. As you can guess from the name of our club, we paint. We also do volunteer work from time to time. Last summer, our club members ⓐparticipated in the "Change Our Neighborhood" project. On the dirty old walls of the buildings in our neighborhood,

we painted birds ⓑflying high in the sky and dolphins jumping over blue waves. As a result, the old neighborhood changed into a bright and beautiful place. The neighbors were happy to see our work and thanked us. You don't have to be a good painter. Anyone who likes to paint can join. Come and be a member of the Picasso Art Club.

18 위 글의 밑줄 친 ⓐparticipated in과 바꿔 쓸 수 있는 것을 모두 고르시오.

① joined
② made a plan for
③ prepared for
④ took part in
⑤ took care of

19 아래 보기에서 위 글의 밑줄 친 ⓑflying과 문법적 쓰임이 다른 것의 개수를 고르시오.

┤ 보기 ├
① She was watching TV in the living room.
② Thank you for visiting our house.
③ Talking behind others' back is not good.
④ He enjoyed listening to her stories.
⑤ Is your hobby playing tennis?

① 1개　② 2개　③ 3개　④ 4개　⑤ 5개

20 다음 빈칸 (A)와 (B)에 알맞은 단어를 넣어 피카소 미술 동아리의 가입 조건을 완성하시오.

You can be a member of the Picasso Art Club if you like (A)_____ _____ but there is no need for you to be (B)_____ _____.

[21~23] 다음 글을 읽고 물음에 답하시오.

The Boram Orchestra

Hi! I am Minsu Jang, the leader of the Boram Orchestra. Did you see several students playing music at the main gate when you came to school today? We were those students. We play music for our friends every morning. You need to know how to play an instrument a little bit to join our club. But don't worry if you don't play well. We will practice hard and get better together. We also teach children how to play musical instruments ⓐ a service to our community. I am teaching an eleven-year-old boy to play the violin. At first, he did not know ⓑhow to read a note. Now he can play a simple song. ⓒ그가 바이올린을 연주하는 걸 듣는 것은 저를 매우 행복하게 합니다. ⓓ joining our club, you can have an opportunity to help others. Come and join our club. We are waiting for you.

21 위 글의 빈칸 ⓐ와 ⓓ에 들어갈 전치사가 바르게 짝지어진 것은?

① to – By
② as – To
③ as – By
④ at – In
⑤ on – For

22 위 글의 밑줄 친 ⓑhow to read와 to부정사의 용법이 다른 것을 모두 고르시오.

① It is interesting to play tennis.
② Tell me the way to play tennis well.
③ I think it interesting to play tennis.
④ He got up early to play tennis.
⑤ I'm healthy enough to play tennis.

23 위 글의 밑줄 친 ⓒ의 우리말에 맞게 주어진 어휘를 이용하여 9 단어로 영작하시오.

hearing

➡ _____

Lesson 4

The Two Roads

 의사소통 기능

- 걱정 표현하기와 안심시키기
  A: I'm worried about your health.
  B: Don't worry. I'm going to the doctor tomorrow.
- 의견 묻기
  A: What do you think of my bike?
  B: It looks light and fast.

언어 형식

- 현재완료
  I **have lived** quietly and well.

- 접속사 'if'
  How can we know **if** we don't try?

Words & Expressions

Key Words

- □ **besides** [bisáidz] 부 게다가
- □ **character** [kǽriktər] 명 등장인물
- □ **comfortable** [kʌ́mfərtəbl] 형 편안한
- □ **correct** [kərékt] 형 올바른
- □ **cub** [kʌb] 명 (곰, 사자 등의) 새끼
- □ **disappointed** [dìsəpɔ́intid] 형 실망한, 기대에 어긋난
- □ **ever** [évər] 부 언제든, 한 번이라도
- □ **foreign** [fɔ́ːrən] 형 외국의
- □ **foreigner** [fɔ́ːrənər] 명 외국인
- □ **friendly** [fréndli] 형 친절한
- □ **happiness** [hǽpinis] 명 행복
- □ **item** [áitəm] 명 품목
- □ **join** [dʒɔin] 동 함께 하다
- □ **journey** [dʒə́ːrni] 명 여행
- □ **nearby** [níərbài] 부 근처에
- □ **nervous** [nə́ːrvəs] 형 불안한
- □ **noisy** [nɔ́izi] 형 시끄러운
- □ **opinion** [əpínjən] 명 의견
- □ **regret** [rigrét] 동 후회하다
- □ **reply** [riplái] 동 대답하다
- □ **review** [rivjúː] 명 감상문, 논평
- □ **rule** [ruːl] 동 지배하다
- □ **scary** [skɛ́əri] 형 무서운
- □ **scene** [siːn] 명 장면
- □ **school cafeteria** 학교 식당
- □ **seagull** [síːgʌl] 명 갈매기
- □ **separate** [sépəreit] 동 헤어지다
- □ **such** [sʌtʃ] 형 그러한, 너무나 ~한
- □ **support** [səpɔ́ːrt] 명 지지 동 지지하다
- □ **teenager** [tínèidʒər] 명 십 대
- □ **throne** [θroun] 명 왕좌, 왕위
- □ **title** [táitl] 명 제목
- □ **weather** [wéðər] 명 날씨
- □ **wide** [waid] 형 넓은

Key Expressions

- □ **be good at**: ~을 잘하다
- □ **be scared of**: ~을 두려워하다
- □ **be worried about**: ~에 대해 걱정하다
- □ **break out**: 발발하다
- □ **by the way**: 그런데(대화에서 화제를 바꿀 때 씀)
- □ **get**+형용사: ~하게 되다
- □ **get better**: (병·상황 등이) 나아지다
- □ **go into**: ~에 들어가다
- □ **go to the doctor**: 병원에 가다
- □ **have a good time**: 좋은 시간을 보내다
- □ **look for**: ~을 찾다
- □ **look good** (**on** 사람): (~에게) 잘 어울리다
- □ **look like**+명사: ~처럼 보이다
- □ **not anymore**: 더 이상 ~ 않다
- □ **take away**: ~을 빼앗다
- □ **take ~ for a walk**: ~을 산책하러 데리고 가다
- □ **try to**+동사원형: ~하는 것을 노력하다
- □ **What do you think of/about** ~?: ~에 대해 어떻게 생각해?
- □ **What if** 주어 동사 ~?: 만약 ~이라면 어떻게 될까?
- □ 비교급 **and** 비교급: 점점 더 ~한[하게]

Word Power

※ 서로 비슷한 뜻을 가진 단어
- □ **correct**(올바른) : **right**(바른, 옳은)
- □ **happiness**(행복) : **pleasure**(즐거움, 기쁨)
- □ **nervous**(불안한) : **worried**(걱정되는), **concerned**(우려하는)

- □ **journey**(여행) : **trip**(여행)
- □ **rule**(지배하다) : **control**(통제하다)
- □ **reply**(대답하다) : **answer**(답하다)

※ 서로 반대의 뜻을 가진 단어
- □ **correct**(올바른) ↔ **incorrect**(올바르지 않은)
- □ **happiness**(행복) ↔ **unhappiness**(불운, 불행)
- □ **separate**(헤어지다) ↔ **unite**(통합하다)

- □ **friendly**(친절한) ↔ **unfriendly**(불친절한, 쌀쌀맞은)
- □ **noisy**(시끄러운) ↔ **quiet**(조용한)
- □ **wide**(넓은) ↔ **narrow**(좁은)

※ 형용사에 -ness를 붙여 명사가 되는 단어
- □ **happy**(행복한) ↔ **happiness**(행복)
- □ **dark**(어두운) ↔ **darkness**(어두움)

- □ **sad**(슬픈) ↔ **sadness**(슬픔)
- □ **kind**(친절한) ↔ **kindness**(친절)

English Dictionary

- □ **besides** 게다가
  → used to give an additional reason for something
  무언가에 대해 추가적인 이유를 제시할 때 사용되는 말
- □ **character** 등장인물
  → a person in a film, book, or play
  영화, 책 또는 연극에 있는 인물
- □ **correct** 올바른
  → having no errors 잘못을 가지고 있지 않은
- □ **cub** (곰, 사자 등의) 새끼
  → the young of a bear, lion or other mammals
  곰, 사자 또는 다른 포유류의 어린 새끼
- □ **ever** 언제든, 한 번이라도
  → at any time 언제든지
- □ **foreign** 외국의
  → from a country other than one's own
  자기 나라 이외의 다른 나라로부터
- □ **happiness** 행복
  → the feeling of pleasure 기쁨의 감정
- □ **journey** 여행
  → a trip from one place to another
  한 장소에서 다른 장소로 가는 여행
- □ **nervous** 불안한
  → worried and anxious about something that is happening or might happen
  일어나고 있는 일 또는 일어날 수도 있는 일에 대해서 걱정하고 염려하는
- □ **noisy** 시끄러운
  → making a lot of loud noise
  많은 시끄러운 소음을 만드는
- □ **opinion** 의견
  → a thought or belief about something
  어떤 것에 대한 생각이나 믿음

- □ **reply** 대답하다
  → to say or write something in response to something
  어떤 것에 응답하여 무언가를 말하거나 쓰다
- □ **review** 감상문, 논평
  → a critical comment in a newspaper that gives an opinion about a new book or film
  새로운 책이나 영화에 대해 의견을 내는 신문의 비평적인 언급
- □ **rule** 지배하다
  → to be in control of an area and its people
  한 지역과 그곳의 사람들을 제어하다
- □ **seagull** 갈매기
  → a bird with white or gray feathers that lives near the sea
  바다 근처에서 사는 하얗거나 회색의 깃털을 가진 새
- □ **separate** 헤어지다
  → to move apart 따로 이동하다
- □ **such** 너무나 ~한
  → so great (often used to emphasize a quality)
  너무 엄청난(보통 질을 강조하기 위해 사용됨)
- □ **support** 지지, 후원
  → help, encouragement, or comfort given to someone during a difficult or unhappy time
  어렵거나 불행한 시기 동안 누군가에게 주어지는 도움, 격려 또는 위로
- □ **teenager** 십대
  → a person between the ages of thirteen and nineteen
  13살에서 19살 사이의 사람
- □ **throne** 왕좌, 왕위
  → a decorative chair that a king, queen, or emperor sits on 왕, 여왕 또는 황제가 앉는 장식용 의자
- □ **title** 제목
  → the name of a book, film, or other artistic works
  책, 영화 또는 다른 예술 작품의 이름

01 주어진 단어 뒤에 ness를 붙여 명사를 만들 수 <u>없는</u> 것을 고르시오.

① happy   ② silent   ③ sad
④ kind   ⑤ dark

[02~03] 밑줄 친 부분과 의미가 가장 가까운 것을 고르시오.

02

> <u>Besides</u>, it's very cold outside.

① Next   ② Despite
③ Likewise   ④ In addition
⑤ However

03

> I didn't know how to <u>reply</u>.

① react   ② answer
③ explain   ④ consider
⑤ understand

[04~05] 다음 빈칸에 알맞은 단어를 고르시오.

04

> You look ____ a totally new person in that suit.

① as   ② so   ③ with   ④ in   ⑤ like

05

> Some people are worried that a war could break _____.

① out   ② away   ③ into
④ up   ⑤ off

06 다음 밑줄 친 부분의 의미로 알맞지 <u>않은</u> 것은? <서답형>

① It was a long <u>journey</u>. (여행)
② Would you mind giving me your <u>opinion</u> about that? (의견)
③ Most <u>teenagers</u> are under a lot of stress. (십대)
④ The <u>seagulls</u> are flying above my head. (갈매기)
⑤ Your uncle looks like a <u>foreigner</u>. (외국의)

07 다음 주어진 우리말에 맞게 빈칸을 채우시오. (철자가 주어진 것도 있음) <서답형>

(1) 너무나 아름다운 날씨예요!
➡ It is _____ a beautiful day!

(2) 이 홀은 백 명을 수용할 정도로 충분히 넓다.
➡ This hall is _____ enough to accommodate one hundred.

(3) 아이에게서 가위를 빼앗아라.
➡ T_____ the scissors _____ from the child.

(4) 나는 드디어 병원에 가기로 결정했어.
➡ I finally decided to _____ _____ the doctor.

(5) 어렸을 때, 난 어둠이 무서웠다.
➡ As a child, I _____ s_____ _____ the dark.

(6) 만약 그 애가 한 말들이 사실이 아니라면 어떻게 될까?
➡ _____ _____ the things she said are not true?

01 다음 짝지어진 단어의 관계가 같도록 주어진 철자로 시작하여 빈칸에 알맞은 말을 쓰시오.

> beautiful : beauty – dark : d_____

[02~03] 다음 빈칸에 공통으로 들어갈 말을 쓰시오.

02
> • I _____ nervous every time I stand on stage to sing.
> • I heard the weather was going to _____ better today.

03
> • He likes to _____ his dogs for a walk along the coast.
> • They _____ bad things away from the air.

04 다음 영영풀이에 해당하는 말을 주어진 철자로 시작하여 쓰고, 알맞은 것을 골라 문장을 완성하시오. (형태 변화 가능)

> • c_____: the young of a bear, lion or other mammal
> • o_____: a thought or belief about something
> • t_____: a decorative chair that a king, queen, or emperor sits on

(1) Who will succeed to the _____?

(2) The _____ are taken care of by a zookeeper.

(3) We have a different _____ about adopting a cat.

05 다음 빈칸에 들어갈 말을 〈보기〉에서 찾아 쓰시오.

> ┌─ 보기 ┤
> good   foreign   scared   worried

(1) What is the most effective way to learn a _____ language?

(2) Do you think those people were _____ of the dentist, too?

(3) His family are _____ about him because of his unhealthy diet.

(4) He is _____ at solving difficult math problems.

06 다음 우리말에 맞게 주어진 단어를 바르게 배열하시오.

(1) 이 영화에서 네가 가장 좋아하는 등장인물이 누구니?
  (this, who, favorite, character, movie, is, your, in, ?)
  ➡ _____

(2) 넌 전에 인도에 가본 적이 있니?
  (ever, before, have, India, to, you, been, ?)
  ➡ _____

(3) 나는 저 드라마의 마지막 장면이 마음에 들었다.
  (last, in, I, that, the, liked, scene, drama)
  ➡ _____

Conditional

Conversation

1 걱정 표현하기와 안심시키기

> **A** I'm worried about your health. 나는 네 건강이 걱정돼.
>
> **B** Don't worry. I'm going to the doctor tomorrow. 걱정하지 마. 내일 진찰받으러 병원에 갈 거야.

■ 걱정 표현하기(I'm worried about ~.)에서 'be worried about'은 걱정을 나타내는 표현으로, '~에 대해 걱정하다'라는 뜻을 지닌다. 걱정의 정도를 강조할 때에는, be so[very] worried about과 같이 worried 앞에 so 또는 very를 사용할 수 있다.

■ 걱정을 표현하는 다른 것으로 'I'm worried (that)+주어+동사'가 있다. 이것은 '나는 (주어)가 ~인 것이 걱정돼'라는 의미로 that절 이하에 걱정하는 내용이 온다. 그 외에 '~에 대해 걱정하다'라는 의미의 표현으로 be anxious about, be concerned about 등이 있다.

걱정 표현하기

- be worried about (동)명사 ~.
- be concerned about (동)명사 ~.
- be anxious about (동)명사 ~.
- be worried that 주어 동사 ~.

걱정에 관련한 표현

- I'm worried about ~. (나는 ~에 대해 걱정하고 있어.)
- I'm not worried about ~. (나는 ~을 걱정하지 않아.)
- I never worry about ~. (나는 ~을 전혀 걱정 안 해.)

안심시키기

- Don't worry. (걱정하지 마.)
- Try not to get worried. You'll do fine[great]. (걱정하지 않도록 해 봐. 넌 잘할 거야.)
- I'm sure everything will be OK. (분명히 모든 일이 잘될 거야.)
- Take it easy. Everything will be all right. (마음 편히 가져. 모든 일이 좋아질 거야.)

핵심 Check

1. 다음 우리말과 일치하도록 빈칸에 알맞은 말을 쓰시오.

   A: _____ worried _____ the English test tomorrow. (나는 내일 영어 시험이 걱정 돼.)

   B: Don't _____. You _____ _____ it. (걱정 마. 넌 합격할 수 있어.)

2. 다음 대화의 순서를 바르게 배열하시오.

   (A) Try not to worry about it too much. You can do well.

   (B) I'm worried about the speech contest.

   (C) You don't look good. Is something wrong?

   ➡ _____

❷ 의견 묻기

> **A** What do you think of my bike? 내 자전거에 대해 어떻게 생각해?
>
> **B** It looks light and fast. 가볍고 빨라 보여.

- 'What do you think of ~?'는 '~에 대해 어떻게 생각해?'의 의미로, 무언가에 대하여 상대방의 의견을 물을 때 사용할 수 있다. 'of' 대신에 'about'을 쓸 수도 있다.

- 의견을 묻는 말에 대한 대답은 'I like it.'이나 'I don't like it.' 등을 말하고 그 이유를 제시할 수 있다.

의견 묻기

- What do you think of[about] ~?
- What's your view on ~?
- How do you like ~?
- What's your opinion of[about/on] ~?
- How do you feel about ~?

의견 답하기

- In my opinion[viewpoint], ~. 내 생각[관점]에는, ~.
- It's terrific[wonderful/excellent/great]. 그것 좋다.
- I recommend it. 나는 그것을 추천해.
- It is terrible. 끔찍해.
- I (don't) like ~. 나는 ~을 (안) 좋아해.
- It is so touching[impressive]. 아주 감동적이야.
- It is not bad. 나쁘지 않아.

핵심 Check

3. 다음 대화의 우리말과 일치하도록 빈칸에 알맞은 말을 쓰시오.

(1) **A:** What do _____ online shopping? (너는 온라인 쇼핑에 대해 어떻게 생각하니?)

B: In my opinion, it saves time. (내 생각에 그것은 시간을 절약해 줘.)

(2) **A:** How _____ about that movie? (너는 저 영화에 대해 어떻게 생각하니?)

B: I like it a lot. (아주 좋아.)

4. 다음 대화의 순서를 바르게 배열하시오.

(A) How did you like it?

(B) I ate a hamburger.

(C) What did you eat yesterday, Jisu?

(D) I liked it a lot. It was delicious.

➡ _____

📍 **Listen & Speak 1 B-1**

B: ❶Do you have any special plans for tomorrow?

G: I'm going to Jejudo in the morning. But ❷I'm worried about the weather.

B: ❸Don't worry. ❹It won't rain on Jejudo tomorrow.

G: Oh, ❺that's good to hear.

B: 내일 특별한 계획 있니?
G: 아침에 제주도에 갈 거야. 그런데 날씨가 걱정돼.
B: 걱정하지 마. 내일 제주도에는 비가 내리지 않을 거야.
G: 오, 반가운 소리네.

❶ 'Do you have any special plans for ~?'는 상대방에게 무엇을 할 계획인지(또는 어떤 계획이 있는지) 물어볼 때 사용하는 표현이다. 'What are you planning to do tomorrow?', 'What are you going to do tomorrow?', 'What are your plans for tomorrow?' 등으로 바꾸어 쓸 수 있다. weather: 날씨

❷ 'be worried about'은 걱정을 나타내는 표현으로, '~에 대해 걱정하다'라는 뜻을 지닌다. 걱정의 정도를 강조할 때에는, be so[very] worried about과 같이 worried 앞에 so 또는 very를 사용할 수 있다.

❸ 'Don't worry.'는 '걱정하지 마.'의 의미로 걱정이나 두려움을 표현한 상대를 안심시키는 표현이다. 비슷한 표현으로 'Try not to get worried. You'll do fine.', 'Everything will be OK.' 등이 있다.

❹ 시간, 거리, 계절, 요일, 명암, 날씨, 날짜 등을 이야기할 때 비인칭 주어 it을 사용한다. won't = will not(~하지 않을 것이다)

❺ 'that's good to hear.'는 안도감을 나타내는 표현이다. 여기서 to hear는 앞의 good을 수식하는 to부정사의 '부사적 용법'에 해당된다.

Check(✓) True or False

(1) It is not going to rain on Jejudo tomorrow.　　　　　　　T ☐ F ☐

(2) The boy is going to Jejudo tomorrow morning.　　　　　T ☐ F ☐

(3) The girl is worried about the weather of Jejudo.　　　　T ☐ F ☐

📍 **Listen & Speak 2 B-1**

G: Did you watch ❶the movie, *The Daughter*?

B: ❷Yes, I saw it last Saturday.

G: ❸What did you think of it?

B: I was ❹disappointed. It wasn't very good.

G: 너 영화 '딸' 봤니?
B: 응, 지난 토요일에 봤어.
G: 어떻게 생각했어?
B: 나는 실망했어. 별로 좋지 않았어.

❶ the movie와 *The Daughter*는 동격이다.

❷ 'Did you 동사원형 ~?'이 질문이므로, see의 과거형 동사 saw를 사용하여 대답한다. 여기서 it은 the movie, *The Daughter*를 의미한다. last Saturday: 지난 토요일

❸ 'What do you think of+명사?'는 '~에 대해 어떻게 생각해?'의 의미로, 무언가에 대하여 상대방의 의견을 물을 때 사용할 수 있다.

❹ disappointed: 실망한, 기대에 어긋난

Check(✓) True or False

(4) The boy saw the movie last Saturday.　　　　　　　　　T ☐ F ☐

(5) The boy thinks the movie was very good.　　　　　　　T ☐ F ☐

(6) The boy was disappointed that the movie wasn't very good.　T ☐ F ☐

Listen & Speak 1 B-2

B: Jina, can you ❶go into your house first?

G: Why? ❷What's wrong?

B: ❸I'm scared of your dog.

G: ❹Don't worry. He's a ❺friendly dog. ❻He just looks scary because he's so big.

---

❶ go into: ～에 들어가다

❷ 상대방이 뭔가에 불만족하거나 실망하고 있는 것을 보고 그 원인을 물을 때 'What's wrong?'이라고 물을 수 있다. 비슷한 표현으로 'What's the matter?', 혹은 'What's the problem?'이 있다.

❸ be scared of: ～을 두려워하다

❹ 걱정하는 상대방을 안심시키는 표현이다.

❺ friendly: 친절한

❻ 어떤 일에 대하여 이유를 말할 때는 'because'를 사용한다. 즉 '결과+because+이유'로 말하면 되는데 보통 여기에서의 결과와 이유는 문장으로 말한다. look+형용사: ～하게 보이다 scary: 무서운

 Listen & Speak 2 B-2

B: ❶What do you think of our school cafeteria food?

G: ❷I think the cafeteria food is delicious.

B: ❸What do you think is the best item?

G: I like the Gimbap the best.

---

❶ 'What do you think of+명사?'는 '～에 대해 어떻게 생각해?'의 의미로, 무언가에 대하여 상대방의 의견을 물을 때 사용할 수 있다. 'of' 대신에 'about'을 쓸 수도 있다. school cafeteria: 학교 식당

❷ think와 the cafeteria 사이에 접속사 that이 생략되어 있다. delicious: 맛있는

❸ What do you think is the best item?: 최고의 품목이 뭐라고 생각하니? best: 최고의

 Listen & Speak 2 B-3

G: ❶What do you think of this painting?

B: It looks great. I like the colors.

G: ❷I'm happy that you like it. I painted it ❸ myself.

---

❶ What do you think of+명사?: ～에 대해 어떻게 생각해? (= What's your opinion of[about/on] ～? = What's your view on ～? = How do you feel about ～? = How do you like ～?)

❷ 'I'm happy that ～.'은 '～해서 나는 기쁘다'라는 뜻으로, that은 생략하기도 한다. that절 이하에는 기쁜 이유가 제시된다.

❸ 주어를 강조하기 위해 재귀대명사를 사용하였다.

 Real-Life Zone

G: I saw you with someone ❶who ❷looked like a foreigner yesterday.

B: Yes. We ❸had lunch together.

G: You looked like you were ❹having a good time.

B: ❺We were. We try to meet twice a month for lunch.

G: ❻I wish I could feel more comfortable talking with a foreigner.

B: I ❼was worried about speaking in English before, but not anymore.

G: I ❽get really nervous when I try to speak in English.

B: Well, the first time is ❾the hardest. After that, it gets easier and easier.

G: ❿What do you think about me ⓫joining both of you for lunch?

B: That's a great idea.

---

❶ 주격 관계대명사로 선행사 someone을 수식한다.

❷ look like 명사: ～처럼 보이다

❸ had는 have(먹다)의 과거형이다. ate으로 바꾸어 쓸 수 있다.

❹ have a good time: 좋은 시간을 보내다

❺ We were 다음에 having a good time이 생략되어 있다.

❻ 현재 사실과 반대되는 일에 대한 소망이나 유감을 나타낼 때 'I wish+주어+could+동사원형 ～.'으로 쓰며 '～라면 좋을 텐데'라고 해석한다. 'I wish+주어+동사의 과거형 ～.'으로도 나타내며 be동사는 were를 쓴다.

❼ 'be worried about'은 걱정을 나타내는 표현으로, '～에 대해 걱정하다'라는 뜻을 지닌다. about은 전치사이므로 뒤에 명사나 동명사가 올 수 있다.

❽ get+감정형용사: ～해지다

❾ the hardest(가장 힘든)는 hard(힘든)의 최상급이다.

❿ 'What do you think about+명사?'는 '～에 대해 어떻게 생각해?'의 의미로, 무언가에 대하여 상대방의 의견을 물을 때 사용할 수 있다.

⓫ 동명사로 전치사 about의 목적어이다. 앞에 있는 me는 joining의 의미상의 주어이다.

● 다음 우리말과 일치하도록 빈칸에 알맞은 말을 쓰시오.

Listen & Speak 1 A

B: I'm w_____ _____ the math test.

W: _____ worry. You'll do fine.

해석
B: 저는 수학 시험이 걱정돼요.
W: 걱정하지 마. 넌 잘할 거야.

Listen & Speak 1 B

1. B: _____ _____ _____ any special _____ for tomorrow?

   G: I'm going _____ Jejudo in the morning. But I'm w_____ _____ the weather.

   B: Don't _____. It _____ rain on Jejudo tomorrow.

   G: Oh, that's good to hear.

2. B: Jina, can you _____ into your house first?

   G: Why? What's _____?

   B: I'm _____ _____ your dog.

   G: Don't worry. He's a f_____ dog. He just _____ _____ _____ he's so big.

1. B: 내일 특별한 계획 있니?
   G: 아침에 제주도에 갈 거야. 그런데 날씨가 걱정돼.
   B: 걱정하지 마. 내일 제주도에는 비가 내리지 않을 거야.
   G: 오, 반가운 소리네.

2. B: 진아야, 네가 먼저 집에 들어갈 수 있어?
   G: 왜? 무슨 일 있니?
   B: 난 네 개가 무서워.
   G: 걱정하지 마. 친절한 개야. 너무 커서 무섭게 보일 뿐이야.

Listen & Speak 1 C

1. A: _____ _____ _____ your health.

   B: _____ _____. I'm going to the doctor tomorrow.

2. A: _____ _____ _____ the speech contest.

   B: Don't worry. _____ _____ _____.

3. A: _____ _____ _____ _____ _____.

   B: Don't _____. You'll _____ _____ you like to do.

1. A: 나는 네 건강이 걱정돼.
   B: 걱정하지 마. 내일 진찰받으러 병원에 갈 거야.

2. A: 나는 말하기 대회가 걱정돼.
   B: 걱정하지 마. 넌 잘할 거야.

3. A: 나는 내 미래가 걱정돼.
   B: 걱정하지 마. 네가 하고 싶은 것을 발견할 거야.

Listen & Speak 2 A

B: _____ _____ _____ think _____ these sunglasses?

G: They're cool! You look _____ a movie star.

B: 이 선글라스에 대해 어떻게 생각해?
G: 멋져! 너는 영화배우 같아.

Listen & Speak 2 B

1. **G:** Did you watch the movie, *The Daughter*?

   B: Yes, I _____ it last Saturday.

   G: _____ _____ _____ _____ _____?

   B: I was d_____. It wasn't very good.

2. **B:** _____ _____ _____ _____ our school

   cafeteria food?

   G: I _____ the cafeteria food is d_____.

   B: _____ do you think is the best item?

   G: I like the Gimbap the best.

3. **G:** What _____ _____ _____ _____ this painting?

   B: It looks great. I like the colors.

   G: I'm _____ _____ you like it. I painted it _____.

Listen & Speak 2 C

1. **A:** What do you _____ _____ my bike?

   B: It _____ _____ and fast.

2. **A:** _____ _____ _____ _____ of these shoes?

   B: They look _____ _____ _____.

Real-Life Zone

G: I saw you with someone _____ _____ _____ a foreigner

yesterday.

B: Yes. We h_____ lunch together.

G: You _____ like you were having a good time.

B: We _____. We try _____ _____ twice a month for lunch.

G: I wish I could feel more _____ talking with a foreigner.

B: I _____ _____ _____ _____ in English before, but not

_____.

G: I get really nervous when I try to speak in English.

B: Well, the first time is _____ _____. After that, it gets easier and

easier.

G: _____ _____ _____ think a_____ me joining both of you

for lunch?

B: That's a great idea.

해석

1. G: 너 영화 '딸' 봤니?
   B: 응, 지난 토요일에 봤어.
   G: 어떻게 생각했어?
   B: 나는 실망했어. 별로 좋지 않았어.

2. B: 학교 식당 음식에 대해 어떻게 생각해?
   G: 식당 음식이 맛있다고 생각해.
   B: 최고의 품목이 뭐라고 생각하니?
   G: 나는 김밥을 제일 좋아해.

3. G: 이 그림에 대해 어떻게 생각해?
   B: 아주 멋있어. 나는 색이 마음에 들어.
   G: 네가 좋아하니 기뻐. 내가 직접 그렸어.

1. A: 내 자전거에 대해 어떻게 생각해?
   B: 가볍고 빨라 보여.

2. A: 이 신발에 대해 어떻게 생각해?
   B: 너에게 잘 어울려.

G: 나는 어제 네가 외국인처럼 보이는 누군가와 있는 것을 봤어.
B: 응. 우리는 점심을 같이 먹었어.
G: 너희들은 좋은 시간을 보내고 있는 것처럼 보였어.
B: 그랬어. 우리는 한 달에 두 번 만나서 점심을 먹으려고 해.
G: 나는 외국인과 더 편하게 이야기할 수 있으면 좋을 텐데.
B: 나는 전에는 영어로 말하는 것에 대해 걱정했었지만, 더 이상은 아니야.
G: 영어로 말하려고 할 때 정말 불안해.
B: 음, 처음이 가장 힘들지. 그 후에 점점 쉬워져.
G: 내가 너희 둘과 함께 점심 먹는 거 어떻게 생각해?
B: 좋은 생각이야.

[01~03] 다음 대화의 빈칸에 알맞은 것을 고르시오.

01

B: I'm worried about the math test.

W: _____ You'll do fine.

① I'm happy about that.   ② What an amazing test!
③ Never mind.   ④ Don't worry.
⑤ I think I should study more.

02

B: Do you have any special plans for tomorrow?

G: I'm going to Jejudo in the morning. But _____

B: Don't worry. It won't rain on Jejudo tomorrow.

G: Oh, that's good to hear.

① I'm worried about the weather.
② the weather was nice.
③ don't worry about the weather.
④ I was concerned about you.
⑤ I'm happy with today's weather.

03

A: What do you think of our history class?

B: _____

① It's difficult for me.   ② It looks good on you.
③ It looks light and fast.   ④ It looks great.
⑤ You'll do great.

04 다음 대화의 순서를 바르게 배열하시오.

(A) Yes, I saw it last Saturday.

(B) What did you think of it?

(C) Did you watch the movie, *The Daughter*?

(D) I was disappointed. It wasn't very good.

➡ _____

01 다음 대화의 빈칸에 알맞은 것을 고르시오.

> A: I'm worried about my smartphone.
> B: Don't worry. _____

① It won't rain.
② You are good at science.
③ Let me teach you how to draw.
④ There is a service center nearby.
⑤ I'm not good at math.

[02~04] 다음 대화를 읽고 물음에 답하시오.

> B: (A)_____
> G: I'm going to Jejudo in the morning. But I'm worried about the (B)_____.
> B: Don't worry. It won't rain on Jejudo tomorrow.
> G: Oh, that's good to hear.

 빈칸 (A)에 알맞은 말을 고르시오.

① What do you think of Jejudo?
② What did you do in the morning?
③ Do you have any special plans for tomorrow?
④ Have you been to Jejudo?
⑤ Where did you go last Sunday?

03 빈칸 (B)에 알맞은 말을 고르시오.

① season   ② weather
③ experience ④ pollution
⑤ climate

04 위 대화의 내용과 일치하지 <u>않는</u> 것을 고르시오.

① The girl has a plan to do tomorrow morning.
② The girl is worried about the weather of Jejudo.
③ The boy knows whether it will rain or not on Jejudo tomorrow.
④ The boy is going to Jejudo tomorrow morning.
⑤ It will not rain on Jejudo tomorrow.

05 다음 중 짝지어진 대화가 <u>어색한</u> 것은?

① A: What do you think of Van Gogh?
   B: I think he is a great artist.
② A: What do you think of Jihun?
   B: I think he's smart and handsome.
③ A: It looks like rain.
   B: Don't worry. It will be fine in the afternoon.
④ A: I'm worried about losing my things.
   B: Why don't you write your name on your things?
⑤ A: What do you think of comic books?
   B: I think you're great.

06 다음 대화의 빈칸에 알맞은 말을 고르시오.

> A: I'm worried _____ my English test.
> B: Don't worry. You'll do great.

① for   ② at
③ about ④ by
⑤ in

[07~08] 다음 대화를 읽고 물음에 답하시오.

> B: What do you think (A)_____ these sunglasses?
> G: They're cool! You look (B)_____ a movie star.

07 빈칸 (A)에 알맞은 말을 <u>모두</u> 고르시오.

① of   ② from   ③ into
④ with   ⑤ about

서답형

08 빈칸 (B)에 알맞은 말을 쓰시오.

➡ _____

[09~10] 다음 대화를 읽고 물음에 답하시오.

> G: I saw you with someone (A)[which / who] looked like a foreigner yesterday.
> B: Yes. We had lunch together.
> G: You looked like you were having a good time.
> B: We were. We try to meet twice a month for lunch.
> G: I wish I could feel more comfortable talking with a foreigner.
> B: I was worried about speaking in English before, (B)[but / and] not anymore.
> G: I get really nervous (C)[that / when] I try to speak in English.
> B: Well, the first time is the hardest. After that, it gets easier and easier.
> G: What do you think about me joining both of you for lunch?
> B: That's a great idea.

서답형

09 (A)~(C)에 알맞은 말을 골라 쓰시오.

➡ (A)_____ (B)_____ (C)_____

10 위 대화를 읽고 대답할 수 <u>없는</u> 질문을 고르시오.

① How does the girl feel when she speaks in English?
② What did the boy do with the foreigner yesterday?
③ What is the boy worried about now?
④ When did the girl see the boy?
⑤ How often does the boy meet the foreigner?

[11~12] 다음 대화를 읽고 물음에 답하시오.

> W: Jimin, you look worried. What's wrong?
> G: Mom, I can't find the book that I borrowed from the library. (①)
> W: What book are you looking (A)_____ ? (②) *Jonathan Livingston Seagull*? I think I saw it in the living room. (③)
> G: Yes, that's it. Thank you, Mom. (④)
> W: By the way, have you read the book? What did you think (B)_____ it? (⑤)
> G: I've read it two times already. It was really interesting. I loved the character of Jonathan a lot.

중요

11 ①~⑤ 중 주어진 문장이 들어갈 곳은?

Have you seen it?

①   ②   ③   ④   ⑤

서답형

12 빈칸 (A)와 (B)에 알맞은 전치사를 쓰시오.

➡ (A) _____ (B) _____

[01~02] 다음 대화에서 어법상 또는 흐름상 어색한 부분을 찾아 고치시오. (1개)

01 중요

> B: Do you have any special plans for tomorrow?
>
> G: I'm going to Jejudo in the morning. But I'm worried about the weather.
>
> B: Don't worry. It will rain on Jejudo tomorrow.
>
> G: Oh, that's good to hear.

➡ _____

02

> B: What do you think of these sunglasses?
>
> G: It's cool! You look like a movie star.

➡ _____

[03~04] 다음 대화를 읽고 물음에 답하시오.

> G: I saw you with someone who looked like a foreigner yesterday.
>
> B: Yes. We had lunch together.
>
> G: You looked like you were having a good time.
>
> B: We were. We try to meet twice a month for lunch.
>
> G: I wish I could feel more comfortable talking with a foreigner.
>
> B: I was worried about speaking in English before, but not anymore.
>
> G: I get really nervous when I try to speak in English.
>
> B: Well, the first time is the hardest. After that, (A)점점 쉬워져.
>
> G: (B)내가 너희 둘과 함께 점심 먹는 거 어떻게 생각해?(for, do, joining, you, both, about, lunch, what, you, me, of, think, ?)
>
> B: That's a great idea.

03 (A)의 밑줄 친 우리말을 주어진 단어를 이용해 영작하시오.

➡ _____ (it, easy, get, and)

04 고난이도

괄호 안의 주어진 단어를 알맞게 배열하여 밑줄 친 (B)의 우리말을 영작하시오.

➡ _____

[05~06] 주어진 문장 다음에 이어질 문장의 순서를 바르게 배열하시오.

05

> What do you think of our school cafeteria food?

> (A) What do you think is the best item?
>
> (B) I think the cafeteria food is delicious.
>
> (C) I like the Gimbap the best.

➡ _____

06

> Jimin, you look worried. What's wrong?

> (A) Mom, I can't find the book that I borrowed from the library. Have you seen it?
>
> (B) Yes, that's it. Thank you, Mom.
>
> (C) What book are you looking for? *Jonathan Livingston Seagull*? I think I saw it in the living room.

➡ _____

Grammar

교과서

① 현재완료

> **I have lived** quietly and well. 나는 조용히 잘 살아 왔어.
> **Have** you ever **written** a diary in English? 영어로 일기를 써 본 적 있니?

■ 현재완료는 'have[has] + 과거분사'의 형태로 과거의 일이 현재까지 영향을 주는 동작 · 상태의 의미를 나타낸다.

■ 부정형은 'have[has] + not[never] + 과거분사'이며, 의문형은 'Have[Has] +주어 + 과거분사 ~?'로 나타낸다.

· **I haven't cleaned** my room yet. 나는 아직 내 방 청소를 안했다.

· **Have** you **read** *The Little Prince* already? 너는 '어린 왕자'를 벌써 읽었니?

■ 현재완료는 '완료(최근에[막] …했다), 경험(…해 본 적이 있다), 계속((지금까지) 계속 …해 왔다), 결과 (…해서 (그 결과) 지금 ~하다)'의 네 가지 용법으로 쓰인다.

완료 용법은 보통 'just, already, yet'과 같은 부사와 함께 쓰이며, 경험은 'ever, never, once, before' 등과 같은 부사와 함께 쓰인다. 계속적 용법은 보통 'for+기간'이나 'since+기준이 되는 때'와 함께 쓰이 며 결과적 용법은 과거에 발생한 사건이 현재 미치고 있는 결과를 포함한다.

· Tom **has** already **finished** his homework. 〈완료〉 Tom은 이미 그의 숙제를 끝마쳤다.

· I **have** never **been** to Vietnam. 〈경험〉 저는 베트남에 가 본 적이 없습니다.

· He **has studied** English for 10 years. <계속> 그는 10년 동안 영어를 공부해 오고 있다.

· She **has lost** her pen in the park. <결과> 그녀는 공원에서 펜을 잃어버렸다. (그 결과 (펜이) 지금 없다.)

*have[has] been to와 have[has] gone to

have[has] been to는 '~에 가 본 적이 있다'는 경험을 나타내고, have[has] gone to는 '~에 가고 없다'는 결과를 나타낸다. 그러므로 have[has] gone to는 3인칭만 주어로 쓸 수 있다.

■ 현재완료는 과거의 일이 현재까지 영향을 주는 동작 · 상태를 나타내므로 과거를 나타내는 어구와 함께 쓸 수 없다.

· He went to London last month.   (○)

· He has gone to London last month. (✕)

핵심 Check

1. 주어진 동사를 어법에 맞게 쓰시오.

(1) Christine _____ _____ to England. So you cannot meet her now. (go)

(2) Hannah _____ _____ the piano for 10 years. (play)

(3) _____ you ever _____ *Alita*? (watch).

② 접속사 if

> How can we know **if** we don't try? 우리가 시도하지 않으면 어떻게 알 수 있어?
>
> **If** it is sunny, I will go shopping. 만약 날씨가 좋으면, 나는 쇼핑하러 갈 거야.

■ if는 '만약 ~한다면'이라는 뜻의 접속사로 종속절 앞에 쓰여 그것을 주절에 연결해 준다. if절은 조건을 나타내는 부사절이다. 접속사가 사용된 문장에서 접속사가 붙은 절을 종속절, 접속사가 붙지 않은 나머지 절을 주절이라고 하는데, 주절이 먼저 나올 수도 있고 종속절이 먼저 나올 수도 있다.

• You can catch the next train **if** you leave now. 너는 지금 출발하면 다음 기차를 탈 수 있어.

■ 접속사 **unless**

'만약 ~하지 않는다면'의 뜻으로 'if ~ not'과 같은 의미이다.

• **If** it doesn't rain, I will go swimming.
  = **Unless** it rains, I will go swimming. 비가 안 오면 나는 수영하러 갈 거야.

■ 시간이나 조건의 부사절에서는 미래의 의미를 갖더라도 will을 쓰지 않고 현재 시제를 쓴다.

• **If** it **snows** tomorrow, I will go skiing. 내일 눈이 오면 나는 스키를 타러 갈 거야.

• Mina will watch TV **after** she **finishes** doing her homework. Mina는 숙제를 끝낸 후에 TV를 볼 거야.

■ 'if절이 명사 역할을 하는 경우도 있으며 (이때 if는 whether와 같은 의미이다.) 이때는 '~인지 아닌지'로 해석하며 미래를 나타낼 때에는 미래 시제를 써야 한다.

• Please ask Ben **if** he is able to attend the meeting. Ben이 그 모임에 참석할 수 있는지 그에게 물어 보세요.

✏️ 핵심 Check

2. 다음 우리말과 일치하도록 빈칸에 알맞은 말을 쓰시오.

(1) 내 추측이 맞는다면 그는 틀림없이 40세 정도 되었다.

➡ _____ my guess is right, he must be about forty.

(2) 지금 출발하면 늦지 않을 거야.

➡ If you _____ right now, you _____ _____ late.

(3) 나는 그녀가 내일 집에 있을지 궁금하다.

➡ I wonder _____ she _____ _____ at home tomorrow.

01 다음 중 어법상 어색한 문장은?

① Marie has studied Chinese for three years.
② The train has just arrived.
③ We have gone to Seoul.
④ Have you ever been to a K-pop concert?
⑤ Jane met her sister yesterday.

02 다음 우리말에 맞게 괄호 안에 주어진 단어를 빈칸에 바르게 배열하시오. (필요하면 어형을 바꿀 것)

(1) 만약 학교가 일찍 끝난다면, 나는 영화를 볼 거야. (school, early, end, if)

➡ _____, I will watch the movie.

(2) Audrey는 초대받지 않으면 그 파티에 참석하지 않을 것이다.

(she, the party, is, attend, won't, invited, not, if)

➡ Audrey _____.

03 다음 문장에서 어법상 어색한 부분을 바르게 고치시오.

(1) I have play the piano for two years.

_____ ➡ _____

(2) She has met John last Saturday.

_____ ➡ _____

(3) Does he have written his report?

_____ ➡ _____

(4) Kate has worn the dress for 2000.

_____ ➡ _____

(5) If it will rain tomorrow, I will stay at home.

_____ ➡ _____

(6) I can't hear you unless you don't turn down the radio.

_____ ➡ _____

01 다음 중 어법상 바르지 않은 것은?

① I have been to San Francisco three times.
② I have lived in this house since I was born.
③ I've never heard that kind of strange story.
④ Marianne has not cleaned her house yet.
⑤ When have you bought your new computer?

02 다음 문장의 빈칸에 알맞은 것은?

> _____ you study hard, you will pass the exam.

① If
② Unless
③ That
④ Although
⑤ What

03 다음 빈칸에 알맞은 말이 바르게 짝지어진 것은?

> • How long _____ you been employed here?
> • The children have _____ to play with their friends.

① were – gone
② were – been
③ have – gone
④ have – been
⑤ did – being

04 다음 중 문맥이나 어법상 바르지 않은 것은?

① I forget things unless I take notes.
② If we don't have homework tomorrow, I will go to see a movie.
③ You should visit the museum if you have some free time.
④ If we arrive on time, she will get angry.
⑤ If you miss the class, you will have to hand in a long report instead.

05 다음 대화의 빈칸에 들어갈 말로 알맞은 것은?

> M: Have you been to Vietnam before?
> W: Yes, I have _____.

① just
② already
③ yet
④ for
⑤ since

06 다음 괄호 안에서 알맞은 말을 고르시오.

(1) Emma (have / has) gone to Germany.
(2) We have (visited / visit) Angkor Wat, Cambodia once.
(3) Lingling is not here now. She has (been / gone) to China.
(4) Melanie (has been / went) to Paris last year.
(5) I will go hiking, (if / unless) it's fine.
(6) If you (will call / call) her, you will know why she left the party so early.

07 다음 중 어법상 옳은 것은?

① Jenny has raised a dog last year.
② Karen have been to Malaysia three times.
③ Susan and I have gone to Paris.
④ Tom has studied English since ten years.
⑤ Have you ever watched the movie?

서답형

08 주어진 어휘를 이용하여 다음 우리말을 두 가지로 영작하시오. (You로 시작할 것)

> 더 빨리 걷지 않으면 버스를 놓칠 거야. (the bus, miss, quickly)

➡ _____

➡ _____

09 다음 질문에 대한 응답으로 알맞은 것은?

> Has she ever been in such a serious situation?

① No, she hasn't.
② No, she isn't.
③ No, she doesn't.
④ Yes, she is.
⑤ Yes, she does.

10 다음 밑줄 친 부분의 의미가 다른 하나는?

① If you exercise regularly, you can lose weight.
② I'm not sure if I can do it.
③ If you study hard, you will pass the exam.
④ She can stay with us if she wants.
⑤ If it's fine tomorrow, I'll go swimming.

11 다음 두 문장을 한 문장으로 바르게 연결한 것은?

> • Julia went back to Ukraine.
> • And she is there now.

① Julia went to Ukraine.
② Julia went to Ukraine already.
③ Julia hasn't been to Ukraine.
④ Julia has gone to Ukraine.
⑤ Julia hasn't come back yet.

12 다음 우리말과 일치하도록 빈칸에 알맞은 단어로 묶은 것은?

> • 수지를 만나면 그녀에게 이 편지를 줄 것이다.
> • If I _____ Suji, I _____ her this letter.

① will meet – will give
② will meet – give
③ meet – will give
④ have met – will give
⑤ meet – give

13 다음 중 밑줄 친 부분의 용법이 다른 것을 두 개 고르시오.

① The train for Busan has just left the station.
② Harry and Jenny have just finished their project.
③ I have known Emily since I was 8 years old.
④ We have already cleaned our classroom.
⑤ Have you heard about the K-pop singer before?

서답형

14 다음 문장을 어법에 맞게 고쳐 쓰시오.

(1) If my friend will move near my house, I can see her more often.

➡ _____

_____

(2) You will be late unless you don't hurry up.

➡ _____

_____

(3) Please let us know if you come to the party tomorrow.

➡ _____

_____

서답형

15 다음 두 문장을 비슷한 뜻을 가진 한 문장으로 고쳐 쓰시오.

(1) Anna fell in love with Sam when she met him first. And she still loves him.

➡ _____

(2) Mariel started to live in Tallinn seven years ago. And she still lives there.

➡ _____

16 다음 문장의 빈칸에 들어가기에 의미상 자연스러운 것은? (2개)

• It is about 5 km to the meeting place. So, _____, you will be late for the meeting.

① unless you go there on foot
② unless you leave right now
③ if you leave immediately
④ if you don't take the subway
⑤ if you don't take time

17 다음 〈보기〉의 밑줄 친 부분과 용법이 같은 것은?

┤ 보기 ├
I <u>have been</u> to Budapest four times.

① Joseph <u>has visited</u> the museum three times.
② Linda <u>has lost</u> her cell phone.
③ I <u>have known</u> the girl since she was a baby.
④ I <u>have finished</u> washing my car.
⑤ She <u>has gone</u> to Thailand.

[18~19] 다음 우리말에 맞게 영작한 것을 고르시오.

18 이 버튼을 누르면 벨이 울릴 것이다.

① If you don't push the button, the bell will ring.
② If you will push the button, the bell will ring.
③ If you push the button, the bell will ring.
④ Unless you push the button, the bell will ring.
⑤ Unless you don't push the button, the bell will ring.

19 너는 일본에 가 본 적 있니?

① Did you go to Japan?
② Do you have visited Japan?
③ Do you have gone to Japan?
④ Have you gone to Japan?
⑤ Have you been to Japan?

01 다음 우리말에 맞게 주어진 어구를 바르게 배열하시오.

(1) 찰리와 초콜릿 공장을 벌써 읽었니?

(you / *Charlie and the Chocolate Factory* / already / have / read)

➡ _____

(2) Jina는 여행을 하면서 많은 것을 경험했다.

(Jina / traveling / while / experienced / lot / has / a)

➡ _____

(3) 웃는 법을 모르면, 가게를 열지 마라.

(you / a shop / how / don't / know / open / smile / unless / to)

➡ _____

(4) 배고프면 간식을 먹는 것이 어떠니?

(why / some snacks / you / you / eat / are / don't / if / hungry)

➡ _____

02 다음 글에서 어법상 잘못 쓰인 것을 찾아 알맞게 고치시오. (3곳)

> This story is about a trumpeter naming Louis. When he was born, he was unable to speak, so he tried lots of things to get over it. I like this story because it has help me learn about the way to overcome my weakness. The book says that I can overcome my weakness unless I work hard.

➡ _____

03 다음 그림을 보고, 주어진 동사를 이용하여 자신의 경험에 대해 쓰시오. (현재완료 시제로 주어와 동사를 갖춘 완전한 문장으로 쓸 것.)

(1) (cook, ramyeon)

➡ _____

(2) (experience, ski)

➡ _____

04 주어진 두 문장을 한 문장으로 바꿔 쓰시오.

(1) • Sophia lost her cap.

　• So, she doesn't have it now.

➡ _____

(2) • I visited Paris again.

　• It was my second visit.

➡ _____

★5 다음 중 어법상 <u>어색한</u> 것을 바르게 고치시오.

(1) You have had a lot of trouble then.

　➡ _____

(2) Mariel has lived in Seoul since 10 years.

　➡ _____

(3) Grace has been to Greece and she is there now.

　➡ _____

(4) If I will go to Paris, I will visit the Louvre museum.

　➡ _____

(5) Unless you are tired, you should have a rest.

　➡ _____

06 다음 우리말을 괄호 안에 주어진 어휘를 이용하여 영작하시오.

(1) Jason은 한국 음식을 먹어 본 적이 있다. (eat, Korean food, 5 단어)

　➡ _____

(2) 인류는 수 천 년 동안 존재해 왔다. (mankind, exist, thousands of years, 7 단어)

　➡ _____

(3) 비가 내린다면 나는 우산을 가져갈 것이다. (rain, take, an umbrella, with, 10 단어)

　➡ _____

(4) 그것이 아주 중요한 일이 아니면 수업에 빠지지 마라. (don't, miss, your classes, it, really, 9 단어)

　➡ _____

★7 다음 문장을 부정문과 의문문으로 각각 바꿔 쓰시오.

(1) Stephanie has used her computer for 3 years.

부정문: _____

의문문: _____

(2) You have seen it before.

부정문: _____

_____

의문문: _____

08 다음 두 문장의 뜻이 같도록 빈칸에 알맞은 말을 쓰시오.

(1) Exercise regularly, and you can stay healthy.

　➡ _____ you exercise regularly, you can stay healthy.

(2) Get up early tomorrow morning, or you'll miss the first train.

　➡ _____ you get up early tomorrow morning, you'll miss the first train.

★9 두 문장의 의미가 같도록 빈칸에 알맞은 말을 쓰시오.

(1) It started to rain two days ago. It still rains.

= It _____ for two days.

(2) Miranda went to her country. She is in her country now.

= Miranda _____ to her country.

(3) My smartphone broke down. And it still doesn't work.

= My smartphone _____ down.

Reading

The Two Brothers

Two brothers <u>went on a journey</u>. They found a rock <u>in front of</u> a
여행을 떠났다   ~ 앞에서

forest. It said, "Go into the forest and swim <u>across the river</u>. There
~ 건너서, ~을 가로질러

you will find a bear and her <u>cubs</u>. Take the bear cubs <u>and</u> <u>run up</u> the
(곰, 사자 등의) 새끼   등위접속사 ~ 위로 달리다

mountain. <u>There</u> you will find <u>happiness</u>."
앞 문장의 'the mountain'을 가리킴   행복

   The younger brother said, "Let's <u>go</u> and <u>find</u> happiness together."
병렬 구문

"No," said the older brother, "How can we know <u>this is true</u>? What
앞에 접속사 'that' 생략 ~하면 어쩌지?

<u>if</u> the river is too <u>wide</u>? Besides, will <u>it</u> be easy <u>to take the cubs away</u>
넓은   가주어   진주어   take away: 빼앗다

from their mother? <u>Instead of</u> finding happiness, we can <u>be killed</u>!"
~하는 대신에   수동태(be동사+과거분사): 죽임을 당하다

The younger brother <u>replied</u>, "How can we know <u>if</u> we don't try?"
대답하다   조건의 접속사: 만약 ~한다면

They <u>separated</u>, and they both <u>went their own way</u>.
떨어지다, 헤어지다   go one's own way: 자신의 길을 가다

   The <u>younger</u> brother went into the <u>forest</u> and swam across the river.
형용사의 비교급: 원급+er   숲

There was the bear. She <u>was sleeping</u>. He took her cubs and ran up the
과거진행형(was/were+~ing): ~하고 있었다

mountain.

journey 여행
cub (곰, 사자 등의) 새끼
happiness 행복
wide 넓은
besides 게다가
reply 대답하다
separate 헤어지다
take away 빼앗다

📎 **확인문제**

● 다음 문장이 본문의 내용과 일치하면 T, 일치하지 <u>않으면</u> F를 쓰시오.

1 Two brothers found a rock in front of a forest. ☐

2 The rock said, "Go into the village and swim across the river." ☐

3 The older brother said, "Let's go and find happiness together." ☐

4 The older brother said, "What if the river is too wide?" ☐

5 The younger brother replied, "How can we know if we don't try?" ☐

6 Two brothers went into the forest and swam across the river. ☐

When he reached the top, some people took him to their city and
시간의 접속사: ~할 때   ~에 도착했다   그를 ~으로 데려갔다

made him their king. There he lived as a king for five years. Then a
5형식(make+목적어+목적격보어): ~을 ~이 되게 하다   전치사: ~로(서)

war broke out, and he lost his throne. He was on the road again.
    발발했다   왕위

One day, the two brothers met again and talked about their lives
어느 날   life의 복수

for the last five years. The older brother said, "I was right. I have
~ 동안

lived quietly and well. You were once a king, but you have had a
현재완료(have/has+p.p.): ~해 왔다   현재완료(have/has + p.p.): ~해 왔다

lot of trouble." The younger brother answered, "I don't regret my
                                                              후회하다

choice. I may have nothing now, but I will always have something to
선택   추측의 조동사: ~일지도 모른다   to부정사의

remember."
형용사적 용법: ~할, ~하는

reach ~에 도착하다
lose 잃다, 지다
throne 왕위, 왕좌
road 길, 도로
regret 후회하다
break out 발발하다
choice 선택

📎 **확인문제**

● 다음 문장이 본문의 내용과 일치하면 T, 일치하지 않으면 F를 쓰시오.

1   Some people took the younger brother to their city and made him their king. ☐

2   After ten years, the younger brother lost his throne. ☐

3   The older brother had a lot of trouble. ☐

4   The younger brother didn't regret his choice. ☐

● 우리말을 참고하여 빈칸에 알맞은 말을 쓰시오.

1 The Two Brothers

2 Two brothers _____ _____ a journey.

3 They found a rock _____ _____ _____ a forest.

4 It _____, "Go _____ the forest and swim _____ the river.

5 There you will find a bear and _____ _____.

6 _____ the bear cubs and _____ _____ the mountain.

7 There you will _____ _____."

8 The younger brother said, "Let's _____ _____ _____ happiness together."

9 "No," said the older brother, "_____ _____ _____ _____ this is true?

10 _____ _____ the river is too wide?

11 _____, will it be easy to take the cubs _____ _____ their mother?

12 _____ _____ finding happiness, we can be killed!"

13 The younger brother replied, "_____ can we know _____ we don't try?"

14 They separated, and they both _____ _____ _____ _____.

15 The younger brother _____ _____ the forest and _____ the river.

16 _____ _____ the bear.

---

1 두 형제

2 두 형제는 여정을 떠났다.

3 그들은 숲 앞에서 바위를 발견했다.

4 거기에 쓰여 있었다. "숲에 들어가 강을 헤엄쳐 건너시오.

5 당신은 거기에서 곰과 새끼들을 발견할 것입니다.

6 곰 새끼들을 데리고 산 위로 뛰어 올라가시오.

7 거기에서 당신은 행복을 찾을 수 있을 것입니다."

8 동생이 말했다. "함께 가서 행복을 찾자."

9 "싫어." 형은 말했다. "이것이 사실인지 우리가 어떻게 알 수 있어?

10 강이 너무 넓으면 어쩌지?

11 게다가, 곰 새끼들을 엄마에게서 빼앗는 것이 쉬울까?

12 행복을 찾는 대신에, 우리는 죽을 수 있어!"

13 동생은 대답했다. "우리가 시도하지 않으면 어떻게 알 수 있어?"

14 그들은 헤어졌고, 둘 다 자신의 길을 갔다.

15 동생은 숲에 들어가서 강을 헤엄쳐 건넜다.

16 곰이 있었다.

17 She was _____ .

18 He _____ _____ _____ and ran up the mountain.

19 When he reached the top, some people _____ _____ _____ their city and _____ him their king.

20 There he lived _____ _____ _____ for five years.

21 Then a war _____ _____ , and he _____ _____ _____ .

22 He was _____ _____ _____ again.

23 One day, the two brothers met again and _____ _____ their lives _____ _____ _____ five years.

24 The older brother said, "_____ _____ _____ .

25 I _____ _____ quietly and well.

26 You were once a king, but you _____ _____ a lot of trouble."

27 The younger brother answered, "I don't _____ _____ _____ .

28 I may have _____ now, but I will always have _____ _____ _____ ."

---

17 그녀는 자고 있었다.

18 그는 새끼들을 데리고 산을 뛰어 올라갔다.

19 그가 정상에 도착했을 때, 어떤 사람들이 그를 자기들 도시로 데려가서 그들의 왕으로 만들었다.

20 그곳에서 그는 5년간 왕으로 살았다.

21 그런 다음 전쟁이 일어났고, 그는 왕좌를 잃었다.

22 그는 다시 길바닥에 나앉았다.

23 어느 날, 두 형제는 다시 만났고 지난 5년 동안의 그들의 삶에 대해 이야기했다.

24 형은 말했다. "내가 옳았어.

25 나는 조용히 잘 살았어.

26 너는 한때 왕이었지만 많은 어려움을 겪었지."

27 동생은 대답했다. "나는 내 선택을 후회하지 않아.

28 나는 지금 아무것도 없지만 언제까지나 기억할 어떤 것이 있어."

● 우리말을 참고하여 본문을 영작하시오.

1 두 형제

➡ _____

2 두 형제는 여정을 떠났다.

➡ _____

3 그들은 숲 앞에서 바위를 발견했다.

➡ _____

4 거기에 쓰여 있었다. "숲에 들어가 강을 헤엄쳐 건너시오.

➡ _____

5 당신은 거기에서 곰과 새끼들을 발견할 것입니다.

➡ _____

6 곰 새끼들을 데리고 산 위로 뛰어 올라가시오.

➡ _____

7 거기에서 당신은 행복을 찾을 수 있을 것입니다."

➡ _____

8 동생이 말했다. "함께 가서 행복을 찾자."

➡ _____

9 "싫어." 형은 말했다. "이것이 사실인지 우리가 어떻게 알 수 있어?

➡ _____

10 강이 너무 넓으면 어쩌지?

➡ _____

11 게다가, 곰 새끼들을 엄마에게서 빼앗는 것이 쉬울까?

➡ _____

12 행복을 찾는 대신에, 우리는 죽을 수 있어!"

➡ _____

13 동생은 대답했다. "우리가 시도하지 않으면 어떻게 알 수 있어?"

➡ _____

14 그들은 헤어졌고, 둘 다 자신의 길을 갔다.

➡ _____

15 동생은 숲에 들어가서 강을 헤엄쳐 건넜다.

➡ _____

16 곰이 있었다.

➡ _____

17 그녀는 자고 있었다.

➡ _____

18 그는 새끼들을 데리고 산을 뛰어 올라갔다.

➡ _____

19 그가 정상에 도착했을 때, 어떤 사람들이 그를 자기들 도시로 데려가서 그들의 왕으로 만들었다.

➡ _____

20 그곳에서 그는 5년간 왕으로 살았다.

➡ _____

21 그런 다음 전쟁이 일어났고, 그는 왕좌를 잃었다.

➡ _____

22 그는 다시 길바닥에 나앉았다.

➡ _____

23 어느 날, 두 형제는 다시 만났고 지난 5년 동안의 그들의 삶에 대해 이야기했다.

➡ _____

24 형은 말했다. "내가 옳았어.

➡ _____

25 나는 조용히 잘 살았어.

➡ _____

26 너는 한때 왕이었지만 많은 어려움을 겪었지."

➡ _____

27 동생은 대답했다. "나는 내 선택을 후회하지 않아.

➡ _____

28 나는 지금 아무것도 없지만 언제까지나 기억할 어떤 것이 있어."

➡ _____

[01~03] 다음 글을 읽고 물음에 답하시오.

Two brothers went ⓐ a journey. They found a rock in front of a forest. ⓑIt said, "Go into the forest and swim ⓒ the river. There you will find a bear and her cubs. Take the bear cubs and run up the mountain. There you will find happiness."

01 위 글의 빈칸 ⓐ와 ⓒ에 들어갈 전치사가 바르게 짝지어진 것은?

① for - by   ② in - across
③ on - across   ④ on - over
⑤ in - by

서답형

02 위 글의 밑줄 친 ⓑIt이 가리키는 것을 본문에서 찾아 쓰시오.

➡ _____

중요

03 위 글의 바위에 쓰여 있는 내용이 아닌 것은?

① 숲에 들어가라.
② 강을 헤엄쳐 건너라.
③ 곰과 새끼들을 발견할 것이다.
④ 곰과 새끼들을 데리고 산 위로 뛰어 올라가라.
⑤ 산 위에서 행복을 찾을 수 있을 것이다.

[04~06] 다음 글을 읽고 물음에 답하시오.

The younger brother said, "Let's go and find happiness together." (①) "No," said the older brother, "How can we know this is true? (②) What if the river is too wide? (③) Besides, will it be easy to take the cubs away from their mother? (④) Instead of ⓐfinding happiness, we can be killed!" (⑤) They separated, and they both went their own way.

The younger brother went into the forest and swam across the river. There was the bear. She was sleeping. He took her cubs and ran up the mountain.

중요

04 위 글의 흐름으로 보아, 주어진 문장이 들어가기에 가장 적절한 곳은?

The younger brother replied, "How can we know if we don't try?"

①   ②   ③   ④   ⑤

05 아래 보기에서 위 글의 밑줄 친 ⓐfinding과 문법적 쓰임이 같은 것의 개수를 고르시오.

┤ 보기 ├
① He gave up finding happiness.
② Finding happiness is not difficult.
③ My goal is finding happiness.
④ She continued finding happiness.
⑤ There are many people finding happiness.

① 1개   ② 2개   ③ 3개   ④ 4개   ⑤ 5개

06 위 글의 내용과 일치하지 않는 것은?

① 형은 행복을 찾는 대신에 죽을 수 있다고 말했다.
② 동생은 위험하므로 시도하지 말자고 말했다.
③ 형과 동생은 헤어져서 자신의 길을 갔다.
④ 동생은 숲에 들어가서 강을 헤엄쳐 건넜다.
⑤ 어미 곰은 자고 있었다.

[07~09] 다음 글을 읽고 물음에 답하시오.

When he reached the top, some people took ①him to their city and made him their king. There he lived as a king for five years. Then a war broke out, and he lost his throne. ②He was on the road again.

One day, the two brothers met again and talked about their lives for the last five years. The older brother said, "I was right. ③I have lived quietly and well. ④You were once a king, but you have had a lot of trouble." The younger brother answered, "⑤I don't regret my choice. I may have nothing now, but I will always have something ⓐto remember."

07 위 글의 밑줄 친 ①~⑤ 중에서 가리키는 대상이 나머지 넷과 다른 것은?

①   ②   ③   ④   ⑤

08 위 글의 밑줄 친 ⓐto remember와 to부정사의 용법이 다른 것을 모두 고르시오.

① She has a few friends to play with.

② The book is too difficult to read.

③ It isn't easy to write good English.

④ I have something to tell you.

⑤ Give me a chance to go abroad.

09 위 글을 읽고 대답할 수 없는 질문은?

① Why did some people make the younger brother their king?

② Why did the younger brother lose his throne?

③ How has the older brother lived for the last five years?

④ What did they talk about when they met again?

⑤ Did the younger brother regret his choice?

[10~12] 다음 글을 읽고 물음에 답하시오.

The younger brother said, "Let's go and find happiness together." "No," said the older brother, "How can we know this is true? What if the river is too wide? Besides, will it be easy ⓐto take the cubs away from their mother? Instead of finding happiness, we can be killed!" The younger brother replied, "ⓑ How can we know if we don't try?" They separated, and they both went their own way.

The younger brother went into the forest and swam across the river. There was the bear. She was sleeping. He took her cubs and ran up the mountain.

10 위 글의 제목으로 알맞은 것을 고르시오.

① Let's Find Happiness Together

② Two Choices toward Happiness

③ What If This Is Not True?

④ The Older Brother's Doubtful Response

⑤ Put It Into Practice

11 위 글의 밑줄 친 ⓐto take와 to부정사의 용법이 다른 것을 모두 고르시오.

① She chose to go there by train.

② There is nothing to see.

③ My desire is to see you again.

④ He grew up to be a great musician.

⑤ To know oneself is difficult.

12 위 글의 밑줄 친 ⓑ에서 알 수 있는 동생의 성격으로 가장 알맞은 것을 고르시오.

① negative   ② selfish   ③ generous

④ passive   ⑤ challenging

[13~15] 다음 글을 읽고 물음에 답하시오.

A Book Review

Title: Jonathan Livingston Seagull: a story
Writer: Richard Bach

This story is about a seagull named Jonathan Livingston. He dreams of flying better than others. To reach ⓐhis goal, he works hard and practices flying. I like this story because it has helped me learn about the power of my own beliefs. The book says ⓑthat I can do anything ⓒthat I want if I do not give up.

서답형

13 위 글의 밑줄 친 ⓐhis goal이 가리키는 것을 본문에서 찾아 쓰시오.

➡ _____

중요

14 아래 보기에서 위 글의 밑줄 친 ⓑthat, ⓒthat과 문법적 쓰임이 같은 것을 각각 모두 고르시오.

┌─ 보기 ┐
① It's true that he was a little hungry.
② This is the house that we live in.
③ It's the best novel that I've ever read.
④ I believe that you'll pass the exam.
⑤ He is the first man that came here.
└────────┘

➡ ⓑ와 같은 것: _____ ,
ⓒ와 같은 것: _____

서답형

15 다음 질문에 대한 알맞은 대답을 빈칸에 쓰시오. (2 단어)

┌──────────────────────────────┐
Q: Why does the reviewer like this book?
A: Because it has helped the reviewer learn about the power of his/her _____ _____.
└──────────────────────────────┘

[16~18] 다음 글을 읽고 물음에 답하시오.

When he reached the top, some people took him to their city and made him their king. There he lived as a king for five years. Then a war broke out, and he lost his throne. ⓐ그는 다시 길바닥에 나앉았다.

One day, the two brothers met again and talked about their lives for the last five years. The older brother said, "I was right. I ⓑhave lived quietly and well. You were once a king, but you have had a lot of trouble." The younger brother answered, "I don't regret my choice. ⓒI may have something now, but I will always have nothing to remember."

서답형

16 밑줄 친 ⓐ의 우리말에 맞게 주어진 어휘를 이용하여 6단어로 영작하시오.

┌──────────────────────────────┐
on, road
└──────────────────────────────┘

➡ _____

17 위 글의 밑줄 친 ⓑhave lived와 현재완료의 용법이 같은 것을 모두 고르시오.

① She hasn't cleaned her room yet.
② I have studied English for two hours.
③ He has lost his car key.
④ Have you ever seen a lion?
⑤ She has been ill since last year.

서답형

18 밑줄 친 ⓒ에서 흐름상 어색한 부분 두 군데를 본문의 단어를 사용하여 고치시오.

➡ _____

[19~21] 다음 글을 읽고 물음에 답하시오.

Title: Jonathan Livingston Seagull: a story
Writer: Richard Bach

  This story is about a seagull ⓐ Jonathan Livingston. He dreams of flying better than (A)[the other / others]. To reach his goal, he works (B)[hard / hardly] and practices flying. I like this story because it has helped me (C)[learn / learning] about the power of my own beliefs. The book says that I can do anything that I want if I do not give up.

서답형

19 위 글의 빈칸 ⓐ에 name을 알맞은 형태로 쓰시오.

➡ _____

서답형

20 위 글의 괄호 (A)~(C)에서 문맥이나 어법상 알맞은 낱말을 골라 쓰시오.

➡ (A)_____ (B)_____ (C)_____

21 위 글의 종류로 알맞은 것을 고르시오.

① essay   ② biography
③ book review   ④ diary
⑤ article

[22~25] 다음 글을 읽고 물음에 답하시오.

[Scene #4]
  One day, the two brothers met again and talked about their lives for the last five years.
OB: Brother, we ⓐhaven't seen each other for a long time.
YB: Yes, it's been several years. ⓑHow have you been?
OB: I have lived quietly and well. And you?
YB: ⓒActually I became a king.

OB: Well.... You look like a traveler, not a king now.
YB: ⓓThat's true. I lost my throne after a war.
OB: So, I was right. I don't think you found happiness because you have had a lot of trouble.
YB: Well, I may have nothing now, but I will always have something to remember. I don't regret my choice.

중요

22 아래 보기에서 위 글의 밑줄 친 ⓐhaven't seen과 현재완료의 용법이 다른 것의 개수를 고르시오.

┌─ 보기 ─┐
① I have already seen the boy.
② How many times have you read it?
③ He has gone to Paris.
④ I have lived in Seoul since 2010.
⑤ How long has she been sick?

① 1개   ② 2개   ③ 3개   ④ 4개   ⑤ 5개

23 위 글의 밑줄 친 ⓑ와 바꿔 쓸 수 없는 말을 모두 고르시오.

① What have you been up to?
② What have you been doing?
③ How do you do?
④ How have you been getting along?
⑤ How are you feeling?

서답형

24 위 글의 밑줄 친 ⓒActually와 바꿔 쓸 수 있는 말을 쓰시오. (in과 as를 이용할 것) (두 개)

➡ _____

서답형

25 위 글의 밑줄 친 ⓓThat이 가리키는 것을 본문에서 찾아 쓰시오.

➡ _____

[01~03] 다음 글을 읽고 물음에 답하시오.

The younger brother said, "Let's go and find happiness together." "No," said the older brother, "How can we know this is true? ⓐ강이 너무 넓으면 어떡해? Besides, will it be easy to take the cubs away from their mother? Instead of finding happiness, we can be killed!" The younger brother replied, "How can we know if we don't try?" ⓑThey united, and they both went their own way.

The younger brother went into the forest and swam across the river. There was the bear. She was sleeping. He took her cubs and ran up the mountain.

01 위 글의 밑줄 친 ⓐ의 우리말에 맞게 다음 빈칸에 들어갈 알맞은 말을 쓰시오.

_____ _____ the river is too wide?

02 다음 빈칸 (A)~(D)에 알맞은 단어를 넣어 형과 동생이 선택한 것을 완성하시오.

The (A)_____ brother chose (B)_____ to go with his brother, and the (C)_____ brother alone went into the forest, swam across the river, took the cubs and (D)_____ up the mountain.

03 위 글의 밑줄 친 ⓑ에서 흐름상 어색한 부분을 찾아 고치시오.

➡ _____

[04~05] 다음 글을 읽고 물음에 답하시오.

When he (A)[reached / reached to] the top, some people took him to their city and made him their king. There he lived as a king for five years. Then a war (B)[broke / was broken] out, and he lost his ____ⓐ____. He was on the road again.

One day, the two brothers met again and talked about their lives for the last five years. The older brother said, "I was right. I have lived (C)[quiet / quietly] and well. You were once a king, but you have had a lot of trouble." The younger brother answered, "I don't regret my choice. I may have nothing now, but I will always have something to remember."

04 위 글의 괄호 (A)~(C)에서 어법상 알맞은 낱말을 골라 쓰시오.

➡ (A)_____ (B)_____ (C)_____

05 주어진 영영풀이를 참고하여 빈칸 ⓐ에 철자 t로 시작하는 단어를 쓰시오.

the position of being king, queen, or emperor

➡ _____

[06~08] 다음 글을 읽고 물음에 답하시오.

The younger brother said, "Let's go and find happiness together." "No," said the older brother, "How can we know this is true? What if the river is too wide? Besides, will it be easy to take the cubs away from their mother? ⓐ Instead of finding happiness, we can kill!" The younger brother replied, "How can we know

ⓑif we don't try?" They separated, and they both went their own way.

The younger brother went into the forest and swam across the river. There was the bear. She was sleeping. He took her cubs and ran up the mountain.

06 위 글의 밑줄 친 ⓐ에서 어법상 틀린 부분을 찾아 고치시오.

➡ _____

07 형이 동생의 제안에 반대하는 이유 네 가지를 우리말로 쓰시오.

➡ (1) _____
　　(2) _____
　　(3) _____
　　(4) _____

08 위 글의 밑줄 친 ⓑ를 unless를 사용하여 고치시오.

➡ _____

[09~11] 다음 글을 읽고 물음에 답하시오.

When he reached the top, some people took him to their city and made him their king. There he lived as a king for five years. Then a war broke out, and he lost his throne. He was on the road again.

One day, the two brothers met again and talked about their lives ⓐ____ the last five years. The older brother said, "I was right. I have lived quietly and well. You were once a king, but you have had a lot of trouble." The younger brother answered, "I don't regret my choice. ⓑ나는 지금 아무것도 없지만 늘 기억할 어떤 것이 있을 거야."

09 위 글의 빈칸 ⓐ에 들어갈 알맞은 전치사를 쓰시오.

➡ _____

10 위 글의 밑줄 친 ⓑ의 우리말에 맞게 한 단어를 보충하여, 주어진 어휘를 알맞게 배열하시오.

something / will / I / have / remember / but / always / I / to / have / may / now / ,

➡ _____
　 _____

11 다음 빈칸 (A)와 (B)에 알맞은 단어를 넣어 지난 5년 동안 두 형제가 각자 어떻게 살았는지를 완성하시오.

The older brother has lived (A)_____ _____ _____ and the younger brother lived (B)_____ _____ _____ for the last five years.

[12~13] 다음 글을 읽고 물음에 답하시오.

A Book Review
Title: Jonathan Livingston Seagull: a story
Writer: Richard Bach
　This story is about a seagull named Jonathan Livingston. He dreams of flying better than others. To reach his goal, he works hard and practices ⓐ____ . I like this story because it has helped me learn about the power of my own beliefs. The book says that I can do anything that I want if I do not give up.

12 위 글의 빈칸 ⓐ에 fly를 알맞은 형태로 쓰시오.

➡ _____

13 본문의 내용과 일치하도록 다음 빈칸에 알맞은 단어를 쓰시오.

According to this book, I can do _____ that I want if I do not stop trying to do it.

교과서

구석구석

Before You Read

A

There is a box filled with gold behind a tree across the river.
there is ~: ~가 있다   filled with: ~로 가득 찬

But watch out! Dangerous animals are in the river.
'주어+be 동사+부사구 ~.'에서 be동사는 '있다'로 해석한다.

B

Mr. Allen chose to go on journey to the city for his vacation.
choose는 to부정사를 목적어로 취한다. go on journey to ~: ~로 여행가다

Sadly the city streets were dirty and noisy. A car even almost hit him. He had
슬프게도(문장 전체 수식)   have trouble: 어려움을 겪다

lots of trouble there. After a few days in the city, he regretted his choice and
= in[at] the city

went back to his hometown.
접속사 and로 regretted와 went는 병렬 관계를 이룬다.

구문해설 ・regret: 후회하다

Writing Workshop

A Book Review

Title: *Jonathan Livingston Seagull*: a story

Writer: Richard Bach

This story is about a seagull named Jonathan Livingston. He dreams of
~라는 이름을 가진

flying better than others. To reach his goal, he works hard and practices flying.
동명사 비교급 than: ~보다 더 잘 to부정사의 부사적 용법(목적)   practice는 목적어로 동명사를 취한다.

I like this story because it has helped me learn about the power of my own
help+목적어+동사원형[to부정사]

beliefs. The book says that I can do anything that I want if I do not give up.
접속사   관계대명사   = unless I

구문해설 ・A named[called] B: B라는 이름을 가진[B라고 불리는] A ・reach: ~에 도달하다
・goal: 목표 ・practice: 연습하다 ・belief: 믿음 ・give up: 포기하다

Into the World

Happiness is when what you think, what you say, and what you do are in
접속사   복수 동사(주어는 3개의 what ~. what ~. and what ~)

harmony.   – Mahatma Gandhi

When one door of happiness closes, another opens. – Helen Keller
또 다른 하나(= another door)

Happiness is not something ready-made. It comes from your own actions.
-thing으로 끝나는 부정대명사는 형용사가 뒤에서 수식 = Happiness   자신의(소유격 강조)
                                                    – Dalai Lama XIV

구문해설 ・harmony: 조화 ・ready-made: 이미 만들어져 나오는[다 만들어서 파는], 기성품의, 준비된

해석

A

강 건너 나무 뒤에 황금으로 가득 찬 상자가 있다. 하지만 조심해! 위험한 동물들이 강에 있어.

B

Allen씨는 휴가를 보내기 위해 도시로 여행을 가기로 결정했다. 슬프게도 도시의 거리는 더럽고 시끄러웠다. 심지어 차가 그를 칠 뻔 했다. 그는 거기서 많은 어려움을 겪었다. 도시에서의 며칠 후, 그는 그의 선택을 후회하고 고향으로 다시 돌아갔다.

독서 감상문

제목: *Jonathan Livingston Seagull*(갈매기의 꿈): 이야기

작가: Richard Bach

이 이야기는 Jonathan Livingston이라는 이름의 갈매기에 대한 것이다. 그는 다른 갈매기들보다 더 잘 나는 것을 꿈꾼다. 그의 목표에 도달하기 위해 그는 열심히 노력하고 비행을 연습한다. 이 이야기가 내 자신의 믿음의 힘에 대해 배우도록 도와주었기 때문에 나는 이 이야기를 좋아한다. 이 책은 내가 포기하시 않으면 내가 원하는 어떤 것이라도 할 수 있다고 말한다.

행복은 생각, 말, 행동이 조화를 이룰 때 찾아온다.

– Mahatma Gandhi

행복의 한쪽 문이 닫히면 다른 쪽 문이 열리게 된다.

– Helen Keller

행복은 준비된 것이 아니다. 행복은 당신 자신의 행동에서 비롯된다.

– Dalai Lama XIV

영역별 핵심문제

01 다음 짝지어진 두 단어의 관계가 같도록 빈칸에 알맞은 말을 쓰시오.

(1) noisy : quiet – friendly : _____

(2) popular : popularity – happy : _____

02 다음 중 밑줄 친 부분의 뜻풀이가 바르지 <u>않은</u> 것은?

① Every <u>item</u> in the store is on sale! (품목)

② I made a <u>review</u> of his work in the paper. (논평)

③ At first, she wanted the role of Cinderella, the most important <u>character</u>. (성격)

④ What is the <u>title</u> of the bestseller? (제목)

⑤ They <u>separated</u> last month. (헤어졌다)

03 다음 영영풀이가 나타내는 말을 고르시오.

having no errors

① correct   ② complete

③ wrong   ④ natural

⑤ entire

04 우리말에 맞게 주어진 단어를 알맞게 배열하시오.

(1) 왕은 오랫동안 자기 나라를 다스렸다. (for, the, his, long, a, ruled, king, time, country)

➡ _____

(2) 당신의 지지에 감사드려요. (thank, support, for, your, you)

➡ _____

05 다음 중 의도하는 바가 나머지 넷과 <u>다른</u> 하나는?

① What's your opinion of that?

② How do you feel about that?

③ What do you think of that?

④ What do you feel like doing?

⑤ How do you feel about that?

06 다음 중 짝지어진 대화가 <u>어색한</u> 것은?

① A: I'm worried that I'm getting fat.
   B: Try not to worry about it too much.

② A: Make sure to come back before dark.
   B: Don't worry. We'll be back soon.

③ A: What do you think about the movie?
   B: It is good. I really enjoyed it.

④ A: The more we have, the more we want.
   B: I'm worried about you.

⑤ A: What do you think of my new shoes?
   B: I like them. They look great.

07 다음 대화의 빈칸에 알맞은 말을 고르시오.

A: What do you think of our history class?

B: _____

① It's difficult for me.

② It looks good on you.

③ I'm happy that you like it.

④ That's a great idea.

⑤ It looks light and fast.

[08~09] 다음 대화를 읽고 물음에 답하시오.

G: What do you think of this painting?
B: It looks (A)[great / greatly]. I like the colors.
G: I'm happy (B)[about / that] you like it. I painted it myself.

08 (A)와 (B)에서 알맞은 것을 골라 쓰시오.

➡ (A)＿＿＿＿＿＿ (B)＿＿＿＿＿＿

09 위 대화의 내용과 일치하도록 빈칸을 채우시오.

> They are talking ＿＿＿＿＿＿＿ which the girl ＿＿＿＿＿＿. The boy likes ＿＿＿＿＿ of the painting.

10 (A)와 (B)에 알맞은 것을 〈보기〉에서 골라 쓰시오

┤ 보기 ├
Who What How Why Where

> B: (A)＿＿＿＿ do you think of our school cafeteria food?
> G: I think the cafeteria food is delicious.
> B: (B)＿＿＿＿ do you think is the best item?
> G: I like the Gimbap the best.

[11~12] 다음 대화를 읽고 물음에 답하시오.

G: I saw you with someone who looked like a foreigner yesterday.
B: ＿＿＿＿＿＿＿＿＿＿＿＿＿＿＿＿
G: ＿＿＿＿＿＿＿＿＿＿＿＿＿＿＿＿
B: ＿＿＿＿＿＿＿＿＿＿＿＿＿＿＿＿
G: ＿＿＿＿＿＿＿＿＿＿＿＿＿＿＿＿
B: 나는 영어로 말하는 것에 대해 걱정했었지만, 더 이상은 아니야.
G: I get really nervous when I try to speak in English.
B: Well, the first time is the hardest. After that, it gets easier and easier.
G: What do you think about me joining both of you for lunch?
B: That's a great idea.

┤ 보기 ├
(A) We were. We try to meet twice a month for lunch.
(B) You looked like you were having a good time.
(C) Yes. We had lunch together.
(D) I wish I could feel more comfortable talking with a foreigner.

11 위 대화의 빈칸에 들어갈 말을 〈보기〉에서 골라 순서대로 옳게 배열한 것은?

① (B)-(A)-(C)-(D) ② (B)-(C)-(D)-(A)
③ (C)-(A)-(B)-(D) ④ (C)-(B)-(A)-(D)
⑤ (C)-(D)-(B)-(A)

12 주어진 단어를 이용해 밑줄 친 우리말을 영작하시오. (총 11 단어)

➡ ＿＿＿＿＿＿＿＿＿＿＿＿＿＿＿＿

＿＿＿＿＿＿＿＿＿＿＿＿＿＿＿＿

(anymore, be, about, in, worried)

Grammar

13 다음 빈칸에 들어갈 표현이 순서대로 바르게 짝지어진 것을 고르시오.

> Three years _____ since he _____ his home.

① have passed – left ② passed – left
③ passed – has left ④ have passed – has left
⑤ have passed – had left

14 다음 표를 보고 괄호 안에 주어진 어휘를 이용하여 빈칸을 알맞게 채우시오.

Spring people	friendly, talkative
Summer people	quiet, thoughtful
Fall people	energetic, active
Winter people	faithful, honest

➡ _____, you must be friendly and talkative. (if)

15 밑줄 친 부분의 쓰임이 나머지 넷과 다른 것은?

① Emily has studied math for 6 hours.
② How long have you played soccer?
③ Sean has lived in Korea for 4 years.
④ We have known Jerry since he was a little boy.
⑤ Someone has stolen my wallet.

16 빈칸에 공통으로 들어갈 접속사를 고르시오.

> • Mike, _____ you're finished, may I use the phone?
> • Let me know _____ you need my advice.

① if ② because ③ as
④ though ⑤ unless

17 다음 ⓐ~ⓔ 중 옳은 것을 모두 고르면?

> ⓐ I have met Mariel two years ago.
> ⓑ I have lost my cell phone.
> ⓒ How long have you been in Korea?
> ⓓ I have gone to Hong Kong.
> ⓔ I like this story because it has helped me learn about the power of my own beliefs.

① ⓐ, ⓒ   ② ⓐ, ⓓ
③ ⓑ, ⓒ   ④ ⓑ, ⓒ, ⓔ
⑤ ⓒ, ⓓ, ⓔ

18 다음 밑줄 친 부분의 쓰임이 나머지 넷과 다른 것은?

① If you leave now, you can catch the next train.
② I will be happy if I have a house someday.
③ I don't know if Sarah will like the idea.
④ If you're free tomorrow, let's go see a movie.
⑤ We will stay home if it rains tomorrow.

19 다음 중 어법상 어색한 문장은?

① If I wear warm clothes, I won't be cold.
② You will be late for school if you don't get up now.
③ The news of the war has caused great sadness around the world.
④ It's been several years since we met after graduation.
⑤ The writer has finished his new novel last week.

Reading

[20~22] 다음 글을 읽고 물음에 답하시오.

Two brothers went on a journey. ⓐ They founded a rock in front of a forest. It said, "Go into the forest and swim across the river. There you will find a bear and her ⓑ . Take the bear ⓑ and run up the mountain. ⓒThere you will find happiness."

20 위 글의 밑줄 친 ⓐ에서 흐름상 어색한 부분을 찾아 고치시오.

➡ _____

21 주어진 영영풀이를 참고하여 빈칸 ⓑ에 철자 c로 시작하는 단어를 쓰시오. (복수형으로 쓸 것)

the young of certain wild animals such as the bear or wolf or lion

➡ _____

22 위 글의 밑줄 친 ⓒThere가 가리키는 것을 본문에서 찾아 영어로 쓰시오.

➡ _____

[23~24] 다음 글을 읽고 물음에 답하시오.

The younger brother said, "Let's go and find happiness together." "No," said the older brother, "How can we know this is true? What if the river is too wide? ⓐBesides, will it be easy to take the cubs away from their mother? Instead of finding happiness, we can be killed!" The younger brother replied, "ⓑHow can we know if we don't try?" They separated, and they both went their own way.

The younger brother went into the forest and swam across the river. There was the bear. She was sleeping. He took her cubs and ran up the mountain.

23 위 글의 밑줄 친 ⓐBesides와 바꿔 쓸 수 있는 어휘를 쓰시오. (in을 이용할 것)

➡ _____

24 위 글의 밑줄 친 ⓑ와 어울리는 속담을 고르시오.

① Look before you leap.
② Nothing ventured, nothing gained.
③ Don't cry over spilt milk.
④ Easier said than done.
⑤ Every dog has his day.

[25~27] 다음 글을 읽고 물음에 답하시오.

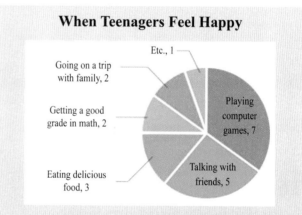

We have asked our classmates ①when they are happy. Seven students say they are happy ②when they play computer games. Five students are happy ③when they talk with friends. Three students say they are happy ④when they eat delicious food. There are two students who are happy ⑤when they get a good grade in math. And there are also two students who are happy when they go on a trip with family.

25 다음 빈칸에 들어갈 알맞은 말을 쓰시오.

_____ percent of the students are happy when they talk with friends.

26 밑줄 친 ①~⑤ 중에서 문법적 쓰임이 나머지 넷과 <u>다른</u> 것은?

①   ②   ③   ④   ⑤

27 위 글의 내용과 일치하지 <u>않는</u> 것은?

① 위 도표는 십대들이 언제 행복하다고 느끼는지를 조사한 표이다.

② 7명의 학생들은 컴퓨터 게임을 할 때 행복하다고 답했다.

③ 친구와 이야기할 때 행복한 학생이 맛있는 음식을 먹을 때 행복한 학생보다 더 많다.

④ 맛있는 음식을 먹을 때 행복한 학생이 수학에서 좋은 점수를 받을 때 행복한 학생보다 더 적다.

⑤ 가족과 여행갈 때 행복한 학생과 수학에서 좋은 점수를 받을 때 행복한 학생의 수는 같다.

[28~29] 다음 글을 읽고 물음에 답하시오.

A Book Review

Title: Jonathan Livingston Seagull: a story

Writer: Richard Bach

This story is about a seagull named Jonathan Livingston. He dreams of flying better than others. ⓐ<u>To reach</u> his goal, he works hard and practices flying. I like this story because it has helped me learn about the power of my own beliefs. The book says that I can do anything that I want if I do not give up.

28 아래 보기에서 위 글의 밑줄 친 ⓐTo reach와 to부정사의 용법이 같은 것의 개수를 고르시오.

┌──── 보기 ────┐

① It wasn't easy <u>to reach</u> his goal.

② He studied hard <u>to reach</u> his goal.

③ He went abroad <u>to reach</u> his goal.

④ He knew the best way <u>to reach</u> his goal.

⑤ He really wants <u>to reach</u> his goal.

└─────────────┘

① 1개   ② 2개   ③ 3개   ④ 4개   ⑤ 5개

29 위 글을 읽고 대답할 수 <u>없는</u> 질문은?

① What's the title of this book?

② Who wrote this book?

③ Who is the main character?

④ What's the dream of Jonathan?

⑤ When does Jonathan practice flying?

[30~31] 다음 글을 읽고 물음에 답하시오.

Mr. Allen chose to go on a journey to the city for his vacation. Sadly, the city streets were dirty and noisy. A car even almost hit him. He had lots of trouble there. After a few days in the city, he ⓐ his choice and went back to his hometown.

30 위 글의 빈칸 ⓐ에 들어갈 알맞은 말을 고르시오.

① accepted   ② regretted

③ improved   ④ achieved

⑤ refused

31 위 글을 읽고 Mr. Allen의 심경 변화로 가장 알맞은 것을 고르시오.

① bored → disappointed

② expectant → pleased

③ frightened → satisfied

④ expectant → disappointed

⑤ satisfied → bored

01 출제율 95%

다음 제시된 단어를 사용하여 자연스러운 문장을 만들 수 없는 것은? (어형 변화 가능)

┌─ 보기 ─┐
regret reply rule support
└───────┘

① Did you _____ a good time on your vacation?

② Rome _____ the world for more than 500 years.

③ I asked her what she does, but she didn't _____.

④ You should respect her choice and _____ her.

⑤ I _____ having been so careless.

[02~03] 다음 대화의 빈칸에 알맞은 말을 쓰시오.

02 출제율 90%

A: What do you think of these shoes?
B: They _____ good _____ you.

03 출제율 100%

A: I'm worried _____ the science project.
B: Don't worry. You _____ good _____ science.

04 출제율 90%

다음 주어진 우리말에 맞게 빈칸을 채우시오. (주어진 철자가 있으면 그 철자로 시작할 것)

(1) 만약 문제를 고치지 않으면, 그것은 점점 더 커질 거예요.
➡ If you don't get your problem fixed, it will get _____. (3 words)

(2) 행복은 돈보다 더 중요하다.
➡ H_____ is more important than money.

05 출제율 90%

다음 글의 빈칸에 알맞은 말을 고르시오.

I'm worried about my math test. I'm not good at math. I think I should _____.

① find the book that I borrowed from the library

② study harder to get good grades

③ speak in English

④ have a good time with friends

⑤ take my dog for a walk in the evening

06 출제율 95%

다음 대화의 순서를 바르게 배열하시오.

(A) Don't worry. It won't rain on Jejudo tomorrow.

(B) Oh, that's good to hear.

(C) Do you have any special plans for tomorrow?

(D) I'm going to Jejudo in the morning. But I'm worried about the weather.

➡ _____

07 출제율 85%

다음 대화의 빈칸 ⓐ~ⓔ에 들어갈 수 없는 표현을 고르시오.

B: Jina, can you go into your house ⓐ _____?
G: Why? What's ⓑ _____?
B: I'm scared of your dog.
G: Don't worry. He's a ⓒ _____ dog. He just looks ⓓ _____ because he's so ⓔ _____.

① friendly   ② big   ③ last
④ wrong   ⑤ scary

[08~11] 다음 대화를 물음에 답하시오.

> W: Jimin, you look worried. What's wrong?
>
> G: Mom, I can't find the book that I borrowed from the library. (①) Have you seen it? (②)
>
> W: What book are you looking for? *Jonathan Livingston Seagull*? (③) I think I saw it in the living room.
>
> G: Yes, that's it. Thank you, Mom. (④)
>
> W: (A)_____, have you read the book? What did you think of it?
>
> G: (⑤) It was really interesting. I loved the character of Jonathan a lot.

출제율 100%

08 ①~⑤ 중 주어진 문장이 들어갈 곳은?

> I've read it two times already.

①   ②   ③   ④   ⑤

출제율 90%

09 위 대화에서 다음 영영풀이에 해당하는 단어를 찾아 쓰시오.

> a person in a film, book, or play

➡ _____

출제율 95%

10 빈칸 (A)에 알맞은 말을 고르시오.

① Finally   ② On the other hand

③ Eventually   ④ By the way

⑤ On the contrary

출제율 100%

11 위 대화를 읽고 알 수 <u>없는</u> 것을 고르시오.

① How many times has the girl read *Jonathan Livingston Seagul*?

② What relationship are they?

③ What character does the woman like in *Jonathan Livingston Seagul*?

④ At first, why did the girl look worried?

⑤ What book did the girl borrow from the library?

출제율 90%

12 밑줄 친 우리말을 주어진 단어를 이용해 영작하시오.

> B: 학교 식당 음식에 대해 어떻게 생각해?
>
> G: I think the cafeteria food is delicious.
>
> B: What do you think is the best item?
>
> G: I like the Gimbap the best.

➡ _____

(think, what, of)

출제율 90%

13 다음 우리말을 주어진 어구를 이용하여 영작하시오.

(1) 그들은 모든 책을 다 팔았다. (그래서 남아 있는 책이 없다.) (sell, all the books)

➡ _____

(2) Mina는 벼룩시장에 한 번 가 본 적이 있다. (once, the flea market)

➡ _____

(3) 나는 태어난 이후로 Paris에서 살고 있다. (live, Paris, was born)

➡ _____

(4) 열차는 이미 역을 떠났다. (have, the station, depart, already)

➡ _____

(5) 내일 날씨가 화창하면, 우리는 해변에 갈 거야. (sunny, the beach)

➡ _____

(6) 그 옷이 너한테 잘 어울릴지 궁금해. (the dress, wonder, look, good, if, on)

➡ _____

14 다음 중 어법상 잘못된 것을 바르게 고치시오.

(1) I have gone to the British Museum before.

➡ _____

(2) When has the technology become available on the market?

➡ _____

(3) Dr. Lee has studied animal diseases for 2002.

➡ _____

(4) Abigail lived in London until now.

➡ _____

(5) If you will push the button, the bell will ring.

➡ _____

[15~17] 다음 글을 읽고 물음에 답하시오.

The younger brother said, "Let's go and find happiness together." "No," said the older brother, "How can we know this is true? What if the river is too wide? Besides, ⓐ곰 새끼들을 엄마에게서 빼앗는 것이 쉬울까? ⓑ_____ finding happiness, we can be killed!" The younger brother replied, "How can we know ⓒif we don't try?" They separated, and they both went their own way.

The younger brother went into the forest and swam across the river. There was the bear. She was sleeping. He took her cubs and ran up the mountain.

15 위 글의 밑줄 친 ⓐ의 우리말에 맞게 한 단어를 보충하여, 주어진 어구를 알맞게 배열하시오.

| their mother / easy / from / to take / will / away / the cubs / be |

➡ _____

_____

16 위 글의 빈칸 ⓑ에 들어갈 알맞은 말을 고르시오.

① In addition to　② Along with
③ Because of　　④ Instead of
⑤ As well as

17 위 글의 밑줄 친 ⓒif와 의미가 다른 것을 고르시오.

① I wonder if I should wear a coat.
② If you see him, give him this note.
③ If necessary, I can come at once.
④ You can stay for a week if you like.
⑤ If you work hard, you will succeed.

[18~20] 다음 글을 읽고 물음에 답하시오.

When he ⓐreached the top, some people took him to their city and made him their king. There he lived as a king for five years. Then a war broke out, and he lost his throne. He was on the road again.

One day, the two brothers met again and talked about their lives for the last five years. (①) The older brother said, "I was right. (②) I have lived quietly and well. (③) You were once a king, but you have had a lot of trouble." (④) The younger brother answered, "(⑤) I may have nothing now, but I will always have something to remember."

18 위 글의 흐름으로 보아, 주어진 문장이 들어가기에 가장 적절한 곳은?

> I don't regret my choice.

①   ②   ③   ④   ⑤

19 위 글의 밑줄 친 ⓐreached와 바꿔 쓸 수 있는 말을 모두 고르시오.

① started from   ② left for
③ arrived at   ④ contacted
⑤ got to

20 위 글의 제목으로 알맞은 것을 고르시오.

① The Younger Brother Lived as a King!
② I'm Satisfied with My Choice!
③ Get along with Your Brother
④ The Quarrel between Two Brothers
⑤ How to Keep Harmonious Relations

[21~23] 다음 글을 읽고 물음에 답하시오.

When he reached the top, some people took him to their city and made him their king. There he lived as a king for five years. Then ⓐ전쟁이 일어났고, and he lost his throne. He was on the road again.

One day, the two brothers met again and talked about their lives for the last five years. The older brother said, "I was right. I have lived quietly and well. You were once a king, but you have had a lot of trouble." The younger brother answered, "I don't regret my choice. I ⓑmay have nothing now, ⓒbut I will always have something to remember."

21 위 글의 밑줄 친 ⓐ의 우리말을 네 단어로 쓰시오.

➡ _____

22 위 글의 밑줄 친 ⓑmay와 같은 의미로 쓰인 것을 고르시오.

① May I come in?
② He works hard so that he may succeed.
③ May she rest in peace.
④ The rumor may be true.
⑤ You may go there at any moment.

23 위 글의 밑줄 친 ⓒ를 읽고, 자신의 선택에 대한 'I'의 심경을 나타내는 가장 알맞은 말을 고르시오.

① bored   ② regretful
③ satisfied   ④ disappointed
⑤ anxious

[24~25] 다음 글을 읽고 물음에 답하시오.

Have You Ever Read *The Little Prince*?
It is a story about a prince who takes a trip to the stars. ⓐThe main character, the Little Prince, understands how important is his friend to him after his trip. It is such an interesting book. ⓑ Why don't you read it?

24 위 글의 밑줄 친 ⓐ에서 어법상 틀린 부분을 찾아 고치시오.

➡ _____

25 위 글의 밑줄 친 ⓑ를 How를 사용하여 고치시오.

➡ _____

[01~02] 대화의 ①~⑤ 중 흐름상이나 어법상 어색한 곳을 고치시오.

01

> G: ①Did you watch the movie, *The Daughter*?
> B: Yes, ②I saw it ③last Saturday.
> G: ④What did you think of it?
> B: ⑤I was excited. It wasn't very good.

➡ _____

02 (2개)

> G: ①What do you think with this painting?
> B: ②It looks great. ③I like the colors.
> G: ④I'm happy that you like it. ⑤I painted it mine.

➡ _____
_____

03 대화의 밑줄 친 부분과 같은 뜻이 되도록 빈칸을 완성하시오.

> A: I'm worried about my math test.
> B: Don't worry. You'll do great.

➡ (1) _____ a_____ about my math test.
  (2) _____ c_____ about my math test.

04 다음 빈칸에 알맞은 단어를 〈보기〉에서 골라 쓰시오.

> ┤ 보기 ├
> ago   before   for   since

(1) I met Juliet 5 years ago. We have known each other _____ five years.
(2) Yesterday I went to the zoo and saw a tiger. I have never seen it _____.
(3) I have taken piano lessons _____ I was young.

05 다음 두 문장의 의미가 같도록 문장의 빈칸을 완성하시오.

(1) Eunji began to live in Kwangju 5 years ago, and she still lives there.
  = Eunji _____ _____ in Kwangju for 5 years.
(2) Brian went to New York, so he isn't here now.
  = Brian _____ _____ _____ New York.
(3) I visited the museum and it was my third visit.
  = I _____ _____ the museum _____ _____.

06 두 문장을 한 문장으로 쓰시오.

(1) Finish your report by 6, and you can play the computer games.
  ➡ _____
  _____
(2) Work hard, or you won't overcome your weakness.
  ➡ _____
  _____

07 다음 중 어법상 <u>어색한</u> 문장을 찾아 바르게 고쳐 쓰시오.

① We have asked our classmates when they are happy.
② If I will meet Suji, I will give her this letter.
③ Jim will go hiking if it is sunny tomorrow.
④ Work hard if you aim for the sky.
⑤ I like this story because it has helped me learn about the way to overcome my weakness.

➡ _____

[08~10] 다음 글을 읽고 물음에 답하시오.

When he reached the top, some people took him to their city and made him their king. There he lived as a king for five years. Then a war broke out, and he lost his throne. He was on the road again.

One day, the two brothers met again and talked about their lives for the last five years. The older brother said, "I was right. I have lived quietly and well. You were once a king, but you have had a lot of trouble." The younger brother answered, "I don't regret my ___@___. I may have nothing now, but I will always have something to remember."

08 다음 문장에서 위 글의 내용과 <u>다른</u> 부분을 찾아서 고치시오.

• When a war broke out, the older brother lost his throne and was on the road again.

➡ _____

09 위 글의 빈칸 @에 choose를 알맞은 형태로 쓰시오.

➡ _____

10 위 글을 읽고 자신들이 내렸던 선택에 대한 두 형제의 생각을 각각 우리말로 쓰시오.

➡ 형의 생각: "_____"
   동생의 생각: "_____"

[11~13] 다음 글을 읽고 물음에 답하시오.

The younger brother said, "Let's go and find happiness together." "No," said the older brother, "(A)[How / What] can we know this is true? What if the river is too wide? (B)[Beside / Besides], will it be easy to take the cubs away from their mother? @행복을 찾는 대신에, 우리는 죽을 수 있어!" The younger brother replied, "How can we know (C)[if / that] we don't try?" They separated, and they both went their own way.

The younger brother went into the forest and swam across the river. There was the bear. ⓑShe was sleeping. ⓒHe took her cubs and ran up the mountain.

11 위 글의 괄호 (A)~(C)에서 문맥과 어법상 알맞은 낱말을 골라 쓰시오.

➡ (A)_____ (B)_____ (C)_____

12 위 글의 밑줄 친 @의 우리말에 맞게 주어진 어휘를 이용하여 8 단어로 영작하시오.

killed

➡ _____

13 위 글의 밑줄 친 ⓑShe와 ⓒHe가 가리키는 것을 본문에서 찾아 쓰시오.

➡ ⓑ_____ ⓒ_____

01 주어진 정보와 그림을 이용해 빈칸에 알맞은 말을 쓰시오..

<조건>
- 걱정을 나타내는 표현을 사용할 것
- worry, read, finish를 이용할 것
- 접속사 that을 꼭 넣을 것

A: _____
B: Don't worry. I know you'll do great.

02 주어진 어구와 조건의 부사절을 이용하여 3 문장 이상을 쓰시오.

sunny	go to Jejudo	know the result	exercise hard
go hiking	swim in the sea	let me know	become healthy

(1) _____
(2) _____
(3) _____
(4) _____

03 자신이 좋아하는 책의 주인공을 소개하는 글을 완성하시오.

Have You Ever Read *the Little Prince*?

It is a story about a prince (A)_____ takes a trip to the stars. The main (B)_____, *the Little Prince*, understands (C)_____ important his friend is to him after his trip. It is (D)_____ an interesting book. (E)_____ read it?

단원별 모의고사

01 다음 짝지어진 단어의 관계가 나머지 넷과 <u>다른</u> 하나를 고르시오.

① separate – unite
② disappointed – discouraged
③ character – role
④ happiness – pleasure
⑤ correct – right

02 빈칸에 알맞은 말을 〈보기〉에서 골라 쓰시오.

┌─ 보기 ┐
at for to about in as
└──────────────────┘

I'm worried _____ my dog. She has _____ stay alone during the day. I think I should take her _____ a walk _____ night.

03 다음 제시된 단어를 사용하여 자연스러운 문장을 만들 수 <u>없는</u> 것은?

┌─ 보기 ┐
comfortable scary nervous noisy
└──────────────────────┘

① It's _____ being all alone in this big house.
② I feel very _____ before an exam.
③ Select the _____ date and time.
④ I can't concentrate on my work in _____ places.
⑤ It helps people feel happier and more _____.

04 단어와 영영풀이의 연결이 <u>잘못된</u> 것을 고르시오.

① support: help, encouragement, or comfort given to someone during a difficult or unhappy time
② reply: to say or write something in response to something
③ teenager: a person between the ages of thirteen and nineteen
④ ever: at no time in the past or at no time in the future
⑤ separate: to move apart

05 다음 대화의 빈칸에 알맞은 말을 고르시오.

┌──────────────────────┐
A: _____
B: Don't worry. You'll find something you like to do
└──────────────────────┘

① I never worry about your grades.
② I'm concerned about my dog.
③ I'm worried about speaking English.
④ I'm anxious about my speech test.
⑤ I'm worried about my future.

06 다음 괄호 안의 단어를 알맞게 배열하여 문장을 만드시오.

┌──────────────────────┐
A: (think, this, painting, what, of, do, you, ?)
B: It's wonderful.
└──────────────────────┘

➡ _____

[07~08] 다음 대화를 읽고 물음에 답하시오.

> B: Do you have any special plans for tomorrow?
> G: I'm going to Jejudo in the morning. But I'm (A)_____ about the weather.
> B: Don't worry. It (B)_____ rain on Jejudo tomorrow.
> G: Oh, (C)_____

07 대화의 단어를 이용해 빈칸 (A)를 채우시오.

➡ _____

08 빈칸 (B)와 (C)에 들어갈 말로 알맞게 연결된 것을 고르시오.

	(B)	(C)
①	will	you'll do fine.
②	will	that's good to hear.
③	won't	you'll do fine.
④	won't	that's good to hear.
⑤	won't	I'm sorry to hear that.

[09~10] 다음 대화를 읽고 물음에 답하시오.

> B: Jina, can you go into your house first?
> G: Why? What's wrong?
> B: 난 네 개가 무서워.
> G: Don't worry. He's a friendly dog. He just looks scary (A)_____ he's so big.

09 밑줄 친 우리말을 주어진 단어를 이용하여 영작하시오.

➡ _____ (scare)

10 빈칸 (A)에 알맞은 말을 고르시오.

① when   ② while

③ although   ④ which

⑤ because

[11~12] 다음 대화를 읽고 물음에 답하시오.

> G: I saw you with someone who looked like a foreigner yesterday.
> B: Yes. We had lunch together. (①)
> G: You looked like you were having a good time. (②)
> B: We were. We try to meet twice a month for lunch.
> G: I wish I could feel more comfortable talking with a foreigner. (③)
> B: I was worried about speaking in English before, but not anymore. (④)
> G: I get really nervous when I try to speak in English.
> B: Well, the first time is the hardest. (⑤)
> G: What do you think about me joining both of you for lunch?
> B: That's a great idea.

11 ①~⑤ 중 주어진 문장이 들어갈 곳은?

> After that, it gets easier and easier.

①   ②   ③   ④   ⑤

12 대화에서 다음 영영풀이에 해당하는 단어를 찾아 쓰시오.

> worried and anxious about something that is happening or might happen

➡ _____

13 대화의 빈칸 ⓐ~ⓔ에 들어갈 수 없는 표현을 고르시오.
(대·소문자 무시)

> W: Jimin, you ⓐ_____. What's wrong?
> G: Mom, I can't find the book ⓑ_____ from the library. ⓒ_____ it?
> W: What book are you looking for? *Jonathan Livingston Seagull*? I think I saw it in the living room.

G: Yes, that's it. Thank you, Mom.

W: By the way, ⓓ_____ the book? ⓔ
_____ of it?

G: I've read it two times already. It was really interesting. I loved the character of Jonathan a lot.

① that I borrowed
② have you seen
③ look interested
④ what did you think
⑤ have you read

14 다음 주어진 문장의 밑줄 친 부분과 쓰임이 같은 것은?

• If you have any problems, I will help you.

① I don't know if Sarah will like the idea.
② The woman was not sure if the thief was a man or a woman.
③ You can go out and play if you finish your homework by three.
④ Please see if the children are dressed for school.
⑤ Only time will tell if I was wrong or not.

15 다음 중 어법상 어색한 것을 고르시오.

① I have never seen Minho since he moved to Yongin.
② I have already had lunch an hour ago.
③ If I can stand the cold, I will help the prince more.
④ You will get wet if you go out now.
⑤ I was ill yesterday and don't feel any better today.

16 다음 문장에서 어법상 어색한 것을 바르게 고치시오.

(1) When have you started working at the company?

➡ _____

(2) Today is July 10, and I arrived here on July 1. So, I was here for 10 days.

➡ _____

(3) She has taught them English since two years.

➡ _____

(4) If you will sleep in class, your teacher will be angry.

➡ _____

(5) Unless she doesn't wear a muffler, she will be cold.

➡ _____
_____

17 주어진 두 문장을 현재완료를 이용해 한 문장으로 만드시오.

(1) Judy arrived at her friend's house two hours ago. She is still in her friend's house.

➡ _____

(2) Someone took away my umbrella. So, I don't have my umbrella now.

➡ _____

[18~20] 다음 글을 읽고 물음에 답하시오.

The younger brother said, "Let's go and find happiness together." "No," said the older brother, "How can we know this is true? What if the river is too wide?   ⓐ   , will ⓑ it be easy to take the cubs away from their mother? Instead of finding happiness, we can be killed!" The younger brother replied, "How can we know if we don't try?" They separated, and they both went their own way.

The younger brother went into the forest and swam across the river. There was the bear. She was sleeping. He took her cubs and ran up the mountain.

18 위 글에서 알 수 있는 형의 성격으로 가장 알맞은 것을 고르시오.

① positive   ② doubtful
③ active   ④ confident
⑤ diligent

19 위 글의 빈칸 ⓐ에 들어갈 알맞은 말을 고르시오.

① However   ② Therefore
③ Besides   ④ For example
⑤ In other words

20 위 글의 밑줄 친 ⓑit과 문법적 쓰임이 같은 것을 고르시오.

① Did you make it?
② It was raining this morning.
③ I make it a rule to get up early.
④ It is 2 miles from here to the airport.
⑤ It is impossible to get there in time.

[21~24] 다음 글을 읽고 물음에 답하시오.

When he reached the top, some people took him ⓐ their city and made him their king. There he lived ⓑas a king for five years. Then a war broke out, and he lost his throne. He was on the road again.

One day, the two brothers met again and talked ⓒ their lives for the last five years. The older brother said, "I was right. I have lived quietly and well. You were once a king, but you have had a lot of trouble." The younger brother answered, "I don't regret my choice. I may have nothing now, but I will always have something to remember."

21 위 글의 빈칸 ⓐ와 ⓒ에 들어갈 전치사가 바르게 짝지어진 것은?

① to - for   ② for - about
③ for - to   ④ to - about
⑤ on - to

22 위 글의 밑줄 친 ⓑas와 같은 의미로 쓰인 것을 고르시오.

① As we go up, the air grows colder.
② He is famous as a statesman.
③ As I was tired, I soon fell asleep.
④ Do in Rome as the Romans do.
⑤ Take as much as you want.

23 다음 질문에 대한 알맞은 대답을 빈칸에 쓰시오.

Q: Why did the younger brother answer that he didn't regret his choice?
A: Because maybe he didn't have anything then, but there would always be something that he could _____.

24 위 글의 내용과 일치하지 않는 것은?

① 동생이 도시에 도착했을 때, 어떤 사람들이 그를 그들의 왕으로 만들었다.
② 동생은 5년간 왕으로 살았다.
③ 지난 5년 동안 형은 조용히 잘 살았다.
④ 동생은 자신의 선택을 후회하지 않는다고 말했다.
⑤ 동생은 지금 아무것도 없지만 언제까지나 기억할 거리가 있다고 말했다.

Lesson 5

We Love Baseball

 의사소통 기능

- 선호하는 것 묻고 답하기
  A: Which story book do you like? *Peter Pan* or *The Last Leaf*?
  B: I like *Peter Pan*.

- 희망, 기대 표현하기
  A: What are you going to do on your vacation?
  B: I'm going to take a boat ride. I can't wait.

 언어 형식

- 부가의문문
  Jian, this is your first time to come to the baseball stadium, **isn't it**?

- 수동태
  The numbers **were determined** by the players' batting order.

교과서

Words & Expressions

Key Words

- □ **anxious**[ǽŋkʃəs] 형 불안한
- □ **base**[beis] 명 (야구의) 루, 베이스
- □ **batter**[bǽtər] 명 타자
- □ **better**[bétər] 형 더 좋은, 더 나은(**good**의 비교급)
- □ **competition**[kὰmpətíʃən] 명 대회
- □ **crack**[kræk] 명 찢어지는 듯한[날카로운] 소리
- □ **decide**[disáid] 동 결정하다
- □ **determine**[ditə́:rmin] 동 결정하다
- □ **dirt**[dəːrt] 명 먼지, 때
- □ **either**[íːðər] 부 (부정문에서) ~도
- □ **fit**[fit] 동 맞다
- □ **forget**[fərgét] 동 잊다
- □ **get**[get] 동 획득하다, 사다
- □ **hide**[haid] 동 감추다, 숨기다
- □ **home run** 홈런
- □ **home team** 홈팀
- □ **international**[ìntərnǽʃənəl] 형 국제적인
- □ **match**[mætʃ] 명 경기, 성냥
- □ **mean**[miːn] 동 의미하다

- □ **miss**[mis] 동 놓치다, 그리워하다
- □ **order**[ɔ́ːrdər] 명 순서, 명령
- □ **past**[pæst] 명 과거
- □ **pet**[pet] 명 애완동물
- □ **pitch**[pitʃ] 명 투구
- □ **rock climbing** 암벽 등반
- □ **rule**[ruːl] 명 규칙
- □ **shorts**[ʃɔːrts] 명 반바지
- □ **sometime**[sʌ́mtàim] 부 언젠가
- □ **stadium**[stéidiəm] 명 경기장
- □ **support**[səpɔ́ːrt] 동 (특정 스포츠 팀을) 응원하다, 지원하다
- □ **team**[tiːm] 명 팀
- □ **then**[ðen] 부 (시간적·공간적으로) 그 뒤에, 그런 다음
- □ **thunder**[θʌ́ndər] 명 천둥
- □ **ticket**[tíkit] 명 티켓
- □ **vacation**[veikéiʃən] 명 휴가
- □ **visit**[vízit] 동 방문하다
- □ **visiting team** 원정 팀

Key Expressions

- □ **at bat** 타석에 서서
- □ **be a big fan of** ~의 열렬한 팬이다
- □ **be about to** 동사원형 막 ~하려고 하다
- □ **be excited about** ~에 신나다, ~에 들뜨다
- □ **between A and B** A와 B 사이에
- □ **can't wait to** 동사원형 ~을 몹시 기대하다
- □ **come back to** ~로 돌아오다
- □ **come out** 나오다
- □ **hurry up** 서둘러 ~하다
- □ **I can't wait** 너무 기다려져
- □ **in a hurry** 서둘러
- □ **in the past** 과거에
- □ **live in** ~에서 살다
- □ **look at** ~을 보다

- □ **look forward to** (동)명사 ~을 기대하다
- □ **over there** 저기, 저쪽에
- □ **think about** ~에 대해 생각하다
- □ **twice a week** 일주일에 두 번
- □ **wait for** ~을 기다리다
- □ **warm up** (스포츠나 활동 전에) 몸을 천천히 풀다, 준비 운동을 하다
- □ **Which** 명사 **do you like** (**better/more**), **A or B**? A나 B 중 어느 것이 (더) 좋습니까?
- □ **which** 명사 어느 명사
- □ **while**+동사**ing** ~하는 동안
- □ **Why don't you** ~? ~하는 게 어때?
- □ **Why not**? 좋아, 왜 아니겠어?
- □ **would like to** 동사원형 ~하고 싶다

Word Power

※ 동작 동사에 'er'을 붙여 동작의 행위자가 되는 단어 (어미가 e로 끝나면 r만 붙임)

- □ **bake**(굽다) – **baker**(제빵사)
- □ **bat**(공을 치다) – **batter**(타자)
- □ **drive**(운전하다) – **driver**(운전자)
- □ **lead**(지휘하다, 이끌다) – **leader**(지도자)
- □ **manage**(경영하다) – **manager**(경영자)

- □ **play**(경기를 하다) – **player**(선수)
- □ **run**(달리다) – **runner**((달리기) 주자)
- □ **sing**(노래하다) – **singer**(가수)
- □ **teach**(가르치다) – **teacher**(교사)
- □ **write**(쓰다) – **writer**(작가)

※ 'go' vs 'play'

- □ **go skiing** 스키 타러 가다
- □ **go surfing** 서핑하러 가다
- □ **go swimming** 수영하러 가다

- □ **play baseball** 야구를 하다
- □ **play soccer** 축구를 하다
- □ **play tennis** 테니스를 치다

English Dictionary

- □ **anxious** 불안한
  → very nervous or worried about something
  매우 긴장하거나 어떤 것에 대해 걱정을 하는
- □ **base** (야구의) 루, 베이스
  → each corner of the square that makes a baseball diamond
  (야구) 내야를 만드는 사각형의 각 모퉁이
- □ **competition** 대회
  → an event or contest in which people try to win something by defeating others
  사람들이 다른 사람들을 물리침으로써 어떤 것을 얻으려고 하는 행사나 경기
- □ **crack** 찢어지는 듯한[날카로운] 소리
  → the sudden loud explosive sound of something when it falls or bumps into itself or something else
  어떤 것이 떨어지거나 자체로 또는 다른 것과 부딪칠 때 나는 갑작스러운 큰 폭발음
- □ **determine** 결정하다
  → to decide or establish something conclusively
  최종적으로 어떤 것을 결정하거나 수립하다
- □ **either** (부정문에서) ~도
  → used in a negative sentence to indicate a similarity with a statement just made
  부정문에서 방금 언급된 진술에 대해 비슷함을 보여주기 위해 사용되는 것
- □ **fit** 맞다
  → to be the right size and shape for someone or something
  어떤 사람이나 사물에 알맞은 크기나 모양이 되다
- □ **hide** 감추다, 숨기다
  → to put something out of sight
  보이지 않는 곳에 무언가를 두다
- □ **home team** 홈팀
  → a sports team playing on its own ground
  홈그라운드에서 경기를 하는 스포츠 팀

- □ **international** 국제적인
  → relating to or involving different countries
  다른 나라들을 포함하거나 관련된
- □ **order** 순서
  → the arrangement or disposition of people or things in a list from first to last
  어떤 목록에서 처음부터 끝까지 사람이나 사물의 배열이나 배치
- □ **past** 과거
  → the time before the moment of speaking or writing
  말하거나 쓰는 순간 이전의 시간
- □ **pitch** 투구
  → a throw of the ball for the batter to hit it
  타자가 치도록 공을 던지는 것
- □ **stadium** 경기장
  → an athletic or sports ground used for playing and watching sports with rows of seats
  운동 경기를 하고 그 경기를 보기 위해 사용되는 여러 줄의 의자가 있는 육상경기나 운동경기장
- □ **team** 팀
  → a group of people who play a sport or game together against other groups of people
  다른 모임의 사람들에 대항해서 운동이나 경기를 함께 하는 사람들의 모임
- □ **thunder** 천둥
  → the loud noise in the sky heard after a lightning flash during a storm
  폭풍우 동안 번개가 번쩍인 후에 들리는 하늘에서 나는 큰 소리
- □ **ticket** 티켓
  → an official piece of paper or card that shows you have paid to enter a place or do something
  어느 장소에 들어가기 위해 또는 어떤 것을 하기 위해 당신이 돈을 지불했다는 것을 보여 주는 공식적인 종이나 카드
- □ **visiting team** 원정 팀
  → a sports team playing on the competing team's field or court
  경쟁하는 팀의 경기장이나 코트에서 경기를 하는 스포츠 팀

01 다음 중 낱말의 관계가 나머지와 다른 하나는?

① lead – leader ② bake – baker
③ sing – singer ④ teach – teacher
⑤ cook – cooker

서답형

02 다음 우리말을 주어진 어휘를 알맞게 배열하여 영작하시오.

내가 네게 막 전화를 걸려던 참인데 네가 전화했어.
(I, me, you, you, was, call, called, when, to, about) (I로 시작할 것)

➡ _____

 03 다음 빈칸에 들어갈 말로 알맞은 것은?

Let's take the problems in a different _____.

① order ② class
③ lesson ④ kind
⑤ nature

서답형

04 다음 빈칸에 공통으로 들어갈 말을 쓰고 그 뜻을 쓰시오.

(1) Is there a particular baseball team that you _____?
(2) His parents wanted to _____ the community center.
(3) Without the _____ of your friends you will not succeed.

(1) _____ (2) _____ (3) _____

05 다음 빈칸에 공통으로 알맞은 말을 고르시오. (대·소문자 무시)

• You can go slow because this work is not _____ a hurry.
• _____ the past, doctors didn't know the reason.

① at ② from ③ to
④ in ⑤ as

06 다음 중 밑줄 친 'miss'의 뜻이 〈보기〉와 다른 것을 고르시오.

┤ 보기 ├
Hurry up or you'll miss the school bus.

① I hate to miss the beginning of a movie.
② Do not miss this exciting festival next year.
③ I'm sure you will miss your school days.
④ Don't miss this chance to learn and experience science!
⑤ It's a pity to miss the match.

 07 다음 영영 풀이에 해당하는 단어를 고르시오.

the loud noise in the sky heard after a lightning flash during a storm

① earthquake ② wave
③ hurricane ④ thunder
⑤ typhoon

01 다음 〈보기〉와 같은 관계가 되도록 빈칸에 알맞은 말을 쓰시오.

┌─ 보기 ─┐
act – actor
└────────┘

(1) bat – _____ (2) write – _____

02 다음 주어진 두 문장이 비슷한 의미가 되도록 빈칸을 알맞게 채우시오.

┌──────────────────────────────┐
I'm looking forward to the New Year's Eve party.
➡ I _____ _____ for the New Year's Eve party.
└──────────────────────────────┘

03 다음 빈칸에 알맞은 단어를 〈보기〉에서 골라 쓰시오.

┌─ 보기 ─┐
home team   match   stadium   thunder
└────────┘

(1) This _____ is so huge, isn't it?
(2) The _____ beat the visiting team 3 to 0.
(3) The alarm sounds like _____.
(4) The Spanish team is leading the soccer _____.

04 다음 대화의 빈칸에 공통으로 들어갈 말을 쓰시오.

┌──────────────────────────────┐
A: _____ don't we go skiing together this afternoon?
B: _____ not?
└──────────────────────────────┘

[05~06] 다음 빈칸에 공통으로 들어갈 말을 쓰시오.

05
┌──────────────────────────────┐
• He wanted to _____ back to Paris.
• New novels _____ out almost every day.
└──────────────────────────────┘

06
┌──────────────────────────────┐
• Can you hurry _____? I don't have much time.
• Warm _____ before lifting heavy weights.
└──────────────────────────────┘

07 다음 주어진 우리말에 맞게 빈칸을 채우시오. (철자가 주어진 것도 있음)

(1) 나는 비틀즈의 열렬한 팬이다.
➡ I a m _____ _____ _____ _____ the Beatles.
(2) 내가 가장 좋아하는 선수가 타석에 선다.
➡ My favorite player is _____ _____.
(3) 조용히 해 주세요. 영화가 곧 시작합니다.
➡ Be quiet, please. The movie _____ _____ _____ start.
(4) 저기 검정색 재킷을 입은 여자는 누구인가요?
➡ Who is that woman _____ _____ in the black jacket?
(5) 나는 일주일에 두 번 요가를 한다.
➡ I do yoga _____ _____ _____.
(6) 음악 클럽에 가입하고 싶어요.
➡ I would _____ _____ join a music club.

Conversation

1 선호하는 것 묻고 답하기

A Which story book do you like? *Peter Pan* or *The Last Leaf*?

너는 어느 이야기책을 좋아하니? "피터팬" 아니면 "마지막 잎새?"

B I like *Peter Pan*. "피터팬"을 좋아해.

■ 주어진 대상 가운데 어느 것을 더 좋아하는지를 물을 때는 'Which do you like better[more], A or B?' 또는 'Which do you prefer, A or B?' 등으로 표현한다. which는 뒤에 나오는 명사를 수식하는 의문형 용사로 쓰일 수 있다.

• Which (sport) do you like more[better], baseball or soccer?

• Which do you prefer, baseball or soccer?

■ 더 좋아하는 것에 대해 말할 때는 'I like A.', 'I like A better[more] than B.' 또는 'I prefer A to B.'로 표현한다. 이때 비교 대상이 되는 'than B'나 'to B'는 생략할 수 있다. 'prefer A to B'에서 to가 전치사 이므로 뒤에 (동)명사가 오는 것에 유의해야 한다.

• A: Which color do you prefer, red or blue?

B: I prefer red (to blue). / I love red (more than blue). / I like red (more than blue).

선호 묻기

• Which (명사) do[would] you like better[more], A or B?

• Which (명사) do you prefer?

• Which (명사) do you prefer, A or B?

선호 대답하기

• I like A.   • I like A better[more] than B.   • I prefer A (to B).

핵심 Check

1. 다음 우리말과 일치하도록 빈칸에 알맞은 말을 쓰시오.

   A: _____ do you like better, meat _____ _____? (너는 어느 것을 더 좋아하니? 고기 아니면 생선?)

   B: I prefer _____ to fish. (나는 생선보다 고기를 더 좋아해.)

2. 다음 우리말과 일치하도록 주어진 단어를 배열하여 문장을 완성하시오.

   A: _____ _____ _____ _____ _____, _____ _____ _____?

   (cats, do, dogs, which, you, or, better, like)

   (너는 어느 것을 더 좋아하니, 개 아니면 고양이?)

   B: I like dogs. (나는 개를 좋아해.)

---

② 희망, 기대 표현하기

> **A** What are you going to do on your vacation? 휴가 때 무엇을 할 예정이니?
>
> **B** I'm going to take a boat ride. I can't wait. 나는 보트를 타러 갈 거야. 너무 기다려져.

- 'I can't wait.'는 '너무 기다려져.' 또는 '나는 빨리 ~했으면 좋겠다.'라는 의미로 희망이나 기대를 나타내는 표현이다. 'I can't wait.' 뒤에는 'for+명사'나 'to+동사원형'을 덧붙여 쓸 수 있다. 'I'm going to take a boat ride. I can't wait.'에서 'I can't wait'를 'I can't wait for a boat ride.'나 'I can't wait to take a boat ride.'로 쓸 수 있다.

- 유사한 표현으로는 'I'm looking forward to+(동)명사'가 있다. 'I can't wait' 다음의 to 다음에는 동사원형이 오는 것과 달리, 'I'm looking forward to'의 to는 전치사이므로, 뒤에는 (동)명사가 오는 것에 주의해야 한다.

희망, 기대 표현하기

- I can't wait. 너무 기다려져.
- I can't wait for 명사.
- I can't wait to 동사원형.
- I'm looking forward to (동)명사.

핵심 Check

3. 다음 대화의 순서를 바르게 배열하시오.

   (A) That sounds great.

   (B) What are your plans for this weekend?

   (C) Yes. I'm looking forward to it.

   (D) I'm going to go to the party this Saturday.

   ➡ _____

4. 다음 주어진 단어를 이용하여 대화의 밑줄 친 부분과 같은 의미의 문장을 쓰시오.

   A: I heard that you are going to take the trip this summer.

   B: Yeah! <u>I'm looking forward to taking the trip.</u>

   ➡ _____ (for, wait)

   _____ (to, wait)

5. 다음 대화의 우리말과 일치하도록 빈칸에 알맞은 말을 쓰시오.

   A: Do you want to watch *Harry Potter* with me this weekend? (나와 이번 주말에 해리 포터 볼래?)

   B: Sure, I'd love to. I _____ wait _____ watch it. (물론, 그리고 싶어. 그것을 정말 보고 싶어.)

Listen & Speak 1 B-2

G: I'm ❶thinking about getting a pet. Do you have a pet?

B: Yes, I do. I have a dog and a cat.

G: ❷What do you think? ❸Which pet is better for me? A cat or a dog?

B: ❹Why don't you come to my house someday and play with my pets? ❺Then you can decide.

G: 나는 애완동물을 기르는 것에 대해 생각 중이야. 넌 애완동물을 기르니?
B: 응, 길러. 개와 고양이가 있어.
G: 어떻게 생각해? 어떤 애완동물이 나에게 더 나아? 고양이 아니면 개?
B: 어느 날 우리 집에 와서 내 애완동물과 놀아 보는 게 어때? 그런 다음 너는 결정할 수 있을 거야.

❶ think about: ~에 대해서 생각하다 (= think of)

❷ What do you think?: 어떻게 생각해? (의견을 묻는 표현) 대화의 흐름상 애완동물을 기르는 것에 대해 어떻게 생각하는지 상대방의 의견을 묻고 있다. (= What do you think about[of] getting a pet?)

❸ better는 good의 비교급으로 '더 좋은'의 의미를 가진다.

❹ Why don't you ~?: ~하는 게 어때? (상대방에게 권유) come과 play는 접속사 and로 연결되어 있다.

❺ then: (시간적·공간적으로) 그 뒤에, 그런 다음 decide 다음에 내용상 'which pet is better for you(어떤 동물이 더 나을지)'가 생략되어 있다.

Check(√) True or False

(1) The girl has a dog and a cat.　　　　　　　　　　　　　　　T ☐ F ☐

(2) The boy advises the girl to come to his house and play with his pets.　　T ☐ F ☐

Listen & Speak 2 B-1

G: Do you ❶want to see my new mountain bike?

B: Sure. ❷When did you get it?

G: ❸Yesterday my father bought it for me. Can you come to my house this afternoon?

B: Of course. ❹I can't wait to see it.

G: 내 새 산악 자전거를 보고 싶니?
B: 물론이지. 언제 생긴 거야?
G: 어제 아빠가 나에게 사 주셨어. 오늘 오후에 우리 집에 올래?
B: 당연하지. 나는 그것을 빨리 보고 싶어.

❶ mountain bike: 산악 자전거 want는 to부정사를 목적어로 갖는다.

❷ when: 언제 get: 얻다, 사다

❸ bought는 buy(사다)의 과거형이다. it은 my new mountain bike를 받는 대명사이다. buy+간접목적어(~에게)+직접목적어(~을, 를)[4형식] = buy+직접목적어+for+간접목적어[3형식]

❹ 'I can't wait.'는 '너무 기다려져.' 또는 '나는 빨리 ~했으면 좋겠다.'라는 의미로, 희망이나 기대를 표현할 때 사용한다. I can't wait to see it. = I'm looking forward to seeing it.

Check(√) True or False

(3) The girl bought a new mountain bike yesterday.　　　　　　　T ☐ F ☐

(4) The boy is going to go to the girl's house this afternoon.　　　　T ☐ F ☐

Listen & Speak 1 A

M: ❶Which sport do you like? Soccer or basketball?

G: ❷I like soccer more. I play soccer ❸twice a week.

❶ Which 명사 do you like (better/more), A or B?: 어떤 ~가 더 좋아? A 아니면 B?
❷ 더 좋아하는 것에 대해 말할 때는 'I like A.', 'I like A better[more] than B.' 또는 'I prefer A to B.'로 표현한다. 이때 비교 대상이 되는 'than B'나 'to B'는 생략할 수 있다.
❸ twice a week: 일주일에 두 번

Listen & Speak 1 B-1

G: ❶What are you doing?

B: ❷I'm looking at a world map.

G: You checked two countries. ❸Which country would you like to visit first? The U.S. or Mexico?

B: I want to visit the U.S. I'd like to see a basketball game there.

❶ What are you doing?: 뭐 하고 있어?
❷ 대상의 동작이나 현재의 상태를 묘사할 때 현재진행형을 사용할 수 있다. look at: ~을 보다
❸ would like to 동사원형: ~하고 싶다 visit: 방문하다

Listen & Speak 2 A

G: Did you ❶get the tickets?

B: ❷Yes! ❸I can't wait to watch the game.

❶ get: 얻다, 사다
❷ Yes! 다음에 'I did.'가 생략되어 있다.
❸ can't wait to 동사원형: ~하기를 몹시 기대하다(희망, 기대 표현하기) 'can't wait for+명사'나 'can't wait to+동사원형'의 형태를 취할 수 있다. I can't wait to watch the game. = I'm looking forward to watching the game.)

Listen & Speak 2 B-2

B: ❶Don't forget that we're going rock climbing this weekend!

G: ❷Don't worry. ❸I won't forget.

B: I'm excited about going. I can't wait.

❶ 상대방에게 어떠한 일을 할 것을 상기시켜 줄 때는 'Don't forget that 주어+동사 ~.' 또는 'Don't forget to+동사원형 ~.'으로 말할 수 있다. 의미는 '~할 것을 잊지 마' 정도로 볼 수 있다.
❷ 'Don't worry.'는 '걱정 마.'의 의미로 상대방을 안심시킬 때 사용한다.
❸ won't는 will not을 줄여 쓴 말이다. forget 다음에 'that we're going rock climbing this weekend'가 생략되어 있다.

Listen & Speak 2 B-3

G: Did you hear about Jisu?

B: What about her? She ❶lives in Canada.

G: She ❷came back to Korea last month. She wants to see you.

B: Oh, ❸I can't wait to see her.

❶ live in: ~에서 살다
❷ come back to: ~로 돌아오다
❸ I can't wait: 너무 기다려져

Real-Life Zone A

B1: Jiho, why are you ❶in such a hurry?

B2: Hi, Alex! I ❷have to be home before 6:00. The game ❸between the Thunders and the Cobras starts at 6:00.

B1: Oh, are you a baseball fan? ❹Which team do you support? The Cobras or the Thunders?

B2: The Cobras.

B1: Me, too! ❺I don't want to miss the game either.

B2: ❻Hurry up! We only have thirty minutes ❼left.

B1: Okay. Maybe we can watch a game together ❽sometime.

B2: That's a great idea! ❾How about going to the next Cobras home game together?

B1: Okay. They have a game next Saturday. We can eat fried chicken ❿while watching the game!

B2: That sounds great. I can't wait!

❶ in a hurry: 서둘러
❷ have to 동사원형: ~해야 한다
❸ between A and B: A와 B 사이의
❹ support: (특정 스포츠 팀을) 응원하다
❺ miss: 놓치다 either: (부정문에서) ~도
❻ hurry up: 서두르다
❼ leave: 남아 있다 → left: 남겨진
❽ sometime: 언젠가
❾ How about (동)명사 ~?: ~하는 게 어때?, ~하지 않을래?(제안하기)
❿ while+동사ing: ~하는 동안

● 다음 우리말과 일치하도록 빈칸에 알맞은 말을 쓰시오.

Listen & Speak 1 A

M: _____ _____ do you like? Soccer _____ basketball?

G: I like soccer _____. I play soccer _____ a _____.

Listen & Speak 1 B

1. G: What are you _____?

   B: _____ looking _____ a world map.

   G: You checked two countries. _____ _____ would you like to visit first? The U.S. _____ Mexico?

   B: I want _____ _____ the U.S. I'd _____ _____ see a basketball game there.

2. G: _____ _____ about _____ a pet. Do you _____ a pet?

   B: Yes, I do. I have a dog and a cat.

   G: _____ do you think? _____ pet is _____ for me? A cat _____ a dog?

   B: _____ _____ you come to my house someday and _____ _____ my pets? Then you _____ _____.

Listen & Speak 2 A

G: _____ you get the tickets?

B: Yes! I _____ _____ _____ _____ the game.

Listen & Speak 2 B

1. G: Do you _____ _____ _____ my new mountain bike?

   B: Sure. _____ _____ you get it?

   G: Yesterday my father _____ _____ _____ _____. Can you _____ to my house this afternoon?

   B: Of course. I _____ _____ _____ _____ it.

해석

M: 너는 어떤 운동을 좋아하니? 축구 아니면 농구?
G: 축구를 더 좋아해요. 저는 일주일에 두 번 축구를 해요.

1. G: 뭐 하고 있어?
   B: 세계 지도를 보고 있어.
   G: 두 나라에 표시를 했네. 어떤 나라를 먼저 방문하고 싶어? 미국 아니면 멕시코?
   B: 미국을 방문하고 싶어. 거기서 농구 경기를 보고 싶어.

2. G: 나는 애완동물을 기르는 것에 대해 생각 중이야. 넌 애완동물을 기르니?
   B: 응, 길러. 개와 고양이가 있어.
   G: 어떻게 생각해? 어떤 애완동물이 나에게 더 나아? 고양이 아니면 개?
   B: 어느 날 우리 집에 와서 내 애완동물과 놀아 보는 게 어때? 그런 다음 너는 결정할 수 있을 거야.

W: 너 티켓 구했니?
B: 응! 나는 경기를 빨리 보고 싶어.

G: 내 새 산악 자전거를 보고 싶니?
B: 물론이지. 언제 생긴 거야?
G: 어제 아빠가 나에게 사 주셨어. 오늘 오후에 우리 집에 올래?
B: 당연하지. 나는 그것을 빨리 보고 싶어.

2. B: Don't _____ _____ we're going rock climbing this weekend!

   G: Don't worry. I _____ _____.

   B: I'm _____ about going. _____ _____ _____.

3. G: Did you hear about Jisu?

   B: What _____ her? She lives _____ Canada.

   G: She _____ back to Korea last month. She _____ _____ _____ you.

   B: Oh, I _____ _____ _____ _____ her.

Real-Life Zone A

B1: Jiho, why are you in _____ a hurry?

B2: Hi, Alex! I have to be home _____ 6:00. The game _____ the Thunders and the Cobras _____ at 6:00.

B1: Oh, are you a baseball fan? _____ _____ do you _____? The Cobras or the Thunders?

B2: The Cobras.

B1: Me, too! I don't want to _____ the game _____.

B2: _____ up! We only have thirty minutes _____.

B1: Okay. Maybe we can watch a game together _____.

B2: That's a great idea! How _____ _____ _____ the next Cobras home game together?

B1: Okay. They have a game next Saturday. We can eat fried chicken _____ _____ the game!

B2: That sounds great. _____ _____ _____!

Wrap Up

B: Jimin, _____ _____ _____ _____ _____ _____? Soccer _____ table tennis?

G: I love table tennis. How _____ you, Yunho?

B: I like soccer. I'm a _____ _____ _____ James Hood. He's a great soccer player.

G: Oh, really? There's a soccer match this weekend _____ Korea and Turkey. _____ you heard about it?

B: Of course. I already have a ticket. _____ _____ _____ _____ the game on Saturday. I _____ _____.

G: That's _____.

해석

2. B: 이번 주말에 암벽 등반하러 가기로 한 거 잊지 마.
   G: 걱정 마. 잊지 않을게.
   B: 등반하러 가는 거 너무 신난다. 너무 기다려져.

3. G: 너 지수에 대해 들었니?
   B: 그녀에 대한 거 뭐? 그녀는 캐나다에 살고 있잖아.
   G: 지난달에 그녀는 한국에 돌아왔어. 너를 보고 싶어해.
   B: 오, 그녀를 빨리 보고 싶어.

B1: 지호야, 너 왜 그렇게 서두르니?
B2: 안녕, 알렉스! 나는 6시 전에 집에 있어야 해. 천둥 대 코브라의 경기가 6시에 시작돼.
B1: 오, 너 야구 팬이니? 어느 팀을 응원해? 코브라 아니면 천둥?
B2: 코브라.
B1: 나도야! 나도 이 경기를 놓치고 싶지 않아.
B2: 서둘러! 우리는 30분밖에 안 남았어.
B1: 알겠어. 언젠가 함께 경기를 볼 수도 있겠다.
B2: 좋은 생각이야! 다음 코브라 홈 경기를 함께 보러 가지 않을래?
B1: 좋아. 다음 주 토요일에 경기가 있어. 우리는 경기를 보면서 프라이드 치킨을 먹을 수 있어!
B1: 굉장해. 너무 기다려져!

B: 지민아, 너는 어떤 운동을 좋아하니? 축구 아니면 탁구?
G: 탁구를 좋아해. 윤호야, 너는 어때?
B: 축구가 좋아. 나는 제임스 후드의 열렬한 팬이야. 그는 위대한 축구 선수야.
G: 오, 정말? 이번 주말에 한국 대 터키의 축구 경기가 있어. 그것에 대해 들었니?
B: 물론이지. 나는 이미 표가 있어. 토요일에 경기를 보러 갈 거야. 너무 기다려져.
G: 환상적이다.

01 다음 대화의 밑줄 친 부분의 의도로 알맞은 것은?

> A: What are you going to do on your vacation?
> B: I'm going to take a boat ride. <u>I can't wait.</u>

① 관심 표현하기   ② 확신 표현하기   ③ 기대 표현하기

④ 거절 표현하기   ⑤ 불가능 표현하기

02 다음 대화의 빈칸에 알맞은 말은?

> A: Which sport do you like? Soccer or basketball?
> B: _____ I play soccer twice a week.

① I like basketball better.   ② I like soccer more.

③ I don't like sports.   ④ I like basketball more than baseball.

⑤ I prefer basketball.

03 다음 대화의 빈칸에 알맞은 말을 <u>모두</u> 고르시오.

> A: _____ *Peter Pan* or *The Last Leaf*?
> B: I like *Peter Pan*.

① Which shorts do you like?

② Which do you prefer?

③ Why don't we read a story book?

④ Which story book do you like?

⑤ How did you like the story book?

04 다음 대화의 밑줄 친 문장 대신 쓸 수 있는 것을 고르시오.

> A: Which sport do you like? Bowling or tennis?
> B: <u>I like tennis.</u> I'm going to play it with my friends this weekend. I can't wait.

① I prefer bowling to tennis.

② I like bowling more than tennis.

③ I prefer tennis and bowling.

④ I like tennis more.

⑤ I like tennis and bowling.

[01~03] 다음 대화를 읽고 물음에 답하시오.

G: ⓐI'm thinking about getting a pet. Do you have a pet? (①)

B: Yes, I do. (②)

G: ⓑWhat do you think? (③) ⓒWhich pet is better for me? A cat or a dog? (④) ⓓI can't wait to play with your pets.

B: ⓔWhy don't you come to my house someday and play with my pets? (⑤) Then you can decide.

01 위 대화의 ①~⑤ 중 다음 주어진 말이 들어갈 알맞은 곳은?

> I have a dog and a cat.

① ② ③ ④ ⑤

02 위 대화의 문장 ⓐ~ⓔ 중 흐름상 어색한 것을 고르시오.

① ⓐ ② ⓑ ③ ⓒ ④ ⓓ ⑤ ⓔ

03 위 대화를 읽고 알 수 없는 것을 고르시오.

① Does the boy have a pet?
② Why does the boy suggest that the girl come to his house someday?
③ Which animal does the girl like more? A dog or a cat?
④ How many dogs does the boy have?
⑤ What kind of pet does the boy have?

04 주어진 문장 이후에 이어질 대화의 순서가 바르게 배열된 것을 고르시오.

> What are you doing?

(A) You checked two countries. Which country would you like to visit first? The U.S. or Mexico?

(B) I want to visit the U.S. I'd like to see a basketball game there.

(C) I'm looking at a world map.

① (A) – (C) – (B) ② (B) – (A) – (C)
③ (B) – (C) – (A) ④ (C) – (A) – (B)
⑤ (C) – (B) – (A)

05 다음 중 짝지어진 대화가 어색한 것은?

① A: Which do you like more, hotdogs or waffles?
   B: I like waffles more.
② A: Which do you prefer, dogs or cats?
   B: I prefer dogs to cats.
③ A: Which do you like more, to buy the books or to borrow them from the library?
   B: I like to borrow the books from the library more.
④ A: Which do you prefer, hiking or swimming?
   B: Of course I do.
⑤ A: Which shirt do you prefer, the red one or the yellow one?
   B: I think the red one is better.

[06~07] 다음 대화를 읽고 물음에 답하시오.

G: Do you want to see my new mountain bike? (①)

B: Sure. (②) When did you get it? (③)

G: Yesterday my father bought it for me. (④)

B: (⑤) Of course. 나는 그것을 빨리 보고 싶어.
(wait, it, see, I, can't, to)

중요

06 위 대화의 ①~⑤ 중 다음 주어진 말이 들어갈 알맞은 곳은?

Can you come to my house this afternoon?

①   ②   ③   ④   ⑤

서답형

07 위 대화의 밑줄 친 우리말 해석에 맞게 괄호 안의 단어를 배열하여 영작하시오.

➡ _____

[08~09] 다음 대화를 읽고 물음에 답하시오.

B1: Jiho, why are you in such a hurry?

B2: _____

B1: _____

B2: _____

B1: _____

B2: Hurry up! We only have thirty minutes left.

B1: Okay. Maybe we can watch a game together sometime.

B2: That's a great idea! How about going to the next Cobras home game together?

B1: Okay. They have a game next Saturday. We can eat fried chicken while watching the game!

B2: That sounds great. I can't wait!

08 위 대화의 빈 부분에 들어갈 순서가 올바른 것을 고르시오.

(A) The Cobras.

(B) Hi, Alex! I have to be home before 6:00. The game between the Thunders and the Cobras starts at 6:00.

(C) Oh, are you a baseball fan? Which team do you support? The Cobras or the Thunders?

(D) Me, too! I don't want to miss the game either.

① (B)–(A)–(C)–(D)   ② (B)–(C)–(A)–(D)
③ (B)–(D)–(A)–(C)   ④ (C)–(A)–(B)–(D)
⑤ (C)–(D)–(B)–(A)

09 위 대화를 읽고 질문에 답할 수 없는 것은?

① What time will the next Cobras home game start?

② What can they eat while watching the game?

③ When will the next Cobras home game be held?

④ Which team do they like more, the Cobras or the Thunders?

⑤ What time is it now?

서답형

10 다음 대화의 빈칸에 알맞은 말을 쓰시오.

A: What are you going to do on your vacation?

B: _____ I can't wait to go surfing.

➡ _____

Conversation 서술형 시험대비

[01~03] 다음 대화를 읽고 물음에 답하시오.

B: Don't forget (A)[to / that] we're going rock climbing this weekend!
G: Don't worry. I won't ___ⓐ___.
B: I'm excited (B)[about / to] going. I can't wait.

01 (A)와 (B)에 알맞은 말을 골라 쓰시오.

(A) _____ (B) _____

02 위 대화의 빈칸 ⓐ에 알맞은 말을 대화에서 찾아 쓰시오.

➡ _____

03 위 대화의 내용과 일치하도록 주어진 질문에 대한 대답을 영어로 쓰시오. (9 단어, 주어진 단어를 이용할 것)

> What is the boy looking forward to?

➡ _____

(wait, to)

[04~05] 주어진 문장 다음에 이어질 대화의 순서를 바르게 배열하시오.

04

> Did you hear about Jisu?

(A) She came back to Korea last month. She wants to see you.
(B) Oh, I can't wait to see her.
(C) What about her? She lives in Canada.

➡ _____

05

> Which sport do you like to play? Tennis or baseball?

(A) I like to play tennis.
(B) Why not?
(C) Why don't we play tennis together this afternoon?

➡ _____

[06~07] 다음 대화를 읽고 물음에 답하시오.

B: Jimin, which sport do you like? Soccer or table tennis?
G: I love table tennis. How about you, Yunho?
B: I like soccer. I'm a big fan of James Hood. He's a great soccer player.
G: Oh, really? There's a soccer match this weekend between Korea and Turkey. __(A)__ you heard about it?
B: Of course. I already __(B)__ a ticket. I'm going to see the game on Saturday. (C)I can't wait.
G: That's fantastic.

06 위 대화의 빈칸 (A)와 (B)에 공통으로 들어갈 말을 쓰시오.

(A) _____ (B) _____

07 밑줄 친 (C)의 뒤에 생략된 부분을 주어진 단어를 넣어 쓰시오. (6 단어)

➡ _____ (see)

Grammar

교과서

1 부가의문문

- Jian, this is your first time to come to the baseball stadium, **isn't it**?
  지안아, 네가 야구 경기장에 온 건 이번이 처음이야, 그렇지 않니?

- You don't like English, **do you**? 너 영어를 싫어하지, 그렇지?

■ 문장의 끝에 붙은 의문문으로, 상대방의 동의를 구하거나 사실을 확인하기 위해 사용된다.

- The post office is a few blocks from your office, **isn't it**?
  우체국은 네 사무실에서 몇 블록 떨어져 있잖아, 그렇지 않니?

- She didn't tell a lie, **did she**? 그녀는 거짓말을 하지 않았어, 그렇지?

부가의문문을 만드는 법은 다음과 같다.

1. 앞 문장에 be동사나 조동사가 사용되었으면 be동사나 조동사를 사용하며 일반 동사가 사용된 경우에는 'do/does/did'를 사용한다.

2. 앞 문장이 긍정이면 부정, 부정이면 긍정으로 쓴다.

3. 주어는 반드시 인칭대명사로 받는다.

4. 부정형의 경우 반드시 축약형을 쓴다.

- You aren't tired, **are you**? 너 피곤하지 않지, 그렇지?

- You want to go to the amusement park, **don't you**? 너 놀이 공원에 가고 싶지, 그렇지 않니?

■ 명령문의 부가의문문은 will you?나 won't you?를 쓰고 권유문(Let's ~)의 경우에는 shall we?를 쓴다.

- Clean your room, **won't you**? 네 방을 청소해, 그러지 않을래?

- Let's work together, **shall we**? 함께 일하자, 그럴래?

핵심 Check

1. 다음 괄호 안에서 알맞은 말을 고르시오.

(1) People usually buy presents to celebrate, (don't / aren't) they?

(2) Ted wasn't at home yesterday, was (he / Ted)?

(3) Your cellphone looks nice, (does / doesn't) it?

(4) Mary felt happy, (did / didn't) she?

② 수동태

> • Jake **made** this table. 〈능동태〉 Jake가 이 탁자를 만들었다.
>
> • This table **was made** by Jake. 〈수동태〉 이 탁자는 Jake에 의해 만들어졌다.

■ 수동태는 '주어+be동사+동사의 과거분사+by+행위자'의 형식을 가지며 '…에 의해 ~되다[당하다]'라는 의미로 주어가 동작의 영향을 받거나 행위를 당할 때 사용한다.

능동태를 수동태로 만드는 법

1. 능동태의 목적어를 문장의 주어로 둔다.

2. 동사를 'be동사+과거분사'로 쓴다. 이때 be동사의 시제는 능동태 문장에 맞추고 수와 인칭은 수동태 문장의 주어에 맞춘다.

3. 능동태의 주어는 'by+행위자(목적격)'의 형태로 문장 끝에 쓴다. 이때 행위자가 중요치 않거나 확실하지 않은 경우 'by+행위자'는 생략한다. • The chair **was broken** by Jerry. 그 의자는 Jerry에 의해 부서졌다.

■ 4형식 문장의 수동태는 간접목적어와 직접목적어 각각을 주어로 하는 수동태가 가능하다. 직접목적어를 주어로 한 수동태에서는 간접목적어 앞에 특정한 전치사를 써야 한다. 전치사 to를 쓰는 동사는 'give, send, tell, teach, show, bring' 등이고, 전치사 for를 쓰는 동사는 'buy, make, choose, cook, get' 등이며, 전치사 of를 쓰는 동사에는 'ask' 등이 있다. 또한 make, buy, read, write 등은 직접목적어를 주어로 하는 수동태만 가능하다.

• Mom **bought** Jane a book. 엄마가 Jane에게 책을 사주셨다.

• A book **was bought** for Jane by Mom. 책이 엄마에 의해 Jane에게 사 주어졌다.

■ 조동사가 있는 문장의 수동태는 '조동사+be+p.p.' 형식을 갖는다.

• The work **will be finished** by me. 그 일은 나에 의해 끝내질 것이다.

■ 목적격보어가 원형부정사인 경우, 수동태 문장에서는 to부정사로 바뀐다.

• Harry **was made** to do the dishes by her. Harry는 그녀에 의해 설거지하도록 시켜졌다.

■ by 이외의 전치사를 사용하는 수동태에 유의한다.

• be interested in: ~에 흥미가 있다 be surprised at: ~에 놀라다

• be covered with: ~로 덮여 있다 be filled with: ~로 가득 차다

• be pleased with: ~로 기뻐하다 be satisfied with: ~에 만족하다

• be made of: ~로 만들어지다(물리적 변화) be made from: ~로 만들어지다(화학적 변화)

핵심 Check

2. 다음 괄호 안에서 알맞은 말을 고르시오.

(1) Some nice presents were given (for / to) her by her friends.

(2) She is interested (in / with) working indoors.

01 다음 빈칸에 알맞은 것은?

> My cousin played the violin.
> ➡ The violin _____ by my cousin.

① plays   ② played   ③ is played

④ was played   ⑤ has played

02 다음 빈칸에 들어갈 말로 적절한 것은?

> Visiting teams wear dark uniforms, _____?

① aren't they   ② are they   ③ don't they

④ do they   ⑤ aren't them

03 다음 우리말에 맞게 빈칸에 알맞은 말을 쓰시오.

(1) 그 방은 Harold에 의해 청소되었다.

     ➡ The room _____ _____ by Harold.

(2) *Romeo and Juliet*은 William Shakespeare에 의해 쓰여졌다.

     ➡ *Romeo and Juliet* _____ _____ by William Shakespeare.

(3) 그녀는 그와 친구가 되고 싶어 해, 그렇지 않니?

     ➡ She wants to be friends with him, _____ _____?

(4) Sam은 운전할 수 없어, 그렇지?

     ➡ Sam cannot drive, _____ _____?

04 다음 문장에서 어법상 <u>어색한</u> 부분을 바르게 고쳐 쓰시오.

(1) The Golden Gate Bridge built in 1937.

     _____ ➡ _____

(2) Dorothy has a book, doesn't Dorothy?

     _____ ➡ _____

01 다음 빈칸에 알맞은 것은?

> The dirt _____ by the dark colors of the uniforms.

① hides ② hid ③ to hide
④ is hiding ⑤ is hidden

02 다음 중 밑줄 친 부분의 쓰임이 올바른 것은?

① You can speak Japanese very well, <u>can you</u>?
② Yuna looks kind, <u>doesn't she</u>?
③ Yollanda gave the book to Petric, <u>doesn't she</u>?
④ Sophie bought a cell phone, <u>wasn't she</u>?
⑤ Mike isn't diligent, <u>doesn't he</u>?

03 다음 괄호 안에서 알맞은 것을 고르시오.

(1) Some flowers were given (to / for) her by Tim.
(2) The spaghetti was made (to / for) me by my mom.
(3) No questions were asked (to / of) us by the teacher.
(4) Laura likes roses, (does / is / doesn't / isn't) she?
(5) It is a kind of Korean traditional food, (does / is / doesn't / isn't) it?

04 다음 중 수동태로의 전환이 <u>어색한</u> 것은?

① Auguste Rodin made *the Thinker* in 1902.
  → *The Thinker* was made by Auguste Rodin in 1902.
② Harriot chose Grace a beautiful song.
  → A beautiful song was chosen for Grace by Harriot.
③ They built the Namdaemoon in 1398.
  → The Namdaemoon was built in 1398.
④ Emily gave me a nice pen.
  → A nice pen was given for me by Emily.
⑤ My teacher asked me to come to the library.
  → I was asked to come to the library by my teacher.

05 다음 중 어법상 옳은 것을 고르시오.

① Dorothy is wearing black shoes, doesn't she?
② My mom is going to make *gimbap* tonight, is she?
③ The children didn't play the violin, did they?
④ Angelina was kind to others last night, was not she?
⑤ Samanda bought a cute pink dress, didn't Samanda?

06 다음 우리말을 바르게 영작한 것은?

> 이 가방은 내 동생을 위해 엄마에 의해 만들어졌다.

① This bag was made for my sister by my mom.
② This bag was made to my sister by my mom.
③ This bag was made of my sister by my mom.
④ This bag was made to my mom by my sister.
⑤ My sister was made for this bag by my mom.

07 다음 문장의 빈칸에 알맞은 말은?

> You had dinner at the hotel last night, _____ you?

① hadn't   ② haven't   ③ have
④ didn't   ⑤ did

08 다음 문장을 수동태로 바르게 바꾼 것은?

> In the past, they determined the numbers by the players' batting order.

① In the past, the numbers determined the players' batting order.
② In the past, the numbers were determined the players' batting order.
③ In the past, the players' batting order was determined by the numbers.
④ In the past, the numbers was determined by the players' batting order.
⑤ In the past, the numbers were determined by the players' batting order.

09 다음 빈칸에 알맞은 것은?

> Kate looks friendly, _____?

① isn't she   ② does she
③ doesn't she   ④ does Kate
⑤ doesn't Kate

10 다음 중 어법상 틀린 것을 고르시오.

① In the early 1800s, soccer was invented in Newgate Prison in London by the prisoners.
② The article was wrote for the school newspaper by Harry.
③ A mouse was caught by a cat.
④ Is English spoken in many countries around the world?
⑤ A nice gift was given to Stephanie on her birthday by her dad.

11 다음 중 빈칸에 들어갈 말이 다른 하나는?

① A man was waiting for Jane outside, _____?
② Jim worked at the bank, _____?
③ He made Ann do the work, _____?
④ Chris went on a vacation, _____?
⑤ A boy played the piano, _____?

12 다음 빈칸에 공통으로 들어갈 알맞은 것은?

> • His heart was filled _____ pride at that time.
> • Does that mean that you're pleased _____ the present?

① at   ② with   ③ from
④ in   ⑤ of

서답형

13 주어진 어구를 이용하여 다음 우리말을 영어로 쓰시오.

(1) 이 편지가 David에 의해 배달되었나요?
(deliver)

➡ _____

(2) 나의 삼촌 집이 홍수에 의해 무너졌다.
(the flood, destroy)

➡ _____

(3) 그 탁자는 나무로 만들어졌다.
(wood, make)

➡ _____

(4) 그 십대들은 유럽에 여행갈 거야, 그렇지 않니?
(the teenagers, travel)

➡ _____

(5) 테니스 치러 가자, 그럴래? (let, to play)

➡ _____

서답형

14 다음 빈칸에 알맞은 부가의문문을 쓰시오.

(1) Sharon studies English very hard,
_____ _____?

(2) You played computer games last night,
_____ _____?

(3) Marylin can't play the guitar, _____
_____?

(4) Alex wasn't angry, _____ _____?

(5) Always do the dishes after each meal,
_____ _____?

(6) Let's take a walk after dinner, _____
_____?

서답형

15 다음 문장에서 어법상 어색한 부분을 찾아 바르게 고치시오.

(1) The dress was chosen to her daughter
for the party by Eveline.

_____ ➡ _____

(2) Playing tennis is reduced my stress.

_____ ➡ _____

(3) The changes will not be appeared
immediately.

_____ ➡ _____

(4) Mina finished washing the dishes, didn't
Mina?

_____ ➡ _____

(5) You will leave a message, will you?

_____ ➡ _____

(6) She isn't going to go hiking tomorrow,
does she?

_____ ➡ _____

16 다음 밑줄 친 부분 중 어법상 어색한 것은?

He ①was known as a marathon winner at
the Rome and Tokyo international sports
competitions. When he ②was prepared
to run the marathon in Rome, he found
out that his shoes did not fit well, so he
decided ③to run the race without shoes.
He felt pain during the race, but he finished
the race as the winner. He was ④one of the
greatest runners in the world, ⑤wasn't he?

①   ②   ③   ④   ⑤

서답형

17 주어진 단어의 형태를 알맞게 바꿔 문장을 완성하시오.

Hana Middle School Sports Day
_____ (hold) on the school
playing field next week.

01 다음 문장을 수동태는 능동태로, 능동태는 수동태로 고치시오.

(1) Tino cleans the big house on Sundays.

➡ _____

(2) Sarang Middle School Sports Day will be held on the school playing field on Wednesday, June 15.

➡ _____
_____
_____

(3) Jonathan made Judy delicious spaghetti.

➡ _____
_____

(4) Does your job as a tour guide satisfy you?

➡ _____

(5) Who painted *Water Lilies* in 1906?

➡ _____

(6) Cathy will make him take part in the science camp.

➡ _____
_____

(7) They are looking after the animals.

➡ _____

02 다음 빈칸에 공통으로 들어갈 말을 쓰시오.

> • Mike studied hard, _____ _____?
> • Joseph did his best at all times, _____ _____?

➡ _____

03 다음 빈칸에 알맞은 부가의문문을 쓰시오.

(1) These cars are really expensive, _____ _____?

(2) Her little son can't read the book, _____ _____?

(3) Matt didn't make his daughter a doll, _____ _____?

(4) Jenny isn't watching TV, _____ _____?

(5) The rock looks like a rabbit, _____ _____?

(6) Be careful when you drive a car at night, _____ _____?

(7) Let's go to the shop at which you bought your skirt, _____ _____?

04 다음 괄호 안에 주어진 어휘를 어법에 맞게 빈칸에 쓰시오.

(1) The computer _____ _____ by my father yesterday. (repair)

(2) The book _____ _____ _____ me by my father yesterday. (buy)

(3) Many smartphones _____ _____ in Korea. (make)

(4) Kathy _____ _____ _____ finish the report by her teacher. (make)

05 다음 그림을 보고 대화의 빈칸에 알맞은 말을 쓰시오.

A: She plays the game really well, _____
   _____?
B: Yes, she does.

06 다음 그림을 보고 주어진 단어를 이용하여 빈칸을 알맞게 채우시오.

I and the Village _____ _____
by Marc Chagall in 1911. (paint)

07 다음 문장에서 어법상 <u>어색한</u> 부분을 바르게 고쳐 다시 쓰시오.

(1) The boy was bought the pens.
   ➡ _____
   _____

(2) Soy sauce is made of soy beans and salt.
   ➡ _____

(3) Cloe was written a letter by Jack.
   ➡ _____

(4) Vivian was heard open the window by her son.
   ➡ _____

(5) *Samgyupsal* is cooked to Emma by her husband next weekend.
   ➡ _____
   _____

(6) Whom this table was made?
   ➡ _____

08 다음 우리말을 괄호 안에 주어진 어휘를 이용하여 영작하시오.

(1) 내 자전거는 지난 금요일에 도둑맞았다.
   (bike, steal)
   ➡ _____

(2) 이 과자들은 나의 엄마에 의해 만들어졌다.
   (these cookies, make, my mom)
   ➡ _____

(3) 그의 집은 책으로 가득 차 있었다. (fill)
   ➡ _____

(4) Jenny는 어젯밤에 파티에 없었어, 그렇지?
   (at the party)
   ➡ _____

(5) 좋아하는 운동에 대해서 말해 보자, 그럴래?
   (let's, our favorite sport, about)
   ➡ _____

Reading

A Day at the Baseball Stadium

Today the Thunders and the Cobras have a game. Jihun's family is at
~에 있다
the baseball stadium.

Jihun: Jian, this is your first time to come to the baseball stadium, isn't it?
to부정사의 형용사적 용법 　　　　　　　　　　　　　　　부가의문문

Jian: Yes, I'm so excited. I can't wait for the game to start.
신이 난, 흥분된　무엇인가를 너무나 하고 싶을 때 쓸 수 있는 표현

Dad: Look, the players are coming out now!
현재진행형 be+~ing

Jian: Which team is the Thunders?
의문형용사 which: 어느 ~

Jihun: Over there, behind third base. They are wearing dark gray

uniforms because they are the visiting team.
~이기 때문에　　　　　　　　원정 팀

Jian: Does the visiting team always wear a dark color?
빈도부사: 일반동사 앞에 위치

Jihun: Yes, that's the rule. Home teams have bright uniforms and
= the visiting team always wear a dark color
visiting teams have dark uniforms.

Jian: Why is that?
앞 문장의 내용을 받음

Mom: There is an interesting story about that. In the past, visiting
~이 있다
teams could not wash their uniforms after every game. So they

started wearing dark colors to hide the dirt.
start+~ing: ~하기 시작하다　　　　to부정사의 부사적 용법(~하기 위해)

Jihun: Hahaha! That was a good idea!
wearing dark colors to hide the dirt

base (야구의) 루, 베이스
visiting team 원정 팀
come out 나오다
dark 어두운
dirt 먼지, 때
hide 숨다, 숨기다
rule 규칙, 법칙

 확인문제

● 다음 문장이 본문의 내용과 일치하면 T, 일치하지 않으면 F를 쓰시오.

1 Jihun's family is at the baseball stadium. ☐

2 This is Jihun's first time to come to the baseball stadium. ☐

3 Jian is so excited that she can't wait for the game to start. ☐

4 The Cobras are the visiting team. ☐

5 Home teams have bright uniforms and visiting teams have dark uniforms. ☐

6 In the past, visiting teams could wash their uniforms after every game. ☐

The players are warming up.

Jian: Who's your favorite player?
Who is의 줄임말

Jihun: Number 77.

Jian: What does the number mean?

Jihun: Hmm…. Players choose a number they like.
관계대명사 which나 that 생략

Dad: You know what? In the past, the numbers were determined by
저 있잖아, 그거 알아?　　　　　　　수동태: be동사+과거분사

the players' batting order.

Jihun: That means there were no players with number 77!
앞 문장의 내용을 받는 지시대명사

Now, Jihun's favorite player is about to bat. Jihun looks anxious.
막 ~하려는 참이다　　　　　　~처럼 보이다

Jian: Your favorite player is at bat.
타석에 서서

Jihun: Yes. He has hit 21 home runs already this year. If he hits one
현재완료(완료)　　　　　　　　접속사 if: ~라면　　조건 부사절에서
　　　　　　　　　　　　　　　　　　　　현재시제가 미래를 나타냄.

more today, he will be the home run leader this season.

The batter misses several balls. Now he has a full count. He is
놓치다　　　　　　　야구에서 스트라이크가 둘이고 볼이 셋인 상태

waiting for the next pitch.

Jihun: HOME RUN! HOME RUN!

Crack!

The ball flies fast. It is going, going, going, gone!

warm up 준비 운동을 하다. 몸을 풀다
determine 결정하다
order 순서
anxious 불안해하는
be about to 막 ~하려고 하다
pitch 투구
wait for ~을 기다리다
crack 찢어지는 듯한 [날카로운] 소리
at bat 타석에 서서

확인문제

● 다음 문장이 본문의 내용과 일치하면 T, 일치하지 않으면 F를 쓰시오.

1 The players are warming up. ☐

2 In the past, players chose a number they liked. ☐

3 Jihun's favorite player is at bat. ☐

4 Jihun's favorite player has hit 20 home runs already this year. ☐

5 Jihun's favorite player misses several balls. ☐

6 Jihun's favorite player has a full count and he is out on a fly ball. ☐

● 우리말을 참고하여 빈칸에 알맞은 말을 쓰시오.

1 A Day at the _____ _____

2 Today the Thunders and the Cobras _____ _____ _____ .

3 Jihun's family _____ _____ the baseball stadium.

4 Jihun: Jian, this is _____ _____ _____ to come to the baseball stadium, _____ _____ ?

5 Jian: Yes, I'm so excited. I _____ _____ _____ the game to start.

6 Dad: Look, the players _____ _____ _____ now!

7 Jian: _____ _____ is the Thunders?

8 Jihun: Over there, _____ _____ _____ .

9 They are wearing dark gray uniforms because they are the _____ _____ .

10 Jian: Does the visiting team always _____ _____ _____ _____ ?

11 Jihun: Yes, that's the _____ .

12 Home teams _____ _____ _____ and visiting teams have dark uniforms.

13 Jian: _____ is that?

14 Mom: There is an _____ _____ about that.

15 In the past, visiting teams could not _____ _____ after every game.

16 So they started wearing dark colors _____ _____ _____ .

17 Jian: Hahaha! That was _____ _____ _____ !

1 야구 경기장에서의 하루

2 오늘 천둥 대 코브라 게임이 있다.

3 지훈이네 가족은 야구 경기장에 있다.

4 지훈: 지안아. 네가 야구 경기장에 온 건 이번이 처음이야, 그렇지 않니?

5 지안: 응, 나 아주 흥분돼. 나는 경기가 빨리 시작했으면 좋겠어.

6 아빠: 봐, 선수들이 지금 나오고 있어!

7 지안: 어떤 팀이 천둥이야?

8 지훈: 저기, 3루 뒤.

9 그들은 원정 팀이기 때문에 어두운 회색 유니폼을 입고 있어.

10 지안: 원정 팀은 항상 어두운 색을 입어?

11 지훈: 응, 그게 규칙이야.

12 홈팀은 밝은 유니폼을 입고 원정팀은 어두운 유니폼을 입어.

13 지안: 왜?

14 엄마: 그것에 대한 흥미로운 이야기가 있단다.

15 과거에는 원정 팀이 매 경기 후 유니폼을 세탁할 수가 없었어.

16 그래서 그들은 때를 숨기기 위해 어두운 색을 입기 시작했지.

17 지안: 하하하! 좋은 생각이었네요!

18 The players are _____ _____.

19 Jian: Who's your _____ _____?

20 Jihun: _____ 77.

21 Jian: _____ does the number _____?

22 Jihun: Hmm…. Players _____ a number _____ _____.

23 Dad: You know _____?

24 In the past, the numbers were determined _____ _____ _____ _____ _____.

25 Jihun: That means there were _____ players _____ number 77!

26 Now, Jihun's favorite player _____ _____ _____ bat.

27 Jihun looks _____.

28 Jian: Your favorite player is _____ _____.

29 Jihun: Yes. He _____ _____ 21 home runs already this year.

30 If he _____ _____ _____ today, he will be the home run leader this season.

31 The batter _____ several balls.

32 Now he has _____ _____ _____.

33 He is waiting for the _____ _____.

34 Jihun: HOME RUN! HOME RUN!

35 _____! The ball _____ fast.

36 It is going, going, going, _____!

18 선수들이 몸을 풀고 있다.

19 지안: 가장 좋아하는 선수가 누구야?

20 지훈: 77번.

21 지안: 그 숫자는 무엇을 의미해?

22 지훈: 음... 선수들이 원하는 번호를 선택해.

23 아빠: 그거 알아?

24 과거에는 번호가 선수들의 타순에 의해 결정되었단다.

25 지훈: 77번 선수가 없었다는 뜻이네요!

26 이제 지훈이의 가장 좋아하는 선수가 막 공을 치려고 한다.

27 지훈이는 불안해 보인다.

28 지안: 오빠가 가장 좋아하는 선수가 타석에 서네.

29 지훈: 응. 그는 올해 이미 21개의 홈런을 쳤어.

30 그가 오늘 하나를 더 치면, 그는 이번 시즌 홈런 리더가 될 거야.

31 타자는 여러 개의 공을 놓친다.

32 이제 그는 풀카운트가 되었다.

33 그는 다음 투구를 기다리고 있다.

34 지훈: 홈런! 홈런!

35 땅! 공은 빠르게 날아간다.

36 그것은 가고, 가고, 가고, 사라져 버렸다!

● 우리말을 참고하여 본문을 영작하시오.

1 야구 경기장에서의 하루

➡ _____

2 오늘 천둥 대 코브라 게임이 있다.

➡ _____

3 지훈이네 가족은 야구 경기장에 있다.

➡ _____

4 지훈: 지안아, 네가 야구 경기장에 온 건 이번이 처음이야, 그렇지 않니?

➡ _____

5 지안: 응, 나 아주 흥분돼. 나는 경기가 빨리 시작했으면 좋겠어.

➡ _____

6 아빠: 봐, 선수들이 지금 나오고 있어!

➡ _____

7 지안: 어떤 팀이 천둥이야?

➡ _____

8 지훈: 저기, 3루 뒤.

➡ _____

9 그들은 원정 팀이기 때문에 어두운 회색 유니폼을 입고 있어.

➡ _____

10 지안: 원정 팀은 항상 어두운 색을 입어?

➡ _____

11 지훈: 응, 그게 규칙이야.

➡ _____

12 홈팀은 밝은 유니폼을 입고 원정팀은 어두운 유니폼을 입어.

➡ _____

13 지안: 왜?

➡ _____

14 엄마: 그것에 대한 흥미로운 이야기가 있단다.

➡ _____

15 과거에는 원정 팀이 매 경기 후 유니폼을 세탁할 수가 없었어.

➡ _____

16 그래서 그들은 때를 숨기기 위해 어두운 색을 입기 시작했지.

➡ _____

17 지안: 하하하! 좋은 생각이었네요!

➡ _____

18 선수들이 몸을 풀고 있다.

➡ _____

19 지안: 가장 좋아하는 선수가 누구야?

➡ _____

20 지훈: 77번.

➡ _____

21 지안: 그 숫자는 무엇을 의미해?

➡ _____

22 지훈: 음... 선수들이 원하는 번호를 선택해.

➡ _____

23 아빠: 그거 알아?

➡ _____

24 과거에는 번호가 선수들의 타순에 의해 결정되었단다.

➡ _____

25 지훈: 77번 선수가 없었다는 뜻이네요!

➡ _____

26 이제 지훈이의 가장 좋아하는 선수가 막 공을 치려고 한다.

➡ _____

27 지훈이는 불안해 보인다.

➡ _____

28 지안: 오빠가 가장 좋아하는 선수가 타석에 서네.

➡ _____

29 지훈: 응. 그는 올해 이미 21개의 홈런을 쳤어.

➡ _____

30 그가 오늘 하나를 더 치면, 그는 이번 시즌 홈런 리더가 될 거야.

➡ _____

31 타자는 여러 개의 공을 놓친다.

➡ _____

32 이제 그는 풀카운트가 되었다.

➡ _____

33 그는 다음 투구를 기다리고 있다.

➡ _____

34 지훈: 홈런! 홈런!

➡ _____

35 땅! 공은 빠르게 날아간다.

➡ _____

36 그것은 가고, 가고, 가고, 사라져 버렸다!

➡ _____

[01~03] 다음 글을 읽고 물음에 답하시오.

Today the Thunders and the Cobras have a game. Jihun's family is at the baseball stadium.

Jihun: Jian, this is your first time ⓐto come to the baseball stadium, ____(A)____?

Jian: Yes, I'm so excited. I can't wait for the game to start.

Dad: Look, the players are coming out now!

Jian: Which team is the Thunders?

Jihun: Over there, behind third base. They are wearing dark gray uniforms because they are the visiting team.

01 위 글의 빈칸 (A)에 들어갈 알맞은 부가의문문을 고르시오.

① isn't this ② is it
③ doesn't it ④ isn't it
⑤ is this

02 위 글의 밑줄 친 ⓐto come과 to부정사의 용법이 같은 것을 <u>모두</u> 고르시오.

① He couldn't decide what to eat.
② It's time for you to finish your work.
③ She went there to meet her friend.
④ It's good for your health to jog every day.
⑤ She wanted to buy a book to read on the train.

03 위 글의 내용과 일치하지 <u>않는</u> 것은?

① 오늘 천둥 대 코브라 게임이 있다.
② 지훈이네 가족은 야구 경기장에 있다.
③ 지안이가 야구 경기장에 온 건 이번이 처음이 아니다.
④ 지안이는 경기가 빨리 시작하기를 바란다.
⑤ 천둥 팀은 어두운 회색 유니폼을 입고 있다.

[04~06] 다음 글을 읽고 물음에 답하시오.

Jian: Does the visiting team always wear a dark color?

Jihun: Yes, that's the rule. Home teams have ____(A)____ uniforms and visiting teams have dark uniforms.

Jian: Why is (B)<u>that</u>?

Mom: There is an interesting story about that. In the past, visiting teams could not wash their uniforms after every game. So they started wearing dark colors to hide the ____(C)____.

Jian: Hahaha! That was a good idea!

서답형

04 위 글의 빈칸 (A)에 문맥상 알맞은 말을 쓰시오.

➡ _____

서답형

05 위 글의 밑줄 친 (B)that이 가리키는 것을 본문에서 찾아 쓰시오.

➡ _____
_____

06 위 글의 빈칸 (C)에 들어갈 알맞은 말을 고르시오.

① pattern ② dirt
③ hole ④ shape
⑤ design

[07~10] 다음 글을 읽고 물음에 답하시오.

Abebe Bikila
Marathon Runner
Born: August 7, 1932
Nationality: Ethiopia
Speciality: He was known ___ⓐ___ a marathon winner at the Rome and Tokyo international sports competitions. When he was preparing (A)[to run / running] the marathon in Rome, he found out that his shoes did not fit well, so he decided (B)[to run / running] the race ___ⓑ___ shoes. He felt pain (C)[during / while] the race, but he finished the race ___ⓒ___ the winner. He was one of the greatest runners in the world, wasn't he?

07 위 글의 빈칸 ⓐ와 ⓒ에 공통으로 들어갈 알맞은 말을 고르시오.

① as   ② to   ③ for
④ by   ⑤ in

서답형

08 위 글의 빈칸 ⓑ에 들어갈 알맞은 말을 쓰시오.

➡ _____

서답형

09 위 글의 괄호 (A)~(C)에서 문맥이나 어법상 알맞은 낱말을 골라 쓰시오.

(A) _____ (B) _____ (C) _____

10 Abebe Bikila에 대한 내용과 일치하지 <u>않는</u> 것을 고르시오.

① 에티오피아 출신의 마라톤 선수였다.
② 로마 국제 스포츠 대회의 마라톤 우승자로 알려졌다.
③ 도쿄 국제 스포츠 대회의 마라톤 우승자로 알려졌다.
④ 도쿄 국제 스포츠 대회에서 신발을 신지 않고 달렸다.
⑤ 경주 도중에 통증을 느꼈지만 우승자로 경주를 끝마쳤다.

[11~13] 다음 글을 읽고 물음에 답하시오.

(A)선수들이 몸을 풀고 있다.

Jian: Who's your favorite player?
Jihun: Number 77.
Jian: What does the number mean?
Jihun: Hmm.... Players choose a number they like.
Dad: You know what? In the past, the numbers were determined ___ⓐ___ the players' batting order.
Jihun: That means there were no players ___ⓑ___ number 77!

중요

11 위 글의 빈칸 ⓐ와 ⓑ에 들어갈 전치사가 바르게 짝지어진 것은?

① for – with   ② by – in
③ in – from   ④ for – in
⑤ by – with

서답형

12 위 글의 밑줄 친 (A)의 우리말에 맞게 주어진 어휘를 변형하여 5 단어로 영작하시오.

warm

➡ _____

13 등번호 7번의 과거와 현재의 의미를 우리말로 쓰시오.

과거: _____

현재: _____

[14~16] 다음 글을 읽고 물음에 답하시오.

　　Now, Jihun's favorite player is about to bat. Jihun looks anxious.

Jian: Your favorite player is at bat.

Jihun: Yes. He ⓐhas hit 21 home runs already this year. If he hits one more today, he will be the home run leader this season.

　　The batter misses several balls. Now he has a full count. He is waiting for the next pitch.

Jihun: HOME RUN! HOME RUN!

　　Crack!

　　The ball flies fast. It is going, going, going, gone!

14 아래 〈보기〉에서 위 글의 밑줄 친 ⓐhas hit과 현재완료의 용법이 다른 것의 개수는?

┌─ 보기 ─┐
① Tom has just eaten breakfast.
② Have you solved it yet?
③ I have worked for this company for two years.
④ He has already read the book.
⑤ She has lost her pen.
└────────┘

① 1개　② 2개　③ 3개　④ 4개　⑤ 5개

15 본문의 내용과 일치하도록 다음 빈칸에 알맞은 단어를 쓰시오.

┌──────────────────────────┐
It is likely that Jihun's favorite player will be the ____ ____ ____ this season because he finally hit a home run.
└──────────────────────────┘

16 위 글을 읽고 대답할 수 없는 질문은?

① Now, who is about to bat?
② How many home runs has Jihun's favorite player hit already this year?
③ Does Jihun's favorite player miss several balls?
④ How many foul balls has Jihun's favorite player hit today?
⑤ Does Jihun's favorite player hit a home run in this inning?

[17~19] 다음 글을 읽고 물음에 답하시오.

Seri Park
Professional golfer
Born: September 8, 1977
Nationality: South Korea
Speciality: She was the school's best ___(A)___ golfer when she was young. She turned ___(B)___ golfer in 1996. She played on the LPGA Tours from 1998 to 2016. She was inducted into the World Golf Hall of Fame in November 2007. She was great, ___(C)___?

17 위 글의 빈칸 (A)와 (B)에 들어갈 알맞은 말을 고르시오.

① professional – amateur
② mature – immature
③ amateur – professional
④ professional – expert
⑤ immature – mature

18 위 글의 빈칸 (C)에 들어갈 알맞은 부가의문문을 쓰시오.

➡ _____

19 위 글을 읽고 박세리에 대해 알 수 없는 것을 고르시오.

① 직업
② 골프를 시작한 나이
③ 프로 골프 선수가 된 시기
④ LPGA Tours에 참가한 시기
⑤ 세계 골프 영예의 전당에 가입한 시기

[20~22] 다음 글을 읽고 물음에 답하시오.

> A: Today the Thunders and the Cobras have a big game.
> B: Now, it is the Thunders' ⓐturn to hit the ball.
> A: The batter with number 77 is coming out to the field. He has hit 21 home runs this year.
> B: He is at bat. The Thunders' fans look very anxious. ⓑ누가 이길 것이라고 생각하시나요? (think, win, do, who, will, you, ?)
> A: Home run! Home run!
> B: ⓒHe will be the home run leader this year!

20 위 글의 밑줄 친 ⓐturn과 같은 의미로 쓰인 것을 고르시오.

① The wheels of the car began to turn.
② Please wait for your turn.
③ Turn the sweater inside out before you wash it.
④ Make a left turn into West Street.
⑤ The weather will turn cold.

서답형

21 위 글의 밑줄 친 ⓑ의 우리말에 맞게 주어진 어휘를 알맞게 배열하시오.

➡ _____

서답형

22 위 글의 밑줄 친 ⓒ와 같은 의미가 되도록 빈칸에 들어갈 알맞은 말을 서수로 쓰시오.

> The batter with number 77 succeeds in hitting his _____ home run.

[23~27] 다음 글을 읽고 물음에 답하시오.

> A: On today's show we are going to talk about fun facts in sports! We have here with us, sports reporter Dasom. Welcome, Dasom!
> B: Hi, I'm going to talk about baseball. Do you think catchers in the old days played the same role as catchers ____ⓐ____ these days? ⓑHow do you think?
> A: Well.... I guess so.
> B: No. In the past, catchers stood about one meter behind home base and stopped the ball.
> A: ⓒThat's interesting!

서답형

23 위 글의 빈칸 ⓐ에 들어갈 알맞은 대동사를 쓰시오.

➡ _____

24 위 글의 A와 B의 관계로 알맞은 것을 고르시오.

① announcer – newscaster
② newscaster – sports reporter
③ sports reporter – show host
④ newscaster – announcer
⑤ sports reporter – newscaster

25 위 글의 종류로 알맞은 것을 고르시오.

① summary ② article ③ essay
④ review ⑤ sports news script

서답형

26 위 글의 밑줄 친 ⓑ에서 어법상 틀린 부분을 찾아 고치시오.

_____ ➡ _____

서답형

27 위 글의 밑줄 친 ⓒ가 가리키는 것을 본문에서 찾아 쓰시오.

➡ _____
_____

[01~03] 다음 글을 읽고 물음에 답하시오.

Today the Thunders and the Cobras have a game. Jihun's family is at the baseball stadium.

Jihun: Jian, this is your first time to come to the baseball stadium, isn't it?

Jian: Yes, I'm so excited. ⓐI can't wait for the game to start.

Dad: Look, the players are coming out now!

Jian: Which team is the Thunders?

Jihun: Over there, behind third base. ⓑ그들은 원정 팀이기 때문에 어두운 회색 유니폼을 입고 있어.

01 위 글의 밑줄 친 ⓐ를 다음과 같이 바꿔 쓸 때 빈칸에 들어갈 알맞은 말을 쓰시오.

(1) I can't _____ to watch the game start.
(2) I'm _____ to watch the game start.

02 위 글의 밑줄 친 ⓑ의 우리말에 맞게 한 단어를 보충하여, 주어진 어휘를 배열하시오.

the / wearing / because / uniforms / gray / are / dark / they / they / team / are

➡ _____

_____

03 본문의 내용과 일치하도록 다음 빈칸 (A)와 (B)에 알맞은 단어를 쓰시오.

Jian has (A)_____ come to the baseball stadium before, so she is very (B)_____.

[04~06] 다음 글을 읽고 물음에 답하시오.

Jian: Does the visiting team always wear a dark color?

Jihun: Yes, that's ⓐthe rule. Home teams have bright uniforms and visiting teams have dark uniforms.

Jian: Why is that?

Mom: There is an interesting story about that. In the past, visiting teams could not wash their uniforms after every game. So they started wearing dark colors ⓑ to hide the dirt.

Jian: Hahaha! That was a good idea!

04 위 글의 밑줄 친 ⓐthe rule의 내용을 우리말로 쓰시오.

➡ _____

05 위 글의 밑줄 친 ⓑ를 다음과 같이 바꿔 쓸 때 빈칸에 들어갈 알맞은 말을 쓰시오.

= _____ to hide the dirt
= _____ to hide the dirt
= _____ _____ _____ they _____ hide the dirt
= _____ _____ they _____ hide the dirt

06 다음 문장에서 위 글의 내용과 다른 부분을 찾아서 고치시오.

In the past, as visiting teams could not take a shower after every game, they started wearing dark colors to hide the dirt.

_____ ➡ _____

[07~09] 다음 글을 읽고 물음에 답하시오.

The players are warming up.

Jian: Who's your favorite player?

Jihun: Number 77.

Jian: What does the number mean?

Jihun: Hmm.... ⓐPlayers choose a number they like.

Dad: You know what? In the past, the numbers were determined by the players' batting order.

Jihun: ⓑThat means there were no players with number 77!

07 위 글의 밑줄 친 문장 ⓐ에 생략된 말을 넣어 문장을 다시 쓰시오.

➡ _____

08 본문의 내용과 일치하도록 다음 빈칸에 알맞은 숫자를 쓰시오.

In the past, if a player was the fourth batter in the lineup, his uniform number was _____.
*lineup: 타순

09 위 글의 밑줄 친 ⓑ의 이유를 우리말로 쓰시오.

➡ _____
_____

[10~12] 다음 글을 읽고 물음에 답하시오.

Now, Jihun's favorite player is about to bat. Jihun looks anxious.

Jian: ⓐ오빠가 가장 좋아하는 선수가 타석에 서네.

Jihun: Yes. He ___(A)___ 21 home runs already this year. If he ___(B)___ one more today, he will be the home run leader this season.

ⓑThe batter misses several balls. Now he has a full count. He is waiting for the next pitch.

Jihun: HOME RUN! HOME RUN!

Crack!

The ball flies fast. It is going, going, going, gone!

10 위 글의 빈칸 (A)와 (B)에 hit을 알맞은 형태로 각각 쓰시오.

(A) _____ (B) _____

11 위 글의 밑줄 친 ⓐ의 우리말에 맞게 주어진 어휘를 이용하여 6단어로 영작하시오.

your, at

➡ _____

12 위 글의 밑줄 친 ⓑThe batter가 가리키는 것을 본문에서 찾아 쓰시오.

➡ _____

해석

Real-Life Zone B

A: Which sport do you like? Basketball or soccer?
어떤 ~을 좋아하니? A 아니면 B? Which는 의문형용사로 sport를 수식하며 '어느, 어떤'으로 해석한다

B: I like basketball. I'm going to play it with my friends this weekend. I can't wait.
= basketball 　　　　너무 기다려져(기대를 나타내는 표현)

구문해설 ・be going to 동사원형: ~할 것이다

A: 너는 어떤 운동을 좋아하니? 농구 아니면 축구?
B: 농구를 좋아해. 이번 주말에 친구들이랑 농구를 할 거야. 너무 기다려져.

Writing Workshop

Abebe Bikila

Marathon Runner

Born: August 7, 1932

Nationality: Ethiopia

Speciality: He was known as a marathon winner at the Rome and Tokyo
be known as: ~로 알려져 있다
international sports competitions. When he was preparing to run the marathon
prepare는 목적어로 to부정사를 취한다.
in Rome, he found out that his shoes did not fit well, so he decided to run the
명사절을 이끄는 접속사 　　　　decide는 목적어로 to부정사를 취한다.
race without shoes. He felt pain during the race, but he finished the race as the
신발을 신지 않고, 신발 없이 　　 ~ 중에 　　　　우승자로서
winner. He was one of the greatest runners in the world, wasn't he?
부가의문문은 앞 문장이 긍정이면 부정으로 만든다.

구문해설 ・nationality: 국적 ・speciality: 전문 (분야), 특별 사항 ・competition: 경쟁, 대회, 시합
・prepare: 준비하다 ・find out: 알아내다, 발견하다

Abebe Bikila
마라톤 선수
생일: 1932년 8월 7일
국적: 에티오피아
특별 사항: 그는 로마 국제 스포츠 대회와 도쿄 국제 스포츠 대회의 마라톤 우승자로 알려졌다. 그가 로마에서 달리기를 준비하던 도중에 자신의 신발이 잘 맞지 않는다는 것을 알고 그는 신발을 신지 않고 달리기로 결심했다. 그는 경주 도중에 통증을 느꼈지만 우승자로 경주를 끝마쳤다. 그는 세계에서 가장 위대한 달리기 선수들 중의 한 명이었다. 그렇지 않은가?

Wrap Up

Sarang Middle School Sports Day

Sarang Middle School Sports Day will be held on the school playing field on
조동사(will)+be+pp: 미래시제 수동태 　　　　요일 앞에 전치사 on
Wednesday, June 15. There will be various games such as baseball and soccer.
~ 와 같은(= like)
There will also be table tennis. It sounds like fun, doesn't it?
sound like+명사 　　부가의문문

구문해설 ・various: 다양한, 여러 가지의

사랑 중학교 운동회
사랑 중학교 운동회가 학교 운동장에서 6월 15일 수요일에 열립니다. 야구와 축구 같은 여러 가지 게임이 있을 것입니다. 또한 탁구도 있을 것입니다. 재미있게 들리지요, 그렇지 않나요?

영역별 핵심문제

Words & Expressions

01 다음 중 밑줄 친 부분의 뜻풀이가 바르지 <u>않은</u> 것은?

① After the party Tommy will clean the living room and <u>then</u> do his homework. (그런 다음)

② There are some tips for making the perfect <u>pitch</u>. (투구)

③ I heard a <u>crack</u> when the vase fell over. (날카로운 소리)

④ It's important that you follow the <u>order</u> when adding liquids. (주문)

⑤ Do you think it will <u>fit</u> me? (맞다)

02 다음 밑줄 친 부분과 의미가 가장 가까운 것을 고르시오.

> She seemed <u>anxious</u> about the interview.

① excited　　② pleased　　③ bored
④ nervous　　⑤ interested

03 다음 빈칸에 공통으로 들어갈 말을 쓰시오.

> • The batter _____ed several balls.
> • I don't want to _____ the game.

04 다음 빈칸에 들어갈 말로 적절한 것은?

> He was covered with dust _____ walking along the road.

① for　　② when　　③ unless
④ while　　⑤ therefore

Conversation

[05~07] 다음 대화를 읽고 물음에 답하시오.

B: Jimin, _____(A)_____ (①)
G: I love table tennis. (②)
B: I like soccer. I'm a big fan of James Hood. He's a great soccer player. (③)
G: Oh, really? There's a soccer match this weekend between Korea and Turkey. Have you heard about it? (④)
B: Of course. I already have a ticket. I'm going to see the game on Saturday. I can't wait. (⑤)
G: That's fantastic.

05 위 대화의 ①~⑤ 중 다음 주어진 말이 들어갈 알맞은 곳은?

> How about you?

①　　②　　③　　④　　⑤

06 그림을 참고하여 빈칸 (A) 들어갈 말을 다음 조건에 맞게 쓰시오.

> ┤ 조건 ├
> • 대화에 나온 단어를 이용할 것
> • 선호하는 것을 물을 것
> • 두 문장으로 쓸 것
> • 총 9 단어

➡ _____

07 다음 영영풀이에 해당하는 단어를 대화에서 찾아 쓰시오.

> an official piece of paper or card that shows you have paid to enter a place or do something

➡ _____

08 다음 대화의 밑줄 친 ⓐ~ⓔ 중 어법상 틀린 개수를 고르시오.

> G: What are you doing?
> B: ⓐI looked at a world map.
> G: You checked two countries. ⓑWhat country ⓒwould you like to visiting first? The U.S. ⓓor Mexico?
> B: I want to visit the U.S. ⓔI'd like to seeing a basketball game there.

① 1개 　② 2개 　③ 3개 　④ 4개 　⑤ 5개

[09~10] 다음 대화를 읽고 물음에 답하시오.

> A: <u>너는 어떤 야구 선수를 좋아하니?</u> Mike Hans or Daniel Parker?
> B: (A)<u>I like Mike Hans.</u>

09 위 대화의 밑줄 친 우리말을 영작하시오. (6 words)

➡ _____

10 위 대화의 밑줄 친 (A)의 문장 뒤에 생략된 말을 쓰시오. (4 words)

➡ _____

[11~12] 다음 대화를 읽고 물음에 답하시오.

> G: ⓐDo you want to see my new mountain bike?
> B: ⓑSure. When did you get it?
> G: ⓒMy father bought it for me. ⓓCan you come to my house this afternoon?
> B: ⓔOf course. (A)I can't wait to see it.

11 문장 ⓐ~ⓔ 중에서 대화의 흐름상 어색한 것을 고르시오.

① ⓐ 　② ⓑ 　③ ⓒ 　④ ⓓ 　⑤ ⓔ

12 밑줄 친 (A)를 주어진 단어를 이용해 같은 뜻이 되도록 영작하시오.

➡ _____ (looking)

Grammar

13 다음 중 어법상 올바른 것은?

① James teaches math, isn't he?
② She was great, didn't she?
③ The door was open by Tom.
④ A cake was made for him by his mom.
⑤ The wall is painted by the painters tomorrow.

14 다음 빈칸에 들어갈 말을 바르게 짝지은 것을 고르시오.

> • Our house _____ by Mrs. Green every Thursday.
> • Jejudo has some beautiful scenery, _____?

① are cleaned – does it
② is cleaned – isn't it
③ is cleaned – doesn't it
④ are cleaning – doesn't it
⑤ is cleaning – isn't it

15 다음 문장에서 <u>틀린</u> 것을 고쳐 다시 쓰시오.

(1) At last the thief caught the police last Saturday.

➡ _____

_____

(2) We don't know exactly when the accident was happened.

➡ _____

_____

(3) Delicious *galbitang* is being made to him by Anna.

➡ _____

_____

(4) Your love can show to your partner by saying "I love you."

➡ _____

_____

(5) Mariel was seen go out with her friend by Andy.

➡ _____

_____

(6) The festival put off by the city on account of the bad weather.

➡ _____

_____

(7) She didn't say good-bye, was she?

➡ _____

(8) She can play soccer very well, doesn't she?

➡ _____

(9) Tino is wearing a blue shirt, doesn't Tino?

➡ _____

(10) The hotel where we stayed was near the city hall, didn't there?

➡ _____

_____

16 다음 두 문장을 부가의문을 써서 한 문장으로 바꿔 쓰시오.

(1) Tino likes eating ice cream. Doesn't he like eating ice cream?

➡ _____

(2) It was an interesting movie. Wasn't it an interesting movie?

➡ _____

17 다음 빈칸에 들어갈 전치사가 나머지와 <u>다른</u> 것은?

① He was covered _____ dust while walking along the road.

② I'm interested _____ Switzerland.

③ You should be satisfied _____ what you have.

④ The president was pleased _____ the news.

⑤ The boxes were filled _____ chocolate bars for the children.

18 다음 우리말을 괄호 안에 주어진 어휘를 이용하여 영작하시오.

(1) 네 개는 어제 어디에서 발견되었니?
(your dog, find, 6단어)

➡ _____

(2) 프랑스어는 아프리카에 있는 많은 국가들에서 말해진다. (Africa, speak , 8단어)

➡ _____

(3) 박씨는 매주 일요일마다 쇼핑을 해, 그렇지 않니?
(Mr. Park, go, every, 8단어)

➡ _____

Reading

[19~21] 다음 글을 읽고 물음에 답하시오.

Today the Thunders and the Cobras have a game. Jihun's family is at the baseball stadium.

Jihun: Jian, this is your first time ⓐto come to the baseball stadium, isn't it?

Jian: Yes, I'm so excited. I (A)[can / can't] wait for the game to start.

Dad: Look, the players are coming out now!

Jian: Which team (B)[is / are] the Thunders?

Jihun: Over there, behind third base. ⓑThey are wearing dark gray uniforms because they are the (C)[visiting / visited] team.

19 위 글의 괄호 (A)~(C)에서 문맥이나 어법상 알맞은 낱말을 골라 쓰시오.

(A) _____ (B) _____ (C) _____

20 위 글의 밑줄 친 ⓐcome과 to부정사의 용법이 같은 것을 고르시오.

① He stopped his car to check the engine.
② She needs someone to talk with.
③ They hope to visit us next year.
④ He grew up to be a famous singer.
⑤ It is difficult to solve this problem.

21 위 글의 밑줄 친 ⓑThey가 가리키는 것을 영어로 쓰시오.

➡ _____

[22~24] 다음 글을 읽고 물음에 답하시오.

Jian: Does the visiting team always wear a dark color?

Jihun: Yes, that's the rule. Home teams have _____ⓐ_____ uniforms and visiting teams have _____ⓑ_____ uniforms.

Jian: Why is that?

Mom: There is an interesting story about that. In the past, visiting teams could not wash their uniforms after every game. So they started ⓒwearing dark colors to hide the dirt.

Jian: Hahaha! That was a good idea!

22 위 글의 빈칸 ⓐ와 ⓑ에 들어갈 알맞은 말을 고르시오.

① dark – bright
② bright – light
③ bright – dark
④ strong – dark
⑤ light – strong

23 아래 〈보기〉에서 위 글의 밑줄 친 ⓒwearing과 문법적 쓰임이 같은 것의 개수를 고르시오.

① I'm fond of wearing a pink dress.
② She is wearing a pink dress today.
③ Do you know the girl wearing a pink dress?
④ Wearing a pink dress makes me happy.
⑤ She came to the party wearing a pink dress.

① 1개 ② 2개 ③ 3개 ④ 4개 ⑤ 5개

24 위 글의 내용과 일치하지 <u>않는</u> 것은?

① 홈팀은 밝은 유니폼을 입는다.
② 원정 팀은 어두운 유니폼을 입는다.
③ 과거에는 원정 팀이 매 경기 후 유니폼을 세탁할 수가 없었다.
④ 원정 팀은 때를 숨기기 위해 어두운 색을 입기 시작했다.
⑤ 원정 팀의 유니폼은 더러웠을 것이라고 지안이는 말한다.

[25~26] 다음 글을 읽고 물음에 답하시오.

> The players are warming up.
> Jian: Who's your favorite player?
> Jihun: Number 77.
> Jian: What does the number mean?
> Jihun: Hmm.... Players choose a number they like.
> Dad: You know what? In the past, the numbers were determined by the players' batting ⓐorder.
> Jihun: That means there were no players with number 77!

25 위 글의 밑줄 친 ⓐorder와 같은 의미로 쓰인 것을 고르시오.

① I would like to place an <u>order</u> for ten copies of this book.
② The names are listed in alphabetical <u>order</u>.
③ When did the officer <u>order</u> them to fire?
④ The house was kept in good <u>order</u>.
⑤ He will <u>order</u> a new suit for his son.

26 위 글을 읽고 대답할 수 <u>없는</u> 질문은?

① What are the players doing now?
② Who's Jihun's favorite player?
③ Why does Jihun like the player?
④ What does the number 77 mean?
⑤ In the past, by what were the players' numbers determined?

[27~30] 다음 글을 읽고 물음에 답하시오.

> Now, Jihun's favorite player ⓐis about to bat. Jihun looks anxious.
> Jian: Your favorite player is ___(A)___ bat.
> Jihun: Yes. He has hit 21 home runs already this year. If he hits one more today, he will be the home run leader this season.
> The batter misses several balls. Now he has a full count. He is waiting ___(B)___ the next pitch.
> Jihun: HOME RUN! HOME RUN!
> Crack!
> The ball flies fast. It is going, going, going, ___(C)___!

27 위 글의 빈칸 (A)와 (B)에 들어갈 전치사가 바르게 짝지어진 것은?

① on – for   ② at – by   ③ in – to
④ on – to   ⑤ at – for

28 다음과 같은 뜻이 되도록 위 글의 빈칸 (C)에 go를 알맞은 형태로 쓰시오.

> Jihun's favorite player hits a home run.

➡ _____

29 위 글의 밑줄 친 ⓐ를 다음과 같이 바꿔 쓸 때 빈칸에 들어갈 알맞은 말을 쓰시오.

> is on the point of _____

30 다음 문장에서 위 글의 내용과 <u>다른</u> 부분을 찾아서 고치시오.

> When Jihun's favorite player hits a ball, it falls to the ground.

_____ ➡ _____

01 출제율 95%

다음 빈칸에 알맞은 말이 순서대로 바르게 나열된 것은?

> • My favorite player is _____ bat.
> • The film is about _____.
> • He also takes English lessons _____ a week.

① on – to begin – two
② on – to beginning – twice
③ at – to begin – twice
④ at – to beginning – twice
⑤ at – beginning – two

02 출제율 95%

우리말 해석에 맞게 빈칸을 완성하시오.

(1) 선수는 1루로 걸어갔다.
  ➡ The player walked to _____ _____.
(2) 그는 대회에서 우승하기 위해 열심히 노력했다.
  ➡ He tried hard to win the _____.
(3) 나도 초콜릿을 좋아하지 않는다.
  ➡ I don't like chocolate, _____.
(4) 반드시 순서를 지켜 주세요.
  ➡ Be sure to follow the _____.

03 출제율 90%

〈보기〉에 주어진 단어를 이용해 빈칸 (A)와 (B)를 채우시오.

> A: What are you going to do on your vacation?
> B: I'm going ___(A)___ a boat ride. I can't ___(B)___.

┌─ 보기 ─┐
go play take wait

(A) _____ (B) _____

04 출제율 100%

다음 중 밑줄 친 부분의 뜻풀이가 바르지 않은 것을 모두 고르시오.

① My daughter hid the ring under her bed. (숨겼다)
② Don't forget to check that your helmet fits properly. (맞다)
③ He can't go and I can't, either. (둘 중 하나)
④ It's not easy to decide what to eat. (결정하다)
⑤ Which team do you support? (지원하다)

05 출제율 90%

다음 단어와 영영풀이의 연결이 잘못된 것을 고르시오.

① pitch: a throw of the ball for the batter to hit it
② anxious: very nervous or worried about something
③ fit: to be the right size and shape for someone or something
④ home team: a sports team playing on the competing team's field or court
⑤ base: each corner of the square that makes a baseball diamond

[06~08] 다음 대화를 읽고 물음에 답하시오.

> B1: Jiho, why are you ___ⓐ___ such a hurry?
> B2: Hi, Alex! I have to be home before 6:00. (①) The game between the Thunders ___ⓑ___ the Cobras starts at 6:00.
> B1: Oh, are you a baseball fan? Which team do you ___(A)___? The Cobras or the Thunders?
> B2: The Cobras. (②)
> B1: Me, too! (③)

B2: Hurry _____ⓒ_____ ! We only have thirty minutes left. (④)

B1: Okay. Maybe we can watch a game together sometime. (⑤)

B2: That's a great idea! How about going to the next Cobras home game together?

B1: Okay. They have a game next Saturday. We can eat fried chicken while watching the game!

B2: That sounds great. I can't wait!

출제율 90%

06 위 대화의 ①~⑤ 중 다음 주어진 말이 들어갈 알맞은 곳은?

> I don't want to miss the game either.

①   ②   ③   ④   ⑤

출제율 95%

07 위 대화의 빈칸 (A)에 들어갈 알맞은 단어를 고르시오.

① provide ② support ③ make
④ enjoy   ⑤ play

출제율 100%

08 위 대화의 빈칸 ⓐ~ⓒ에 알맞은 말을 〈보기〉에서 골라 쓰시오.

┌── 보기 ──
│ and at for in or to up
└─────────

ⓐ _____ ⓑ _____ ⓒ _____

[09~10] 다음 대화를 읽고 물음에 답하시오.

G: What are you doing?

B: I'm looking at a world map.

G: You checked two countries. 어떤 나라에 먼저 방문하고 싶어? 미국 아니면 멕시코?

B: I want to visit the U.S. I'd like to see a basketball game there.

출제율 85%

09 밑줄 친 우리말을 주어진 단어를 이용하여 영작하시오.

> (Mexico, would, country, like, The U.S.)

➡ _____
  _____

출제율 95%

10 위 대화를 읽고 답할 수 없는 질문을 고르시오.

① What countries did the boy check on a world map?

② What does the boy want to do in Mexico?

③ What is the boy doing now?

④ Which country does the boy want to go first? Mexico or the U.S.?

⑤ What would the boy like to do when he visits the U.S.?

[11~12] 다음 대화를 읽고 물음에 답하시오.

B: Jimin, which sport do you like? Soccer or table tennis?

G: I love table tennis. How about you, Yunho?

B: I like soccer. I'm a big fan of James Hood. He's a great soccer player.

G: Oh, really? 이번 주말에 한국 대 터키의 축구 경기가 있어. (Korea, between, a, match, Turkey, soccer, there's, weekend, and, this) Have you heard about it?

B: Of course. I already have a ticket. I'm going to see the game on Saturday. I can't wait.

G: That's fantastic.

11 위 대화의 밑줄 친 우리말에 맞게 괄호 안의 단어를 알맞게 배열하여 영작하시오.

➡ _____

_____

12 위 대화의 내용과 일치하는 것을 고르시오.

① Jimin does not like soccer.
② Jimin and Yunho like table tennis.
③ Yunho has heard about the soccer match this weekend.
④ Yunho is going to see the final baseball game.
⑤ Jimin already has the soccer match ticket.

13 다음 밑줄 친 부분을 생략할 수 있는 것은?

① A lot of waste is thrown away in big cities by people.
② This picture was drawn by Lio.
③ The photos were not taken by my brother.
④ Math was taught to us by Mr. Lee.
⑤ This report was written by the student.

14 다음 주어진 문장과 같은 뜻이 되도록 빈칸을 채우시오.

(1) Simon will read his son the book tonight.
➡ The book _____

_____.

(2) Peter fixed the car this morning.
➡ The car _____.

15 다음 빈칸을 두 단어로 채워 상대방의 동의를 구하는 문장으로 완성하시오.

(1) She had her hair cut, _____ _____?
(2) The boys can play the violin, _____

_____?
(3) The movie wasn't interesting at all,

_____ _____?

[16~18] 다음 글을 읽고 물음에 답하시오.

Today the Thunders and the Cobras have a game. Jihun's family is at the baseball stadium.

Jihun: Jian, this is your first time to come to the baseball stadium, ___ⓐ___ ?

Jian: Yes, I'm so (A)[exciting / excited]. I can't wait for the game (B)[starting / to start].

Dad: Look, the players are coming out now!

Jian: Which team is the Thunders?

Jihun: Over there, behind (C)[three bases / third base]. They are wearing dark gray uniforms because they are the visiting team.

16 위 글의 빈칸 ⓐ에 들어갈 알맞은 부가의문문을 쓰시오.

➡ _____

17 위 글의 괄호 (A)~(C)에서 문맥이나 어법상 알맞은 것을 골라 쓰시오.

(A) _____ (B) _____ (C) _____

18 위 글을 읽고 대답할 수 없는 질문은?

① What teams have a game today?
② Where is Jihun's family now?
③ Has Jian come to the baseball stadium before?
④ How does Jian feel to be in the baseball stadium?
⑤ Why are the players of the visiting team wearing dark gray uniforms?

[19~21] 다음 글을 읽고 물음에 답하시오.

Jian: Does the visiting team always wear a dark color?

Jihun: Yes, that's the rule. Home teams have bright uniforms and visiting teams have dark uniforms.

Jian: Why is that?

Mom: There is an interesting story about that. In the past, visiting teams could not wash their uniforms after every game. So they started wearing dark colors ⓐto hide the dirt.

Jian: Hahaha! That was a good idea!

출제율 100%

19 위 글의 주제로 알맞은 것을 고르시오.

① the reason why home teams like bright uniforms

② the reason why visiting teams wear dark uniforms

③ the difficulties that visiting teams experienced

④ the strong points of bright uniforms

⑤ the weak points of dark uniforms

출제율 90%

20 Why did visiting teams start wearing dark colors? Fill in the blanks with the suitable words.

> Because visiting teams could not _____ _____ _____ after every game in the past, they started wearing dark colors _____ _____ the dirt.

출제율 95%

21 위 글의 밑줄 친 ⓐto hide와 to부정사의 용법이 다른 것을 모두 고르시오.

① He studied hard to pass the exam.

② I didn't expect to see you here.

③ Tom needed someone to help him.

④ It's fun to teach the students.

⑤ I have come here to learn English.

[22~24] 다음 글을 읽고 물음에 답하시오.

The players are warming up.

Jian: Who's your favorite player?

Jihun: Number 77.

Jian: What does the number mean?

Jihun: Hmm.... Players choose a number they like.

Dad: ⓐYou know what? In the past, the numbers were determined by the players' batting order.

Jihun: That means there were no players with number 77!

출제율 95%

22 What is the number that Jihun's favorite player likes? Answer in English in a full sentence. (3 words)

➡ _____

출제율 90%

23 위 글의 밑줄 친 ⓐYou know what?과 바꿔 쓸 수 있는 말을 모두 고르시오.

① You know something?

② How do you feel about it?

③ How would you like it?

④ Guess what!

⑤ What do you think about it?

출제율 95%

24 위 글의 내용과 일치하지 않는 것은?

① 선수들이 몸을 풀고 있다.

② 지안이가 가장 좋아하는 선수는 77번 선수이다.

③ 지훈이는 선수들이 원하는 번호를 선택한다고 말한다.

④ 과거에는 번호가 선수들의 타순에 의해 결정되었다.

⑤ 과거에는 77번 선수가 없었다.

[01~02] 다음 대화의 흐름상 어색한 부분을 찾아 고치시오.

01

> B: Don't forget that we're going rock climbing this weekend!
> G: Don't worry. I will forget.
> B: I'm excited about going. I can't wait.

_____ ➡ _____

02

> A: Which sport do you like? Bowling or baseball?
> B: I like baseball. I'm going to play it with my friends this weekend. I can wait.

_____ ➡ _____

03 대화의 밑줄 친 부분과 같은 의미가 되도록 주어진 단어를 이용하여 문장을 완성하시오.

> G: Did you get the tickets?
> B: Yes! I can't wait to watch the game.

➡ _____ (forward)

04 다음 주어진 문장을 능동태는 수동태로, 수동태는 능동태로 바꾸시오.

(1) What did she cook for her family last night?

➡ _____

(2) Dabotap was built in the eighth century by Kimdaesung.

➡ _____

(3) The plants are watered by Kevin every morning.

➡ _____

(4) My friend gave me some flowers two days ago.

➡ _____

_____

_____

05 다음 문장에서 틀린 것을 고쳐 다시 쓰시오.

(1) The light bulb invented Edison.

➡ _____

_____

(2) Sue was made a dress by her mom.

➡ _____

(3) You aren't paying attention, do you?

➡ _____

(4) You forgot to bring your umbrella, were not you?

➡ _____

[06~09] 다음 글을 읽고 물음에 답하시오.

Today the Thunders and the Cobras have a game. Jihun's family is at the baseball stadium.

Jihun: Jian, this is your first time to come to the baseball stadium, isn't it?

Jian: Yes, I'm so ___(A)___ . ⓐ나는 경기가 빨리 시작했으면 좋겠어.

Dad: Look, the players are coming out now!

Jian: Which team is the Thunders?

Jihun: Over there, behind third base. They are ___(B)___ dark gray uniforms because they are the visiting team.

06 위 글의 빈칸 (A), (B)에 알맞은 말을 주어진 어휘를 이용하여 쓰시오.

(A) excite, (B) wear

(A) _____ (B) _____

07 위 글의 밑줄 친 ⓐ의 우리말에 맞게 주어진 어구를 이용하여 8단어로 영작하시오.

can't wait, start

➡ _____

08 Why are the Thunders wearing dark gray uniforms? Fill in the blank with the suitable words.

➡ Because _____ .

09 다음 문장에서 위 글의 내용과 <u>다른</u> 부분을 찾아서 고치시오.

Jian has come to the baseball stadium before.

_____ ➡ _____

[10~13] 다음 글을 읽고 물음에 답하시오.

The players are (A)[warming / warmed] up.

Jian: (B)[Whose / Who's] your favorite player?

Jihun: Number 77.

Jian: What does the number mean?

Jihun: Hmm.... ⓐPlayers choose a number they like.

Dad: You know (C)[how / what]? In the past, ⓑthe numbers were determined by the players' batting order.

Jihun: ⓒThat means there were no players with number 77!

10 위 글의 괄호 (A)~(C)에서 문맥이나 어법상 알맞은 낱말을 골라 쓰시오.

(A) _____ (B) _____ (C) _____

11 위 글의 밑줄 친 ⓐ를 수동태로 고치시오.

➡ _____

_____

12 위 글의 밑줄 친 ⓑ를 능동태로 고치시오.

➡ _____

_____

13 위 글의 밑줄 친 ⓒThat이 가리키는 것을 본문에서 찾아 쓰시오.

➡ _____

_____

01 주어진 동사의 수동태를 사용하여 다양한 문장을 쓰시오.

┌─ 보기 ─┐

choose, donate, turn off, make, write

(1) _____

(2) _____

(3) _____

(4) _____

(5) _____

02 다음 내용을 바탕으로 선수의 프로필을 작성하시오.

Seri Park

Professional golfer

Born: September 8, 1977

Nationality: South Korea

Speciality: • When young: the best amateur golfer

• in 1996: turned professional golfer

• from 1998 to 2016: played on the LPGA Tours

• in November 2007: inducted into the World Golf Hall of Fame

*induct: (조직에) 가입시키다

Seri Park

Professional golfer

Born: September 8, 1977

Nationality: South Korea

Speciality: She was the best (A)_____ golfer when she was young. She turned (B)_____ golfer in 1996. She played on the (C)_____ from 1998 to 2016. She was inducted into the (D)_____ in November 2007. She was great, wasn't she?

단원별 모의고사

01 다음 밑줄 친 부분과 의미가 가까운 것을 고르시오.

> The price is <u>determined</u> by supply and demand.

① decided ② got
③ agreed ④ made
⑤ discussed

02 다음 제시된 의미에 맞는 단어를 주어진 철자로 시작하여 빈칸에 쓰고 알맞은 것을 골라 문장을 완성하시오. (필요하면 어형 변화를 할 것)

> • c_____ : an event or contest in which people try to win something by defeating others
> • c_____ : the sudden loud explosive sound of something when it falls or bumps into itself or something else
> • p_____ : the time before the moment of speaking or writing
> • h_____ : to put something out of sight

(1) The dog _____ the bone in the ground yesterday.
(2) There were huge _____ of thunders all night long.
(3) The _____ is heating up.
(4) In the _____, people traveled on horseback.

03 다음 우리말에 맞게 빈칸에 알맞은 말을 쓰시오.

(1) 제 차는 저기 주차장에 주차되어 있습니다.
➡ My car is in the parking lot _____ _____.

(2) 그녀는 급해서 빨간 불을 무시하고 지나갔다.
➡ She was _____ _____ _____ and drove through a red light.

(3) 언제 그의 새로운 소설이 나오나요?
➡ When will his new novel _____ _____?

(4) 남자는 수하물을 기다리고 있다.
➡ The man is _____ _____ his luggage.

04 다음 중 동사와의 연결이 <u>어색한</u> 것을 고르시오.

① go surfing ② play soccer
③ go swimming ④ go tennis
⑤ play baseball

[05~06] 다음 대화를 읽고 물음에 답하시오.

A: Which shorts do you like? The green ones or the red ones?
B: (A)<u>I like the green ones.</u>

05 위 대화의 밑줄 친 문장 (A)에서 생략된 부분을 쓰시오.
➡ _____

06 밑줄 친 문장 (A)와 같은 의미가 되도록 주어진 단어를 이용해 문장을 완성하시오.
➡ _____ (to, 9단어)

[07~11] 다음 대화를 읽고 물음에 답하시오.

B1: Jiho, why are you in such a hurry?

B2: Hi, Alex! I have to be home before 6:00. The game between the Thunders and the Cobras (A)[start / starts] at 6:00. (①)

B1: Oh, are you a baseball fan? ___@___ The Cobras or the Thunders?

B2: The Cobras. (②)

B1: Me, too! I don't want to miss the game (B)[either / too]. (③)

B2: Hurry up! We only have thirty minutes (C)[left / leaving].

B1: Okay. Maybe we can watch a game together sometime. (④)

B2: That's a great idea! (⑤)

B1: Okay. They have a game next Saturday. We can eat fried chicken while watching the game!

B2: That sounds great. I can't wait!

07 위 대화의 ①~⑤ 중 다음 주어진 문장이 들어갈 알맞은 곳은?

> How about going to the next Cobras home game together?

①   ②   ③   ④   ⑤

08 위 대화의 빈칸 @에 들어갈 알맞은 표현을 고르시오.

① Where can we watch the game?

② Which team do you support?

③ Do you like baseball?

④ What are they going to do at 6:00?

⑤ What do you want to eat while watching TV?

09 위 대화의 (A)~(C)에서 알맞은 말을 골라 쓰시오.

(A) _____ (B) _____ (C) _____

10 다음 영영풀이에 해당하는 단어를 대화에서 찾아 쓰시오.

> a group of people who play a sport or game together against other groups of people

➡ _____

11 위 대화의 내용과 일치하지 않는 것을 고르시오.

① It is five-thirty now.

② They watched the Cobras home game together.

③ Jiho is a baseball fan.

④ There is a baseball game at 6:00.

⑤ Jiho is in a hurry to watch a baseball game.

12 다음 대화의 흐름상 어색한 부분을 찾아 고치시오. (밑줄 친 부분에서 고를 것)

> G: I'm thinking about getting a pet. Do you have a pet?
>
> B: Yes, I do. I have a dog and a cat.
>
> G: What do you think? Which pet is more for me? A cat or a dog?
>
> B: Why don't you come to my house someday and play with my pets? Then you can decide.

_____ ➡ _____

13 다음 중 어법상 바른 것은?

① Cheesecake bakes for Scott every day.

② Mr. Lee was written a letter.

③ My computer was fixed my brother.

④ Mastering English in a year or two is really difficult, isn't it?

⑤ You have a pen, do you?

14 다음 중 능통태를 수동태로 잘못 바꾼 것은?

① People living near the river have eaten fish.

= Fish have been eaten by people living near the river.

② His teacher made him study English every day.

= He was made to study English every day by his teacher.

③ They gave up the plan because of the heavy costs.

= The plan was given because of the heavy costs.

④ Sam gave Alicia a present.

= A present was given to Alicia by Sam.

⑤ Amedeo Modigliani painted *Woman with Blue Eyes* in 1918.

= *Woman with Blue Eyes* was painted by Amedeo Modigliani in 1918.

15 다음 문장에서 틀린 것을 고치시오.

(1) This house is made from stone.

_____ ➡ _____

(2) William was bought a new computer by her mother.

_____ ➡

_____

(3) The Olympic Games are taken place every four years.

_____ ➡ _____

(4) They are doctors, don't they?

_____ ➡ _____

(5) Come home by 8 o'clock tonight, can't you?

_____ ➡ _____

16 다음 밑줄 친 부분의 쓰임이 나머지 넷과 다른 것은?

① The station was <u>built</u> in 1894.

② His words often <u>made</u> no sense.

③ The roof of my house was <u>covered</u> with snow.

④ These cookies were <u>cooked</u> for him by Joanna.

⑤ The greetings are <u>used</u> to welcome people.

17 다음 빈칸에 알맞은 부가의문문을 쓰시오.

(1) You like dogs, _____ _____?

(2) Emily is tired, _____ _____?

(3) He was one of the greatest runners in the world, _____ _____?

(4) The man always parks his car on the street, _____ _____?

(5) You will go there, _____ _____?

(6) You looked so busy, _____ _____?

(7) Be good to yourself, _____ _____?

(8) Let's help that child, _____ _____?

[18~19] 다음 글을 읽고 물음에 답하시오.

Today the Thunders and the Cobras have a game. Jihun's family is at the baseball stadium.

Jihun: Jian, this is your first time to come to the baseball stadium, isn't it?

Jian: Yes, I'm so excited. I can't wait for the game to start.

Dad: Look, the players are coming out now!

Jian: Which team is the Thunders?

Jihun: Over there, behind third base. They are wearing dark gray uniforms because they are the ⓐ<u>visiting</u> team.

18 아래 〈보기〉에서 위 글의 밑줄 친 ⓐvisiting과 문법적 쓰임이 **다른** 것의 개수를 고르시오.

> ① I came home running all the way from school.
> ② He enjoyed studying with his friends.
> ③ Mastering foreign languages is not easy.
> ④ The boy sitting under the tree is my brother.
> ⑤ Thank you for showing me the way to the subway station.

① 1개　② 2개　③ 3개　④ 4개　⑤ 5개

19 Which team is the home team, the Thunders or the Cobras? Answer in English. (2 words)

➡ _____

[20~21] 다음 글을 읽고 물음에 답하시오.

Jian: Does the visiting team always wear a dark color?

Jihun: Yes, that's the rule. Home teams have bright uniforms and visiting teams have dark uniforms.

Jian: Why is that?

Mom: There is an interesting story about that. In the past, visiting teams could not wash their uniforms after every game. So they started wearing dark colors to hide the dirt.

Jian: Hahaha! ⓐThat was a good idea!

20 위 글의 밑줄 친 ⓐThat이 가리키는 것을 본문에서 찾아 쓰시오.

➡ _____

21 위 글을 읽고 대답할 수 **없는** 질문은?

① Does the home team always wear a bright color?
② What's the rule about the color of the uniforms?
③ Why did visiting teams have dark uniforms in the past?
④ What team started wearing dark colors for the first time?
⑤ What does Jian think about the origin of dark uniforms?

[22~23] 다음 글을 읽고 물음에 답하시오.

The players are warming up.

Jian: Who's your favorite player?

Jihun: Number 77.

Jian: What does the number mean?

Jihun: Hmm.... Players choose a number they like.

Dad: You know what? In the past, ⓐ번호가 선수들의 타순에 의해 결정되었단다.

Jihun: That means there were no players with number 77!

22 위 글의 밑줄 친 ⓐ의 우리말에 맞게 한 단어를 보충하여, 주어진 어휘를 알맞게 배열하시오.

> order / were / the numbers / batting / determined / the players'

➡ _____

_____

23 다음 빈칸 (A)와 (B)에 알맞은 단어를 넣어 현재 등번호가 결정되는 방법에 대한 설명을 완성하시오.

> At present, the number is chosen by (A)_____ themselves, which is a number they (B)_____.

INSIGHT
on the textbook

교과서 파헤치기

※ 다음 영어를 우리말로 쓰시오.

01 concert _____

02 grow _____

03 actually _____

04 bit _____

05 clothes _____

06 opportunity _____

07 bright _____

08 dolphin _____

09 elementary school _____

10 musical instrument _____

11 cook _____

12 free time _____

13 hold _____

14 join _____

15 easy _____

16 neighbor _____

17 main gate _____

18 orchestra _____

19 introduce _____

20 own _____

21 garden _____

22 vegetable _____

23 library _____

24 present _____

25 volunteer _____

26 experience _____

27 several _____

28 note _____

29 activity _____

30 leader _____

31 interest _____

32 practice _____

33 neighborhood _____

34 cooking _____

35 as a result _____

36 enjoy+동사ing _____

37 look for _____

38 would like to+동사원형 _____

39 participate in _____

40 change into _____

41 ask for help _____

42 be good at _____

43 how to+동사원형 _____

※ 다음 우리말을 영어로 쓰시오.

01	도넛	22	(사람·동물을) 걷게 하다
02	경험, 경력	23	실제로, 사실은
03	무인 비행기	24	기회
04	선물, 참석한	25	(모임·식 등을) 개최하다
05	연습; 연습하다	26	소개하다
06	활동	27	실제로, 사실은
07	요리, 음식	28	밝은
08	관심	29	옷, 의상
09	날게 하다	30	(동식물을) 기르다
10	봉사, 유익한 활동	31	(모임·식 등을) 개최하다
11	몇몇의	32	이웃
12	동네	33	정문
13	~을 사다, ~을 획득하다	34	채소
14	지도자, 대표	35	~로 변화시키다[바꾸다]
15	도서관	36	아주 조금
16	동아리	37	~에 빠지다
17	그러나, 하지만	38	결과적으로
18	봉사하다	39	~에 참여하다
19	음, 음표	40	(병·상황 등이) 나아지다
20	사업, 계획	41	~에 대해 감사하다
21	스페인어	42	도움을 청하다
		43	(~에 대해서) 조심하다

※ 다음 영영풀이에 알맞은 단어를 <보기>에서 골라 쓴 후, 우리말 뜻을 쓰시오.

1 _____ : strong and easy to see: _____

2 _____ : to develop or increase in size or length: _____

3 _____ : slightly or to a small degree(=a little): _____

4 _____ : to do something regularly in order to do it better: _____

5 _____ : to take a dog for a walk for exercise: _____

6 _____ : to cook something using dry heat, in an oven: _____

7 _____ : aircraft that does not have a pilot, but is operated by radio: _____

8 _____ : to become a member of an organization, society, or group: _____

9 _____ : someone who lives next to you or near you: _____

10 _____ : a part of the area next to a house, which has plants and flowers in it: _____

11 _____ : something that you use for playing music, such as a piano or guitar: _____

12 _____ : the person who directs or controls a group, organization, country, etc.: _____

13 _____ : a chance to do something or an occasion when it is easy for you to do something: _____

14 _____ : to have a meeting, party, election etc in a particular place or at a particular time: _____

15 _____ : a large group of musicians playing many different kinds of instruments and led by a conductor: _____

16 _____ : organization for people who share a particular interest or enjoy similar activities, or a group of people who meet together to do something they are interested in: _____

보기			
join	drone	opportunity	bake
bright	hold	orchestra	walk
a bit	musical instrument	grow	leader
neighbor	club	practice	garden

※ 다음 우리말과 일치하도록 빈칸에 알맞은 말을 쓰시오.

Listen & Speak 1 A

A: Do you _____ _____ _____ _____ a paper cat?

B: Of _____. It's _____.

Listen & Speak 1 B

1. G: I _____ _____ _____ _____ Yuna's violin concert

　　 yesterday. _____ was it?

　 B: It was great. _____ _____ _____ _____ _____ the

　　 violin _____ _____ _____.

　 G: I didn't know you _____ _____ _____ _____ _____

　　 _____.

　 B: I can, but I'm _____ _____ _____ it _____.

2. G: _____ _____ these pictures. I _____ these vegetables

　　 _____. I have my _____ _____.

　 B: Cool! Do you know _____ _____ _____ the vegetables

　　 you _____, _____?

　 G: Yes, my grandmother _____ _____.

Listen & Speak 2 A

A: Do you enjoy _____ _____ the stars _____ _____?

G: Yes, I _____ _____ that.

Listen & Speak 2 B

1. B: _____ _____ _____ _____ books, Yumi?

　 G: Yes, I _____ _____ science books. How _____ you?

　 B: I love _____ books, _____.

　 G: Then, _____ _____ to _____ _____ after school today.

2. G: _____ _____ _____ _____ on the weekend, Minsu?

　 B: I _____ _____ for my family.

　 G: _____ _____ _____ _____ _____?

　 B: Yes, I'm a _____ _____! My family loves my _____.

해석

G: 종이 고양이 만드는 법을 알고 있니?
B: 물론이지. 그건 쉬워.

1. G: 어제 유나의 바이올린 콘서트에
　　 갔다고 들었어. 어땠니?
　 B: 좋았어. 나도 언젠가 그녀처럼 바
　　 이올린을 연주할 수 있기를 바라.
　 G: 나는 네가 바이올린 연주하는 법
　　 을 아는지 몰랐어.
　 B: 할 수 있어, 그러나 아직 잘하지는
　　 못해.
2. G: 이 사진들 좀 봐. 나는 이 채소를
　　 직접 길렀어. 나는 내 자신의 정원
　　 이 있어.
　 B: 멋지다! 네가 기르는 채소로 요리
　　 하는 법도 아니?
　 G: 응, 할머니께서 내게 가르쳐 주셨
　　 어.

B: 너는 밤에 별을 보는 것을 즐기니?
G: 응, 나는 별을 보는 것을 아주 좋아
　 해.

1. B: 유미야, 너는 책 읽는 것을 즐
　　 기니?
　 G: 응, 나는 과학 책을 읽는 것을
　　 좋아해. 너는 어때?
　 B: 나도 책 읽는 것을 좋아해.
　 G: 그럼 오늘 방과 후에 도서관 가
　　 자.
2. G: 민수야, 주말에 뭐 했니?
　 B: 가족을 위해 아침을 만들었어.
　 G: 너는 요리를 즐기니?
　 B: 응, 나는 훌륭한 요리사야! 우
　　 리 가족은 내 요리를 좋아해.

3. **B:** Jiyun, that's a pretty backpack! _____ did you _____ it?

   G: My sister _____ _____ _____ _____.

   B: Wow! She's a _____ _____ _____.

   G: Yes, she is. And she _____ _____ _____, _____.

Real-Life Zone A

B: Hello, Kate. I'm Hamin, _____ _____ of the Nanum Orchestra. _____ you _____ _____ _____ in our club.

G: Hi. Nice _____ _____ you.

B: You play the violin? _____ _____ _____ _____ the violin?

G: I started learning _____ _____ _____ I was ten.

B: Do you have any _____ _____ in a group?

G: Yes. _____, I was a member of _____ _____ _____ I was in _____ _____.

B: Great. We also _____ _____ _____ children. _____ _____ _____ _____ _____?

G: I have no _____ teaching others. But I _____ _____ _____ people, so I'd _____ _____ _____.

B: Good. I think we'll _____ a great time _____ together. _____ _____ the Nanum Orchestra.

Wrap Up

B: These cookies _____ so _____. Did you make them?

G: Yes. I _____ _____ yesterday. I enjoy _____. I'm _____ _____ make doughnuts _____ _____.

B: Oh, I _____ _____ _____ _____ doughnuts. _____ it _____?

G: Not _____ _____. You can come to my house and _____ _____ if you want.

B: Thanks, Bora. _____ _____ _____ I come?

G: _____ 2:00.

B: _____ good. _____ you _____.

3. **B:** 지윤아, 그거 예쁜 배낭이네! 어디서 샀어?
   G: 언니가 내게 만들어 준 거야.
   B: 와! 그녀는 정말 훌륭한 디자이너구나.
   G: 응, 그래. 그리고 그녀는 옷 만드는 것도 즐겨.

B: 안녕, 케이트. 나는 나눔 오케스트라의 대표 하민이야. 우리 동아리에 관심을 가져줘서 고마워.
G: 안녕. 만나서 반가워.
B: 너는 바이올린을 연주하니? 언제 바이올린 연주를 시작했니?
G: 10살 때 바이올린을 연주하는 법을 배우기 시작했어.
B: 그룹에서 연주해 본 경험이 있니?
G: 응. 사실 나는 초등학교 때 오케스트라 단원이었어.
B: 좋아. 우리는 자원봉사로 아이들도 가르쳐. 다른 사람들을 가르치는 것을 즐기니?
G: 나는 다른 사람들을 가르친 경험이 없어. 그러나 나는 사람들과 일하는 것을 즐겨, 그래서 나는 해보고 싶어.
B: 좋아. 나는 우리가 함께 연주하며 좋은 시간을 보낼 것이라고 생각해. 나눔 오케스트라에 온 걸 환영해.

B: 이 쿠키들은 정말 맛있어 보여. 네가 만들었니?
G: 응. 어제 내가 직접 만들었어. 나는 제빵을 즐겨. 이번 주 토요일에 도넛을 만들 예정이야.
B: 오, 나는 도넛 만드는 법을 배우고 싶어. 그건 어렵니?
G: 전혀 아니야. 네가 원한다면 우리 집에 와서 같이 해도 돼.
B: 고마워, 보라야. 내가 몇 시에 가야 해?
G: 2시에.
B: 좋아. 그때 보자.

※ 다음 우리말에 맞도록 대화를 영어로 쓰시오.

Listen & Speak 1 A

A: _____

B: _____

Listen & Speak 1 B

1. G: _____

   B: _____

   G: _____

   B: _____

2. G: _____

   B: _____

   G: _____

Listen & Speak 2 A

A: _____

G: _____

Listen & Speak 2 B

1. B: _____

   G: _____

   B: _____

   G: _____

2. G: _____

   B: _____

   G: _____

   B: _____

해석

G: 종이 고양이 만드는 법을 알고 있니?
B: 물론이지. 그건 쉬워.

1. G: 어제 유나의 바이올린 콘서트에 갔다고 들었어. 어땠니?
   B: 좋았어. 나도 언젠가 그녀처럼 바이올린을 연주할 수 있기를 바라.
   G: 나는 네가 바이올린 연주하는 법을 아는지 몰랐어.
   B: 할 수 있어, 그러나 아직 잘하지는 못해.
2. G: 이 사진들 좀 봐. 나는 이 채소를 직접 길렀어. 나는 내 자신의 정원이 있어.
   B: 멋지다! 네가 기르는 채소로 요리하는 법도 아니?
   G: 응, 할머니께서 내게 가르쳐 주셨어.

B: 너는 밤에 별을 보는 것을 즐기니?
G: 응, 나는 별을 보는 것을 아주 좋아해.

1. B: 유미야, 너는 책 읽는 것을 즐기니?
   G: 응, 나는 과학 책을 읽는 것을 좋아해. 너는 어때?
   B: 나도 책 읽는 것을 좋아해.
   G: 그럼 오늘 방과 후에 도서관 가자.
2. G: 민수야, 주말에 뭐 했니?
   B: 가족을 위해 아침을 만들었어.
   G: 너는 요리를 즐기니?
   B: 응, 나는 훌륭한 요리사야! 우리 가족은 내 요리를 좋아해.

3. B: _____

G: _____

B: _____

G: _____

3. B: 지윤아, 그거 예쁜 배낭이네! 어디서 샀어?

G: 언니가 내게 만들어 준 거야.

B: 와! 그녀는 정말 훌륭한 디자이너구나.

G: 응, 그래. 그리고 그녀는 옷 만드는 것도 즐겨.

Real-Life Zone A

B: _____

_____

G: _____

B: _____

G: _____

B: _____

G: _____

B: _____

G: _____

_____

B: _____

_____

B: 안녕, 케이트. 나는 나눔 오케스트라의 대표 하민이야. 우리 동아리에 관심을 가져줘서 고마워.

G: 안녕. 만나서 반가워.

B: 너는 바이올린을 연주하니? 언제 바이올린 연주를 시작했니?

G: 10살 때 바이올린을 연주하는 법을 배우기 시작했어.

B: 그룹에서 연주해 본 경험이 있니?

G: 응. 사실 나는 초등학교 때 오케스트라 단원이었어.

B: 좋아. 우리는 자원봉사로 아이들도 가르쳐. 다른 사람들을 가르치는 것을 즐기니?

G: 나는 다른 사람들을 가르친 경험이 없어. 그러나 나는 사람들과 일하는 것을 즐겨, 그래서 나는 해보고 싶어.

B: 좋아. 나는 우리가 함께 연주하며 좋은 시간을 보낼 것이라고 생각해. 나눔 오케스트라에 온 걸 환영해.

Wrap Up

B: _____

G: _____

_____

B: _____

G: _____

B: _____

G: _____

B: _____

B: 이 쿠키들은 정말 맛있어 보여. 네가 만들었니?

G: 응. 어제 내가 직접 만들었어. 나는 제빵을 즐겨. 이번 주 토요일에 도넛을 만들 예정이야.

B: 오, 나는 도넛 만드는 법을 배우고 싶어. 그건 어렵니?

G: 전혀 아니야. 네가 원한다면 우리 집에 와서 같이 해도 돼.

B: 고마워, 보라야. 내가 몇 시에 가야 해?

G: 2시에.

B: 좋아. 그때 보자.

※ 다음 우리말과 일치하도록 빈칸에 알맞은 것을 골라 쓰시오.

1 _____ _____ You _____ Our Club?
   A. Join   B. Don't   C. Why

2 _____ in club activities is a great _____ to enjoy your school _____ .
   A. life   B. participating   C. way

3 _____ about _____ a club?
   A. joining   B. how

4 Here _____ two club _____ _____ want students to _____ their clubs.
   A. join   B. who   C. are   D. leaders

5 _____ listen _____ _____ they say.
   A. what   B. to   C. let's

6 The Picasso _____ _____
   A. Club   B. Art

7 Hi! I am Sora Kang _____ the Picasso _____ _____ .
   A. Club   B. from   C. Art

8 _____ you can _____ _____ the name of our club, we _____ .
   A. paint   B. as   C. guess   D. from

9 We also do _____ from time _____ time.
   A. to   B. work   C. volunteer

10 _____ summer, our club members _____ _____ the "_____ Our Neighborhood" project.
   A. in   B. change   C. participated   D. last

11 On the _____ old walls of the buildings in our neighborhood, we painted birds _____ high in the sky and dolphins _____ over blue _____ .
   A. waves   B. dirty   C. flying   D. jumping

12 _____ a result, the old neighborhood changed _____ a _____ and beautiful _____ .
   A. bright   B. into   C. place   D. as

13 The _____ were happy _____ see our work and _____ us.
   A. thanked   B. to   C. neighbors

14 You _____ _____ _____ be a good painter.
   A. to   B. have   C. don't

15 _____ who likes to _____ can _____ .
   A. join   B. paint   C. anyone

1 우리 동아리에 가입하는 게 어때?

2 동아리 활동에 참여하는 것은 학교생활을 즐기는 좋은 방법이에요.

3 동아리에 가입하는 게 어떤가요?

4 여기 학생들이 그들의 동아리에 가입하기를 원하는 두 명의 동아리 대표가 있어요.

5 그들이 하는 말을 들어 봅시다.

6 피카소 미술 동아리

7 안녕하세요! 저는 피카소 미술 동아리의 강소라입니다.

8 우리 동아리의 이름에서 추측할 수 있듯이, 우리는 그림을 그립니다.

9 우리는 가끔 자원봉사도 합니다.

10 지난여름, 우리 동아리 회원들은 "우리 마을 바꾸기" 프로젝트에 참여했습니다.

11 우리 마을에 있는 건물의 더럽고 오래된 벽에 하늘 높이 나는 새들과 푸른 파도 위로 점프하는 돌고래들을 그렸습니다.

12 결과적으로, 오래된 마을은 밝고 아름다운 곳으로 바뀌었습니다.

13 이웃들은 우리의 작품을 보고 행복해 했고 고마워했습니다.

14 여러분은 그림을 잘 그릴 필요는 없습니다.

15 그림 그리는 것을 좋아하는 사람은 누구나 가입할 수 있습니다.

16 _____ and _____ a _____ of the Picasso Art Club.

    A. member   B. be   C. come

17 The _____ _____

    A. Orchestra   B. Boram

18 Hi! I am Minsu Jang, the _____ _____ the Boram _____ .

    A. Orchestra   B. of   C. leader

19 Did you see _____ students _____ music at the _____ _____ when you came to school today?

    A. gate   B. playing   C. main   D. several

20 We _____ _____ students.

    A. those   B. were

21 We _____ music _____ our friends _____ morning.

    A. every   B. for   C. play

22 You _____ to know _____ to play an instrument a _____ _____ to join our club.

    A. bit   B. how   C. need   D. little

23 But don't _____ _____ you don't _____ well.

    A. play   B. if   C. worry

24 We will _____ hard and _____ _____ together.

    A. better   B. get   C. practice

25 We also teach children how to play _____ _____ as a _____ to our _____ .

    A. community   B. service   C. instruments   D. musical

26 I am _____ an _____ boy to _____ the violin.

    A. how   B. teaching   C. eleven-year-old

27 _____ first, he did not know _____ to read a _____ .

    A. note   B. note   C. at

28 Now he _____ play a _____ _____ .

    A. song   B. simple   C. can

29 _____ him _____ the violin _____ me very happy.

    A. makes   B. play   C. hearing

30 _____ _____ our club, you can have an _____ to help _____ .

    A. joining   B. opportunity   C. others   D. by

31 _____ and _____ our _____ .

    A. club   B. join   C. come

32 We are _____ _____ you.

    A. for   B. waiting

---

16 와서 피카소 미술 동아리의 회원이 되세요.

17 보람 오케스트라

18 안녕하세요! 저는 보람 오케스트라의 회장 장민수입니다.

19 오늘 학교에 왔을 때 정문에서 음악을 연주하는 몇 명의 학생들을 보았습니까?

20 우리가 그 학생들이었습니다.

21 우리는 매일 아침 친구들을 위해 음악을 연주합니다.

22 우리 동아리에 가입하기 위해서는 악기 연주하는 법을 조금 알아야 합니다.

23 그러나 여러분이 연주를 잘 못한다고 해서 걱정하지 마세요.

24 우리는 열심히 연습하고 함께 좋아질 것입니다.

25 우리는 지역 사회에 대한 봉사로 아이들에게 악기를 연주하는 법도 가르칩니다.

26 저는 열한 살 소년에게 바이올린을 가르치고 있습니다.

27 처음에 그는 음표를 읽는 법을 알지 못했습니다.

28 이제는 간단한 노래도 연주할 수 있습니다.

29 그가 바이올린을 연주하는 걸 듣는 것은 저를 매우 행복하게 합니다.

30 우리 동아리에 가입함으로써, 여러분은 다른 사람들을 도울 수 있는 기회를 가질 수 있습니다.

31 와서 우리 동아리에 가입하세요.

32 우리는 여러분을 기다리고 있습니다.

※ 다음 우리말과 일치하도록 빈칸에 알맞은 말을 쓰시오.

1 _____ _____ _____ _____ Our Club?

2 _____ _____ _____ _____ is a great way _____ _____ your school life.

3 _____ _____ _____ a club?

4 _____ _____ two club leaders _____ _____ students _____ _____ their clubs.

5 _____ listen _____ _____ they say.

6 The Picasso _____ _____

7 Hi! I am Sora Kang _____ the Picasso _____ _____.

8 _____ you _____ _____ _____ the name of our club, we _____.

9 We also _____ _____ _____ _____ time _____ time.

10 _____ summer, our club members _____ _____ the "_____ Our _____" project.

11 _____ _____ _____ _____ _____ of the buildings in our neighborhood, we _____ birds _____ high in the sky and dolphins _____ _____ _____ _____.

12 _____ _____ _____, the old neighborhood _____ _____ a bright and _____ _____.

13 The neighbors _____ _____ _____ _____ our work and _____ us.

14 You _____ _____ _____ be a good _____.

15 _____ _____ _____ _____ paint can _____.

1 우리 동아리에 가입하는 게 어때?

2 동아리 활동에 참여하는 것은 학교생활을 즐기는 좋은 방법이에요.

3 동아리에 가입하는 게 어떤가요?

4 여기 학생들이 그들의 동아리에 가입하기를 원하는 두 명의 동아리 대표가 있어요.

5 그들이 하는 말을 들어 봅시다.

6 피카소 미술 동아리

7 안녕하세요! 저는 피카소 미술 동아리의 강소라입니다.

8 우리 동아리의 이름에서 추측할 수 있듯이, 우리는 그림을 그립니다.

9 우리는 가끔 자원봉사도 합니다.

10 지난여름, 우리 동아리 회원들은 "우리 마을 바꾸기" 프로젝트에 참여했습니다.

11 우리 마을에 있는 건물의 더럽고 오래된 벽에 하늘 높이 나는 새들과 푸른 파도 위로 점프하는 돌고래들을 그렸습니다.

12 결과적으로, 오래된 마을은 밝고 아름다운 곳으로 바뀌었습니다.

13 이웃들은 우리의 작품을 보고 행복해 했고 고마워했습니다.

14 여러분은 그림을 잘 그릴 필요는 없습니다.

15 그림 그리는 것을 좋아하는 사람은 누구나 가입할 수 있습니다.

16 _____ _____ _____ a member of the Picasso Art Club.

17 The Boram _____

18 Hi! I am Minsu Jang, _____ _____ _____ the Boram Orchestra.

19 Did you _____ several students _____ _____ at the _____ _____ when you _____ _____ today?

20 We _____ _____ students.

21 We _____ _____ _____ our friends every morning.

22 You need to know _____ _____ _____ an instrument _____ _____ _____ _____ _____ our club.

23 But _____ _____ _____ you _____ play well.

24 We will _____ _____ and _____ together.

25 We _____ _____ children _____ _____ play musical instruments _____ _____ _____ _____ our community.

26 I am _____ _____ _____ _____ _____ to play the violin.

27 _____ _____ , he did not know _____ _____ _____ _____ _____ .

28 Now he _____ _____ _____ _____ _____ .

29 _____ _____ _____ the violin makes me very _____ .

30 _____ _____ our club, you can _____ _____ _____ _____ _____ .

31 _____ _____ _____ our club.

32 We are _____ _____ you.

16 와서 피카소 미술 동아리의 회원이 되세요.

17 보람 오케스트라

18 안녕하세요! 저는 보람 오케스트라의 회장 장민수입니다.

19 오늘 학교에 왔을 때 정문에서 음악을 연주하는 몇 명의 학생들을 보았습니까?

20 우리가 그 학생들이었습니다.

21 우리는 매일 아침 친구들을 위해 음악을 연주합니다.

22 우리 동아리에 가입하기 위해서는 악기 연주하는 법을 조금 알아야 합니다.

23 그러나 여러분이 연주를 잘 못한다고 해서 걱정하지 마세요.

24 우리는 열심히 연습하고 함께 좋아질 것입니다.

25 우리는 지역 사회에 대한 봉사로 아이들에게 악기를 연주하는 법도 가르칩니다.

26 저는 열한 살 소년에게 바이올린을 가르치고 있습니다.

27 처음에 그는 음표를 읽는 법을 알지 못했습니다.

28 이제는 간단한 노래도 연주할 수 있습니다.

29 그가 바이올린을 연주하는 걸 듣는 것은 저를 매우 행복하게 합니다.

30 우리 동아리에 가입함으로써, 여러분은 다른 사람들을 도울 수 있는 기회를 가질 수 있습니다.

31 와서 우리 동아리에 가입하세요.

32 우리는 여러분을 기다리고 있습니다.

※ 다음 문장을 우리말로 쓰시오.

1 Why Don't You Join Our Club?

➡ _____

2 Participating in club activities is a great way to enjoy your school life.

➡ _____

3 How about joining a club?

➡ _____

4 Here are two club leaders who want students to join their clubs.

➡ _____

5 Let's listen to what they say.

➡ _____

6 The Picasso Art Club

➡ _____

7 Hi! I am Sora Kang from the Picasso Art Club.

➡ _____

8 As you can guess from the name of our club, we paint.

➡ _____

9 We also do volunteer work from time to time.

➡ _____

10 Last summer, our club members participated in the "Change Our Neighborhood" project.

➡ _____

11 On the dirty old walls of the buildings in our neighborhood, we painted birds flying high in the sky and dolphins jumping over blue waves.

➡ _____

12 As a result, the old neighborhood changed into a bright and beautiful place.

➡ _____

13 The neighbors were happy to see our work and thanked us.

➡ _____

14 You don't have to be a good painter.

➡ _____

15 Anyone who likes to paint can join.

➡ _____

16 Come and be a member of the Picasso Art Club.

➡ _____

17 The Boram Orchestra

➡ _____

18 Hi! I am Minsu Jang, the leader of the Boram Orchestra.

➡ _____

19 Did you see several students playing music at the main gate when you came to school today?

➡ _____

20 We were those students.

➡ _____

21 We play music for our friends every morning.

➡ _____

22 You need to know how to play an instrument a little bit to join our club.

➡ _____

23 But don't worry if you don't play well.

➡ _____

24 We will practice hard and get better together.

➡ _____

25 We also teach children how to play musical instruments as a service to our community.

➡ _____

26 I am teaching an eleven-year-old boy to play the violin.

➡ _____

27 At first, he did not know how to read a note.

➡ _____

28 Now he can play a simple song.

➡ _____

29 Hearing him play the violin makes me very happy.

➡ _____

30 By joining our club, you can have an opportunity to help others.

➡ _____

31 Come and join our club.

➡ _____

32 We are waiting for you.

➡ _____

※ 다음 괄호 안의 단어들을 우리말에 맞도록 바르게 배열하시오.

1 (Don't / Why / Join / You / Club? / Our)
➡ _____

2 (in / participating / activities / club / is / great / a / to / way / enjoy / your / life. / school)
➡ _____

3 (about / how / club? / a / joining)
➡ _____

4 (are / here / two / leaders / club / who / students / want / clubs. / their / join / to)
➡ _____

5 (listen / let's / what / to / say. / they)
➡ _____

6 (Picasso / Club / The / Art)
➡ _____

7 (hi! // am / I / Kang / Sora / from / Picasso / Club. / Art / the)
➡ _____

8 (you / as / guess / can / from / name / the / of / club, / our / paint. / we)
➡ _____

9 (also / do / we / work / volunteer / to / time / from / time.)
➡ _____

10 (summer, / last / club / our / members / in / participated / the / Our / "Change / project. / Neighborhood")
➡ _____

11 (the / on / old / dirty / walls / the / of / buildings / our / in / neighborhood, / painted / we / flying / birds / high / the / in / sky / and / dolphins / over / jumping / waves. / blue)
➡ _____

12 (a / as / result, / old / the / neighborhood / into / changed / a / beautiful / and / place. / bright)
➡ _____

13 (neighbors / the / happy / were / see / to / work / our / and / us. / thanked)
➡ _____

14 (don't / have / you / be / to / painter. / good / a)
➡ _____

15 (who / anyone / likes / to / join. / can / paint)
➡ _____

16 (and / come / be / member / a / of / the / Club. / Art / Picasso)
➡ _____

---

1 우리 동아리에 가입하는 게 어때?

2 동아리 활동에 참여하는 것은 학교생활을 즐기는 좋은 방법이 에요.

3 동아리에 가입하는 게 어떤가요?

4 여기 학생들이 그들의 동아리에 가입하기를 원하는 두 명의 동아리 대표가 있어요.

5 그들이 하는 말을 들어 봅시다.

6 피카소 미술 동아리

7 안녕하세요! 저는 피카소 미술 동아리의 강소라입니다.

8 우리 동아리의 이름에서 추측할 수 있듯이, 우리는 그림을 그립니다.

9 우리는 가끔 자원봉사도 합니다.

10 지난여름, 우리 동아리 회원들은 "우리 마을 바꾸기" 프로젝트에 참여했습니다.

11 우리 마을에 있는 건물의 더럽고 오래된 벽에 하늘 높이 나는 새들과 푸른 파도 위로 점프하는 돌고래들을 그렸습니다.

12 결과적으로, 오래된 마을은 밝고 아름다운 곳으로 바뀌었습니다.

13 이웃들은 우리의 작품을 보고 행복해 했고 고마워했습니다.

14 여러분은 그림을 잘 그릴 필요는 없습니다.

15 그림 그리는 것을 좋아하는 사람은 누구나 가입할 수 있습니다.

16 와서 피카소 미술 동아리의 회원이 되세요.

17 (Boram / The / Orchestra)

➡ _____

18 (hi! // am / I / Jang, / Minsu / leader / the / of / the / Orchestra. / Boram)

➡ _____

19 (you / did / several / see / students / playing / music / the / at / gate / main / when / you / to / came / today? / school)

➡ _____

_____

20 (were / students. / we / those)

➡ _____

21 (play / we / for / music / our / morning. / every / friends)

➡ _____

22 (need / you / know / to / how / play / to / an / instrument / little / a / bit / join / to / club. / our)

➡ _____

23 (don't / but / worry / you / if / play / well. / don't)

➡ _____

24 (will / practice / we / hard / and / together. / better / get)

➡ _____

25 (we / teach / also / children / to / how / play / instruments / musical / as / service / a / to / coummunity. / our)

➡ _____

_____

26 (I / teaching / am / an / boy / eleven-year-old / play / violin. / the / to)

➡ _____

27 (first, / at / did / he / know / not / to / how / read / note. / a)

➡ _____

28 (he / now / play / can / song. / simple / a)

➡ _____

29 (him / hearing / play / violin / the / me / makes / happy. / very)

➡ _____

30 (joining / by / club, / our / can / you / have / opportunity / an / others. / help / to)

➡ _____

31 (join / and / come / club. / our)

➡ _____

32 (are / we / waiting / you. / for)

➡ _____

17 보람 오케스트라

18 안녕하세요! 저는 보람 오케스트라의 회장 장민수입니다.

19 오늘 학교에 왔을 때 정문에서 음악을 연주하는 몇 명의 학생들을 보았습니까?

20 우리가 그 학생들이었습니다.

21 우리는 매일 아침 친구들을 위해 음악을 연주합니다.

22 우리 동아리에 가입하기 위해서는 악기 연주하는 법을 조금 알아야 합니다.

23 그러나 여러분이 연주를 잘 못한다고 해서 걱정하지 마세요.

24 우리는 열심히 연습하고 함께 좋아질 것입니다.

25 우리는 지역 사회에 대한 봉사로 아이들에게 악기를 연주하는 법도 가르칩니다.

26 저는 열한 살 소년에게 바이올린을 가르치고 있습니다.

27 처음에 그는 음표를 읽는 법을 알지 못했습니다.

28 이제는 간단한 노래도 연주할 수 있습니다.

29 그가 바이올린을 연주하는 걸 듣는 것은 저를 매우 행복하게 합니다.

30 우리 동아리에 가입함으로써, 여러분은 다른 사람들을 도울 수 있는 기회를 가질 수 있습니다.

31 와서 우리 동아리에 가입하세요.

32 우리는 여러분을 기다리고 있습니다.

※ 다음 우리말을 영어로 쓰시오.

1 우리 동아리에 가입하는 게 어때?

➡ _____

2 동아리 활동에 참여하는 것은 학교생활을 즐기는 좋은 방법이에요.

➡ _____

3 동아리에 가입하는 게 어떤가요?

➡ _____

4 여기 학생들이 그들의 동아리에 가입하기를 원하는 두 명의 동아리 대표가 있어요.

➡ _____

5 그들이 하는 말을 들어 봅시다.

➡ _____

6 피카소 미술 동아리

➡ _____

7 안녕하세요! 저는 피카소 미술 동아리의 강소라입니다.

➡ _____

8 우리 동아리의 이름에서 추측할 수 있듯이, 우리는 그림을 그립니다.

➡ _____

9 우리는 가끔 자원봉사도 합니다.

➡ _____

10 지난여름, 우리 동아리 회원들은 "우리 마을 바꾸기" 프로젝트에 참여했습니다.

➡ _____

11 우리 마을에 있는 건물의 더럽고 오래된 벽에 하늘 높이 나는 새들과 푸른 파도 위로 점프하는 돌고래들을 그렸습니다.

➡ _____

_____

12 결과적으로, 오래된 마을은 밝고 아름다운 곳으로 바뀌었습니다.

➡ _____

13 이웃들은 우리의 작품을 보고 행복해 했고 고마워했습니다.

➡ _____

14 여러분은 그림을 잘 그릴 필요는 없습니다.

➡ _____

15 그림 그리는 것을 좋아하는 사람은 누구나 가입할 수 있습니다.

➡ _____

16 와서 피카소 미술 동아리의 회원이 되세요.

➡ _____

17 보람 오케스트라

➡ _____

18 안녕하세요! 저는 보람 오케스트라의 회장 장민수입니다.

➡ _____

19 오늘 학교에 왔을 때 정문에서 음악을 연주하는 몇 명의 학생들을 보았습니까?

➡ _____

20 우리가 그 학생들이었습니다.

➡ _____

21 우리는 매일 아침 친구들을 위해 음악을 연주합니다.

➡ _____

22 우리 동아리에 가입하기 위해서는 악기 연주하는 법을 조금 알아야 합니다.

➡ _____

23 그러나 여러분이 연주를 잘 못한다고 해서 걱정하지 마세요.

➡ _____

24 우리는 열심히 연습하고 함께 좋아질 것입니다.

➡ _____

25 우리는 지역 사회에 대한 봉사로 아이들에게 악기를 연주하는 법도 가르칩니다.

➡ _____

26 저는 열한 살 소년에게 바이올린을 가르치고 있습니다.

➡ _____

27 처음에 그는 음표를 읽는 법을 알지 못했습니다.

➡ _____

28 이제는 간단한 노래도 연주할 수 있습니다.

➡ _____

29 그가 바이올린을 연주하는 걸 듣는 것은 저를 매우 행복하게 합니다.

➡ _____

30 우리 동아리에 가입함으로써, 여러분은 다른 사람들을 도울 수 있는 기회를 가질 수 있습니다.

➡ _____

31 와서 우리 동아리에 가입하세요.

➡ _____

32 우리는 여러분을 기다리고 있습니다.

➡ _____

※ 다음 우리말과 일치하도록 빈칸에 알맞은 말을 쓰시오.

After You Read

1. Today, Minsu, the _____ of the Boram Orchestra, came to _____ _____.

2. He _____ _____ me _____ _____ _____ the violin last month.

3. At first, I didn't know _____ _____ _____ _____ _____.

4. I _____ _____ _____ the Boram Orchestra and play the violin at the _____ _____ when I become a middle school student.

Writing Workshop

1. Boram _____ _____ _____ Membership Form

2. • _____ of Club: FC Boram

3. • _____ _____ : Sunho Park

4. • Why You Want _____ _____ the Club: I love soccer and _____ _____ _____ join FC Boram.

5. I am _____ _____ _____ the ball and _____ fast.

6. However, I don't know _____ _____ _____ the ball, _____ I want to learn how to do that.

7. I want to _____ a soccer player _____ can make wonderful heading goals.

8. • Your _____ : If I _____ this club, I will _____ very _____ and become a good team player!

Real Life Zone

1. I _____ _____ to introduce our new orchestra member, Kate.

2. She knows _____ _____ _____ the violin.

3. She also has _____ _____ experience _____ in a group.

4. And she said she _____ _____ with people.

5. _____ all _____ her _____ the Nanum Orchestra.

1. 오늘, 보람 오케스트라의 대표인 민수가 지역 주민회관에 왔다.
2. 그는 지난달에 바이올린을 연주하는 법을 나에게 가르쳐 주기 시작했다.
3. 처음에는 나는 하나의 음표도 읽는 법을 알지 못했다.
4. 나는 보람 오케스트라에 가입하여, 내가 중학생이 될 때 정문에서 바이올린을 연주하기를 희망한다.

1. 보람중학교 동아리 지원서
2. 동아리 이름: FC Boram
3. 학생 이름: 박순호
4. 가입을 원하는 이유: 나는 축구를 사랑하고 FC Boram에 가입하고 싶다.
5. 나는 공을 패스하는 것을 잘하고 빨리 달린다.
6. 그러나, 나는 공을 헤딩하는 법을 모르기 때문에 그것을 하는 법을 배우고 싶다.
7. 나는 멋진 헤딩 골을 만들 수 있는 축구 선수가 되기를 원한다.
8. 당신의 목표: 만약 내가 이 동아리에 가입하면, 나는 매우 열심히 연습해서 좋은 팀 플레이어가 될 것이다.

1. 나는 우리의 새로운 오케스트라 회원인 케이트를 소개하고 싶어.
2. 그녀는 바이올린을 연주하는 법을 알아.
3. 그녀는 또한 그룹에서 연주해 본 경험이 많아.
4. 그리고 그녀는 사람들과 일하는 것을 즐긴다고 말했어.
5. 모두 그녀가 나눔 오케스트라에 온 걸 환영하자.

※ 다음 우리말을 영어로 쓰시오.

After You Read

1. 오늘, 보람 오케스트라의 대표인 민수가 지역 주민회관에 왔다.
   ➡ _____

2. 그는 지난달에 바이올린을 연주하는 법을 나에게 가르쳐 주기 시작했다.
   ➡ _____

3. 처음에는 나는 하나의 음표도 읽는 법을 알지 못했다.
   ➡ _____

4. 나는 보람 오케스트라에 가입하여, 내가 중학생이 될 때 정문에서 바이올린을 연주하기를 희망한다.
   ➡ _____
   _____

Writing Workshop

1. 보람중학교 동아리 지원서
   ➡ _____

2. 동아리 이름: FC Boram
   ➡ _____

3. 학생 이름: 박순호
   ➡ _____

4. 가입을 원하는 이유: 나는 축구를 사랑하고 FC Boram에 가입하고 싶다.
   ➡ _____

5. 나는 공을 패스하는 것을 잘하고 빨리 달린다.
   ➡ _____

6. 그러나, 나는 공을 헤딩하는 법을 모르기 때문에 그것을 하는 법을 배우고 싶다.
   ➡ _____

7. 나는 멋진 헤딩 골을 만들 수 있는 축구 선수가 되기를 원한다.
   ➡ _____

8. 당신의 목표: 만약 내가 이 동아리에 가입하면, 나는 매우 열심히 연습해서 좋은 팀 플레이어가 될 것이다.
   ➡ _____

Real Life Zone

1. 나는 우리의 새로운 오케스트라 회원인 케이트를 소개하고 싶어.
   ➡ _____

2. 그녀는 바이올린을 연주하는 법을 알아.
   ➡ _____

3. 그녀는 또한 그룹에서 연주해 본 경험이 많아.
   ➡ _____

4. 그리고 그녀는 사람들과 일하는 것을 즐긴다고 말했어.
   ➡ _____

5. 모두 그녀가 나눔 오케스트라에 온 걸 환영하자.
   ➡ _____

※ 다음 영어를 우리말로 쓰시오.

01 besides _____

02 correct _____

03 reply _____

04 ever _____

05 character _____

06 rule _____

07 scene _____

08 friendly _____

09 happiness _____

10 seagull _____

11 item _____

12 noisy _____

13 support _____

14 title _____

15 comfortable _____

16 join _____

17 such _____

18 throne _____

19 journey _____

20 nearby _____

21 foreign _____

22 separate _____

23 review _____

24 school cafeteria _____

25 weather _____

26 cub _____

27 disappointed _____

28 nervous _____

29 foreigner _____

30 opinion _____

31 regret _____

32 scary _____

33 teenager _____

34 wide _____

35 be worried about _____

36 get better _____

37 look good (on 사람) _____

38 take away _____

39 be scared of _____

40 look+like+명사 _____

41 be good at _____

42 by the way _____

43 What if+주어+동사 ~? _____

Step2

※ 다음 우리말을 영어로 쓰시오.

01	불안한	
02	대답하다	
03	헤어지다	
04	날씨	
05	장면	
06	(곰, 사자 등의) 새끼	
07	감상문, 논평	
08	외국의	
09	여행	
10	너무나 ～한, 그러한	
11	십 대	
12	지지; 지지하다	
13	친절한	
14	게다가	
15	행복	
16	품목	
17	등장인물	
18	갈매기	
19	함께 하다	
20	근처에	
21	의견	

22	후회하다	
23	편안한	
24	시끄러운	
25	왕좌, 왕위	
26	지배하다	
27	실망한, 기대에 어긋난	
28	무서운	
29	외국인	
30	학교 식당	
31	제목	
32	넓은	
33	올바른	
34	언제든, 한 번이라도	
35	발발하다	
36	더 이상 ～않다	
37	그런데	
38	～하는 것을 노력하다	
39	～에 대해 걱정하다	
40	～처럼 보이다	
41	～을 두려워하다	
42	(병·상황 등이) 나아지다	
43	～에 들어가다	

※ 다음 영영풀이에 알맞은 단어를 <보기>에서 골라 쓴 후, 우리말 뜻을 쓰시오.

1 _____ : to move apart: _____

2 _____ : a trip from one place to another: _____

3 _____ : the feeling of pleasure: _____

4 _____ : used to give an additional reason for something: _____

5 _____ : making a lot of loud noise: _____

6 _____ : a person in a film, book, or play: _____

7 _____ : to be in control of an area and its people: _____

8 _____ : the young of a bear, lion or other mammals: _____

9 _____ : from a country other than one's own: _____

10 _____ : to say or write something in response to something: _____

11 _____ : a person between the ages of thirteen and nineteen: _____

12 _____ : the name of a book, film, or other artistic work: _____

13 _____ : a bird with white or gray feathers that lives near the sea: _____

14 _____ : worried and anxious about something that is happening or might happen:

_____

15 _____ : help, encouragement, or comfort given to someone during a difficult or

unhappy time: _____

16 _____ : a critical comment in a newspaper that gives an opinion about a new

book or film: _____

보기	title	separate	reply	character
	journey	cub	besides	happiness
	review	rule	nervous	seagull
	noisy	support	teenager	foreign

※ 다음 우리말과 일치하도록 빈칸에 알맞은 말을 쓰시오.

Listen & Speak 1 A

B: I'm _____ _____ the math test.

W: _____ _____ . You'll _____ _____ .

B: 저는 수학 시험이 걱정돼요.
W: 걱정하지 마. 넌 잘할 거야.

Listen & Speak 1 B

1. B: _____ _____ _____ any _____ _____ for tomorrow?

   G: I'm _____ _____ Jejudo in the morning. But I'm _____ _____ the weather.

   B: _____ _____ . It _____ _____ on Jejudo tomorrow.

   G: Oh, that's _____ _____ _____ .

2. B: Jina, _____ you _____ _____ your house first?

   G: Why? _____ _____ ?

   B: I'm _____ _____ your dog.

   G: Don't worry. He's a _____ dog. He _____ _____ _____ _____ he's so big.

1. B: 내일 특별한 계획 있니?
   G: 아침에 제주도에 갈 거야. 그런데 날씨가 걱정돼.
   B: 걱정하지 마. 내일 제주도에는 비가 내리지 않을 거야.
   G: 오, 반가운 소리네.

2. B: 진아야, 네가 먼저 집에 들어갈 수 있어?
   G: 왜? 무슨 일 있니?
   B: 난 네 개가 무서워.
   G: 걱정하지 마. 친절한 개야. 너무 커서 무섭게 보일 뿐이야.

Listen & Speak 1 C

1. A: _____ _____ _____ _____ your health.

   B: _____ _____ . I'm _____ _____ the doctor tomorrow.

2. A: _____ _____ the speech contest.

   B: Don't _____ . _____ _____ _____ .

3. A: _____ _____ _____ _____ _____ _____ .

   B: Don't _____ . You'll _____ _____ you _____ _____ _____ .

1. A: 나는 네 건강이 걱정돼.
   B: 걱정하지 마. 내일 진찰받으러 병원에 갈 거야.

2. A: 나는 말하기 대회가 걱정돼.
   B: 걱정하지 마. 넌 잘할 거야.

3. A: 나는 내 미래가 걱정돼.
   B: 걱정하지 마. 네가 하고 싶은 것을 발견할 거야.

Listen & Speak 2 A

B: _____ _____ _____ _____ _____ _____ these sunglasses?

G: They're cool! You _____ _____ a movie star.

B: 이 선글라스에 대해 어떻게 생각해?
G: 멋져! 너는 영화배우 같아.

Listen & Speak 2 B

1. **G:** _____ you _____ the movie, *The Daughter*?

   B: Yes, I _____ it _____ _____.

   G: _____ _____ _____ _____ _____ _____ _____?

   B: I was _____. It _____ very _____.

2. **B:** _____ _____ _____ _____ _____ our school cafeteria food?

   G: I _____ the cafeteria food is _____.

   B: _____ do you think is the _____ _____?

   G: I _____ the Gimbap _____ _____.

3. **G:** What _____ _____ _____ _____ this painting?

   B: It _____ _____. I like the colors.

   G: I'm _____ _____ you like it. I _____ it _____.

Listen & Speak 2 C

1. **A:** _____ do you _____ _____ my bike?

   B: It _____ _____ and _____.

2. **A:** _____ _____ _____ _____ of these shoes?

   B: They _____ _____ _____ _____.

Real-Life Zone

G: I saw you with someone _____ _____ _____ a foreigner yesterday.

B: Yes. We _____ lunch together.

G: You _____ _____ you _____ _____ a good time.

B: We _____. We _____ _____ _____ _____ a month for lunch.

G: I _____ I _____ _____ more _____ talking with a foreigner.

B: I _____ _____ _____ _____ in English before, but not _____.

G: I _____ really _____ when I _____ _____ _____ in English.

B: Well, the first time is _____ _____. After that, it _____ _____ and _____.

G: _____ _____ _____ think _____ me joining _____ _____ you for lunch?

B: That's a _____ _____.

---

1. G: 너 영화 '딸' 봤니?
   B: 응, 지난 토요일에 봤어.
   G: 어떻게 생각했어?
   B: 나는 실망했어. 별로 좋지 않았어.

2. B: 학교 식당 음식에 대해 어떻게 생각해?
   G: 식당 음식이 맛있다고 생각해.
   B: 최고의 품목이 뭐라고 생각하니?
   G: 나는 김밥을 제일 좋아해.

3. G: 이 그림에 대해 어떻게 생각해?
   B: 아주 멋있어. 나는 색이 마음에 들어.
   G: 네가 좋아하니 기뻐. 내가 직접 그렸어.

1. A: 내 자전거에 대해 어떻게 생각해?
   B: 가볍고 빨라 보여.

2. A: 이 신발에 대해 어떻게 생각해?
   B: 너에게 잘 어울려.

G: 나는 어제 네가 외국인처럼 보이는 누군가와 있는 것을 봤어.
B: 응. 우리는 점심을 같이 먹었어.
G: 너희들은 좋은 시간을 보내고 있는 것처럼 보였어.
B: 그랬어. 우리는 한 달에 두 번 만나서 점심을 먹으려고 해.
G: 나는 외국인과 더 편하게 이야기할 수 있으면 좋을 텐데.
B: 나는 전에는 영어로 말하는 것에 대해 걱정했었지만, 더 이상은 아니야.
G: 영어로 말하려고 할 때 정말 불안해.
B: 음, 처음이 가장 힘들지. 그 후에 점점 쉬워져.
G: 내가 너희 둘과 함께 점심 먹는 거 어떻게 생각해?
B: 좋은 생각이야.

※ 다음 우리말에 맞도록 대화를 영어로 쓰시오.

Listen & Speak 1 A

B: _____

W: _____

B: 저는 수학 시험이 걱정돼요.
W: 걱정하지 마. 넌 잘할 거야.

Listen & Speak 1 B

1. B: _____

   G: _____

   B: _____

   G: _____

2. B: _____

   G: _____

   B: _____

   G: _____

1. B: 내일 특별한 계획 있니?
   G: 아침에 제주도에 갈 거야. 그런데 날씨가 걱정돼.
   B: 걱정하지 마. 내일 제주도에는 비가 내리지 않을 거야.
   G: 오, 반가운 소리네.

2. B: 진아야, 네가 먼저 집에 들어갈 수 있어?
   G: 왜? 무슨 일 있니?
   B: 난 네 개가 무서워.
   G: 걱정하지 마. 친절한 개야. 너무 커서 무섭게 보일 뿐이야.

Listen & Speak 1 C

1. A: _____

   B: _____

2. A: _____

   B: _____

3. A: _____

   B: _____

1. A: 나는 네 건강이 걱정돼.
   B: 걱정하지 마. 내일 진찰받으러 병원에 갈 거야.

2. A: 나는 말하기 대회가 걱정돼.
   B: 걱정하지 마. 넌 잘할 거야.

3. A: 나는 내 미래가 걱정돼.
   B: 걱정하지 마. 네가 하고 싶은 것을 발견할 거야.

Listen & Speak 2 A

B: _____

G: _____

B: 이 선글라스에 대해 어떻게 생각해?
G: 멋져! 너는 영화배우 같아.

Listen & Speak 2 B

1. G: _____

   B: _____

   G: _____

   B: _____

2. B: _____

   G: _____

   B: _____

   G: _____

3. G: _____

   B: _____

   G: _____

Listen & Speak 2 C

1. A: _____

   B: _____

2. A: _____

   B: _____

Real-Life Zone

G: _____

B: _____

G: _____

B: _____

G: _____

B: _____

G: _____

B: _____

G: _____

B: _____

1. G: 너 영화 '딸' 봤니?
   B: 응, 지난 토요일에 봤어.
   G: 어떻게 생각했어?
   B: 나는 실망했어. 별로 좋지 않았어.

2. B: 학교 식당 음식에 대해 어떻게 생
      각해?
   G: 식당 음식이 맛있다고 생각해.
   B: 최고의 품목이 뭐라고 생각하니?
   G: 나는 김밥을 제일 좋아해.

3. G: 이 그림에 대해 어떻게 생각해?
   B: 아주 멋있어. 나는 색이 마음에
      들어.
   G: 네가 좋아하니 기뻐. 내가 직접
      그렸어.

1. A: 내 자전거에 대해 어떻게 생각해?
   B: 가볍고 빨라 보여.

2. A: 이 신발에 대해 어떻게 생각해?
   B: 너에게 잘 어울려.

G: 나는 어제 네가 외국인처럼 보이는
   누군가와 있는 것을 봤어.
B: 응. 우리는 점심을 같이 먹었어.
G: 너희들은 좋은 시간을 보내고 있는
   것처럼 보였어.
B: 그랬어. 우리는 한 달에 두 번 만나
   서 점심을 먹으려고 해.
G: 나는 외국인과 더 편하게 이야기할
   수 있으면 좋을 텐데.
B: 나는 전에는 영어로 말하는 것에 대
   해 걱정했지만, 더 이상은 아니야.
G: 영어로 말하려고 할 때 정말 불안해.
B: 음, 처음이 가장 힘들지. 그 후에 점
   점 쉬워져.
G: 내가 너희 둘과 함께 점심 먹는 거
   어떻게 생각해?
B: 좋은 생각이야.

※ 다음 우리말과 일치하도록 빈칸에 알맞은 것을 골라 쓰시오.

1 The _____ _____

A. Brothers   B. Two

2 Two brothers _____ _____ a _____.

A. went   B. journey   C. on

3 They _____ a rock in _____ _____ a forest.

A. front   B. found   C. of

4 It _____, "Go _____ the forest and swim _____ the river.

A. said   B. across   C. into

5 There you will _____ a bear and _____ _____.

A. her   B. find   C. cubs

6 _____ the bear cubs and _____ _____ the mountain.

A. run   B. take   C. up

7 There you will _____ _____."

A. happiness   B. find

8 The younger brother said, "Let's _____ and _____ happiness _____."

A. find   B. go   C. together

9 "No," said the older brother, "_____ _____ we know this is _____?

A. how   B. can   C. true

10 _____ _____ the river is too _____?

A. if   B. wide   C. what

11 _____, will it be easy to take the cubs _____ _____ their mother?

A. from   B. away   C. besides

12 _____ of _____ happiness, we can be _____!"

A. finding   B. killed   C. Instead

13 The younger brother _____, "How can we know _____ we don't _____?"

A. if   B. replied   C. try

14 They separated, and they both _____ their _____ _____.

A. way   B. went   C. own

15 The younger brother _____ _____ the forest and _____ _____ the river.

A. across   B. into   C. swam   D. went

16 _____ _____ the bear.

A. was   B. there

---

1 두 형제

2 두 형제는 여정을 떠났다.

3 그들은 숲 앞에서 바위를 발견했다.

4 거기에 쓰여 있었다. "숲에 들어가 강을 헤엄쳐 건너시오.

5 당신은 거기에서 곰과 새끼들을 발견할 것입니다.

6 곰 새끼들을 데리고 산 위로 뛰어 올라가시오.

7 거기에서 당신은 행복을 찾을 수 있을 것입니다."

8 동생이 말했다. "함께 가서 행복을 찾자."

9 "싫어." 형은 말했다. "이것이 사실인지 우리가 어떻게 알 수 있어?

10 강이 너무 넓으면 어쩌지?

11 게다가, 곰 새끼들을 엄마에게서 빼앗는 것이 쉬울까?

12 행복을 찾는 대신에, 우리는 죽을 수 있어!"

13 동생은 대답했다. "우리가 시도하지 않으면 어떻게 알 수 있어?"

14 그들은 헤어졌고, 둘 다 자신의 길을 갔다.

15 동생은 숲에 들어가서 강을 헤엄쳐 건넜다.

16 곰이 있었다.

17 She _____ _____ .

A. sleeping   B. was

17 그녀는 자고 있었다.

18 He _____ her cubs and _____ _____ the mountain.

A. ran   B. took   C. up

18 그는 새끼들을 데리고 산을 뛰어 올라갔다.

19 When he _____ the top, some people _____ him to their city and _____ him their king.

A. made   B. took   C. reached

19 그가 정상에 도착했을 때, 어떤 사람들이 그를 자기들 도시로 데려가서 그들의 왕으로 만들었다.

20 There he _____ _____ a king _____ five years.

A. as   B. for   C. lived

20 그곳에서 그는 5년간 왕으로 살았다.

21 Then a war _____ _____ , and he _____ his throne.

A. out   B. lost   C. broke

21 그런 다음 전쟁이 일어났고, 그는 왕좌를 잃었다.

22 He was _____ the _____ again.

A. on   B. road

22 그는 다시 길바닥에 나앉았다.

23 _____ day, the two brothers _____ again and talked about their lives _____ the _____ five years.

A. met   B. last   C. for   D. one

23 어느 날, 두 형제는 다시 만났고 지난 5년 동안의 그들의 삶에 대해 이야기했다.

24 The _____ brother said, "I was _____ .

A. right   B. older

24 형은 말했다. "내가 옳았어.

25 I _____ _____ quietly and _____ .

A. lived   B. have   C. well

25 나는 조용히 잘 살았어.

26 You were _____ a king, but you have _____ a _____ of trouble."

A. had   B. once   C. lot

26 너는 한때 왕이었지만 많은 어려움을 겪었지."

27 The _____ brother answered, "I don't _____ my _____ .

A. regret   B. choice   C. younger

27 동생은 대답했다. "나는 내 선택을 후회하지 않아.

28 I may have _____ now, but I will always have _____ _____ ."

A. something   B. remember   C. nothing   D. to

28 나는 지금 아무것도 없지만 언제까지나 기억할 어떤 것이 있어."

※ 다음 우리말과 일치하도록 빈칸에 알맞은 말을 쓰시오.

1 The _____ _____

2 Two brothers _____ _____ a _____.

3 They _____ a rock _____ _____ _____ a forest.

4 It _____, "_____ _____ the forest and _____ _____ the river.

5 There you _____ _____ a bear and _____ _____.

6 _____ the bear cubs and _____ _____ the mountain.

7 There you _____ _____ _____."

8 The younger brother said, "_____ _____ _____ _____ _____ _____."

9 "No," said the _____ _____, "_____ _____ _____ this is _____?

10 _____ _____ the river is _____ _____?

11 _____, will it be _____ _____ _____ the cubs _____ _____ their mother?

12 _____ _____ _____ happiness, we can _____ _____!"

13 The younger brother _____, "_____ can we know _____ we _____ _____?"

14 They _____, and they _____ _____ _____ _____.

15 The younger brother _____ _____ the forest and _____ _____ the river.

16 _____ _____ the bear.

1 두 형제

2 두 형제는 여정을 떠났다.

3 그들은 숲 앞에서 바위를 발견했다.

4 거기에 쓰여 있었다. "숲에 들어가 강을 헤엄쳐 건너시오.

5 당신은 거기에서 곰과 새끼들을 발견할 것입니다.

6 곰 새끼들을 데리고 산 위로 뛰어 올라가시오.

7 거기에서 당신은 행복을 찾을 수 있을 것입니다."

8 동생이 말했다. "함께 가서 행복을 찾자."

9 "싫어." 형은 말했다. "이것이 사실인지 우리가 어떻게 알 수 있어?

10 강이 너무 넓으면 어쩌지?

11 게다가, 곰 새끼들을 엄마에게서 빼앗는 것이 쉬울까?

12 행복을 찾는 대신에, 우리는 죽을 수 있어!"

13 동생은 대답했다. "우리가 시도하지 않으면 어떻게 알 수 있어?"

14 그들은 헤어졌고, 둘 다 자신의 길을 갔다.

15 동생은 숲에 들어가서 강을 헤엄쳐 건넜다.

16 곰이 있었다.

17 She _____ _____ .

18 He _____ _____ _____ and _____ _____ the mountain.

19 When he _____ _____ _____ , some people _____ _____ _____ their city and _____ him their king.

20 There he _____ _____ _____ _____ _____ five years.

21 Then a war _____ _____ , and he _____ _____ _____ .

22 He _____ _____ _____ _____ again.

23 _____ _____ , the two brothers met again and _____ _____ their _____ _____ _____ _____ five years.

24 The older brother said, "_____ _____ _____ .

25 I _____ _____ _____ and _____ .

26 You were _____ a king, but you _____ _____ _____ _____ _____ _____ ."

27 The _____ _____ answered, "I don't _____ _____ _____ .

28 I may have _____ now, but I _____ _____ _____ _____ _____ _____ ."

---

17 그녀는 자고 있었다.

18 그는 새끼들을 데리고 산을 뛰어 올라갔다.

19 그가 정상에 도착했을 때, 어떤 사람들이 그를 자기들 도시로 데려가서 그들의 왕으로 만들었다.

20 그곳에서 그는 5년간 왕으로 살았다.

21 그런 다음 전쟁이 일어났고, 그는 왕좌를 잃었다.

22 그는 다시 길바닥에 나앉았다.

23 어느 날, 두 형제는 다시 만났고 지난 5년 동안의 그들의 삶에 대해 이야기했다.

24 형은 말했다. "내가 옳았어.

25 나는 조용히 잘 살았어.

26 너는 한때 왕이었지만 많은 어려움을 겪었지."

27 동생은 대답했다. "나는 내 선택을 후회하지 않아.

28 나는 지금 아무것도 없지만 언제까지나 기억할 어떤 것이 있어."

※ 다음 문장을 우리말로 쓰시오.

1 The Two Brothers

➡ _____

2 Two brothers went on a journey.

➡ _____

3 They found a rock in front of a forest.

➡ _____

4 It said, "Go into the forest and swim across the river.

➡ _____

5 There you will find a bear and her cubs.

➡ _____

6 Take the bear cubs and run up the mountain.

➡ _____

7 There you will find happiness."

➡ _____

8 The younger brother said, "Let's go and find happiness together."

➡ _____

9 "No," said the older brother, "How can we know this is true?

➡ _____

10 What if the river is too wide?

➡ _____

11 Besides, will it be easy to take the cubs away from their mother?

➡ _____

12 Instead of finding happiness, we can be killed!"

➡ _____

13 The younger brother replied, "How can we know if we don't try?"

➡ _____

14 They separated, and they both went their own way.

➡ _____

15 The younger brother went into the forest and swam across the river.

➡ _____

16 There was the bear.

➡ _____

17 She was sleeping.

➡ _____

18 He took her cubs and ran up the mountain.

➡ _____

19 When he reached the top, some people took him to their city and made him their king.

➡ _____

20 There he lived as a king for five years.

➡ _____

21 Then a war broke out, and he lost his throne.

➡ _____

22 He was on the road again.

➡ _____

23 One day, the two brothers met again and talked about their lives for the last five years.

➡ _____

24 The older brother said, "I was right.

➡ _____

25 I have lived quietly and well.

➡ _____

26 You were once a king, but you have had a lot of trouble."

➡ _____

27 The younger brother answered, "I don't regret my choice.

➡ _____

28 I may have nothing now, but I will always have something to remember."

➡ _____

※ 다음 괄호 안의 단어들을 우리말에 맞도록 바르게 배열하시오.

1 (Brothers / Two / The)
➡ _____

2 (brothers / two / on / a / journey. / went)
➡ _____

3 (found / they / rock / a / front / in / forest. / a / of)
➡ _____

4 (said, / it / into / "go / forest / the / and / across / swim / river. / the)
➡ _____

5 (you / there / find / will / bear / a / cubs. / her / and)
➡ _____

6 (the / take / cubs / bear / and / up / mountain. / run / the)
➡ _____

7 (you / will / there / happiness." / find)
➡ _____

8 (younger / the / said, /. brother / go / "let's / find / and / together." / happiness)
➡ _____

9 ("no," / the / said / brother, / older / "how / we / know / can / true? / is / this)
➡ _____

10 (if / what / river / the / wide? / too / is)
➡ _____

11 (besides, / it / will / easy / be / take / to / cubs / the / from / away / mother? / their)
➡ _____

12 (of / instead / happiness, / finding / can / we / killed!" / be)
➡ _____

13 (younger / the / replied, / brother / "how / we / can / if / know / we / try?" / don't)
➡ _____

14 (separated, / they / and / both / they / their / went / way. / own)
➡ _____

15 (younger / the / went / brother / into / forest / the / swam / and / river. / the / across)
➡ _____

16 (was / bear. / there / the)
➡ _____

1	두 형제
2	두 형제는 여정을 떠났다.
3	그들은 숲 앞에서 바위를 발견했다.
4	거기에 쓰여 있었다. "숲에 들어가 강을 헤엄쳐 건너시오.
5	당신은 거기에서 곰과 새끼들을 발견할 것입니다.
6	곰 새끼들을 데리고 산 위로 뛰어 올라가시오.
7	거기에서 당신은 행복을 찾을 수 있을 것입니다."
8	동생이 말했다. "함께 가서 행복을 찾자."
9	"싫어." 형은 말했다. "이것이 사실인지 우리가 어떻게 알 수 있어?
10	강이 너무 넓으면 어쩌지?
11	게다가, 곰 새끼들을 엄마에게서 빼앗는 것이 쉬울까?
12	행복을 찾는 대신에, 우리는 죽을 수 있어!"
13	동생은 대답했다. "우리가 시도하지 않으면 어떻게 알 수 있어?"
14	그들은 헤어졌고, 둘 다 자신의 길을 갔다.
15	동생은 숲에 들어가서 강을 헤엄쳐 건넜다.
16	곰이 있었다.

17 (was / she / sleeping.)

➡ _____

18 (took / he / cubs / her / and / up / ran / mountain. / the)

➡ _____

19 (he / when / reached / top, / the / people / some / him / took / their / to / city / and / made / king. / him / their)

➡ _____

_____

20 (he / there / lived / a / as / king / years. / five / for)

➡ _____

21 (a / then / broke / war / out, / and / lost / he / throne. / his)

➡ _____

22 (was / he / the / on / again. / road)

➡ _____

23 (day, / one / two / the / brothers / again / met / and / about / talked / lives / their / for / years. / five / the / last)

➡ _____

_____

24 (older / the / said, / brother / right. / was / "I)

➡ _____

25 (have / I / quietly / lived / well. / and)

➡ _____

26 (were / you / once / king, / a / but / have / you / had / trouble." / of / lot / a)

➡ _____

27 (younger / the / answered, / brother / don't / "I / choice. / my / regret)

➡ _____

28 (may / I / nothing / have / now, / but / will / I / always / something / have / remember." / to)

➡ _____

17 그녀는 자고 있었다.

18 그는 새끼들을 데리고 산을 뛰어 올라갔다.

19 그가 정상에 도착했을 때, 어떤 사람들이 그를 자기들 도시로 데려가서 그들의 왕으로 만들었다.

20 그곳에서 그는 5년간 왕으로 살았다.

21 그런 다음 전쟁이 일어났고, 그는 왕좌를 잃었다.

22 그는 다시 길바닥에 나앉았다.

23 어느 날, 두 형제는 다시 만났고 지난 5년 동안의 그들의 삶에 대해 이야기했다.

24 형은 말했다. "내가 옳았어.

25 나는 조용히 잘 살았어.

26 너는 한때 왕이었지만 많은 어려움을 겪었지."

27 동생은 대답했다. "나는 내 선택을 후회하지 않아.

28 나는 지금 아무것도 없지만 언제까지나 기억할 어떤 것이 있어."

※ 다음 우리말을 영어로 쓰시오.

1 두 형제

➡ _____

2 두 형제는 여정을 떠났다.

➡ _____

3 그들은 숲 앞에서 바위를 발견했다.

➡ _____

4 거기에 쓰여 있었다. "숲에 들어가 강을 헤엄쳐 건너시오.

➡ _____

5 당신은 거기에서 곰과 새끼들을 발견할 것입니다.

➡ _____

6 곰 새끼들을 데리고 산 위로 뛰어 올라가시오.

➡ _____

7 거기에서 당신은 행복을 찾을 수 있을 것입니다."

➡ _____

8 동생이 말했다. "함께 가서 행복을 찾자."

➡ _____

9 "싫어." 형은 말했다. "이것이 사실인지 우리가 어떻게 알 수 있어?

➡ _____

10 강이 너무 넓으면 어쩌지?

➡ _____

11 게다가, 곰 새끼들을 엄마에게서 빼앗는 것이 쉬울까?

➡ _____

12 행복을 찾는 대신에, 우리는 죽을 수 있어!"

➡ _____

13 동생은 대답했다. "우리가 시도하지 않으면 어떻게 알 수 있어?"

➡ _____

14 그들은 헤어졌고, 둘 다 자신의 길을 갔다.

➡ _____

15 동생은 숲에 들어가서 강을 헤엄쳐 건넜다.

➡ _____

16 곰이 있었다.

➡ _____

17 그녀는 자고 있었다.

➡ _____

18 그는 새끼들을 데리고 산을 뛰어 올라갔다.

➡ _____

19 그가 정상에 도착했을 때, 어떤 사람들이 그를 자기들 도시로 데려가서 그들의 왕으로 만들었다.

➡ _____

20 그곳에서 그는 5년간 왕으로 살았다.

➡ _____

21 그런 다음 전쟁이 일어났고, 그는 왕좌를 잃었다.

➡ _____

22 그는 다시 길바닥에 나앉았다.

➡ _____

23 어느 날, 두 형제는 다시 만났고 지난 5년 동안의 그들의 삶에 대해 이야기했다.

➡ _____

24 형은 말했다. "내가 옳았어.

➡ _____

25 나는 조용히 잘 살았어.

➡ _____

26 너는 한때 왕이었지만 많은 어려움을 겪었지."

➡ _____

27 동생은 대답했다. "나는 내 선택을 후회하지 않아.

➡ _____

28 나는 지금 아무것도 없지만 언제까지나 기억할 어떤 것이 있어."

➡ _____

※ 다음 우리말과 일치하도록 빈칸에 알맞은 말을 쓰시오.

Before You Read

1. A. _____ is a box _____ _____ gold behind a tree _____ the river.

2. But _____ _____! Dangerous animals _____ in the river.

3. B. Mr. Allen _____ to _____ _____ _____ to the city for his vacation.

4. _____ the city streets were _____ and _____.

5. A car even _____ _____ him.

6. He had _____ _____ _____ there.

7. _____ _____ _____ _____ in the city, he _____ his choice and _____ _____ to his hometown.

| 1. A. 강 건너 나무 뒤에 황금으로 가득 찬 상자가 있다. |
| 2. 하지만 조심해! 위험한 동물들이 강에 있어. |
| 3. B. Allen씨는 휴가를 보내기 위해 도시로 여행을 가기로 결정했다. |
| 4. 슬프게도 도시의 거리는 더럽고 시끄러웠다. |
| 5. 심지어 차가 그를 칠 뻔 했다. |
| 6. 그는 거기서 많은 어려움을 겪었다. |
| 7. 도시에서의 며칠 후, 그는 그의 선택을 후회하고 고향으로 다시 돌아갔다. |

Writing Workshop

1. A _____ _____

2. _____: *Jonathan Livingston Seagull*: a story

3. _____: Richard Bach

4. This story _____ _____ a seagull _____ Jonathan Livingston.

5. He dreams of _____ _____ _____ _____.

6. _____ _____ his goal, he works hard and _____ _____.

7. I like this story _____ it has _____ _____ _____ about the power of my own beliefs.

8. The book says _____ I can do _____ _____ I want if I do not _____ _____.

1. 독서 감상문
2. 제목: Jonathan Livingston Seagull(갈매기의 꿈): 이야기
3. 작가: Richard Bach
4. 이 이야기는 Jonathan Livingston이라는 이름의 갈매기에 대한 것이다.
5. 그는 다른 갈매기들보다 더 잘 나는 것을 꿈꾼다.
6. 그의 목표에 도달하기 위해 그는 열심히 노력하고 비행을 연습한다.
7. 이 이야기가 내 자신의 믿음의 힘에 대해 배우도록 도와주었기 때문에 나는 이 이야기를 좋아한다.
8. 이 책은 내가 포기하지 않으면 내가 원하는 어떤 것이라도 할 수 있다고 말한다.

Into the World

1. Happiness is _____ what you _____, what you _____, and what you do are _____ _____. - Mahatma Gandhi

2. _____ one door of happiness _____, _____ opens. - Helen Keller

3. Happiness is not _____ _____. It _____ _____ your own actions. - Dalai Lama XIV

1. 행복은 생각, 말, 행동이 조화를 이룰 때 찾아온다.– Mahatma Gandhi
2. 행복의 한쪽 문이 닫히면 다른 쪽 문이 열리게 된다.
　　　– Helen Keller
3. 행복은 준비된 것이 아니다. 행복은 당신 자신의 행동에서 비롯된다.
　　　– Dalai Lama XIV

구석구석 지문 Test

※ 다음 우리말을 영어로 쓰시오.

Before You Read

1. A. 강 건너 나무 뒤에 황금으로 가득 찬 상자가 있다.
   ➡ _____

2. 하지만 조심해! 위험한 동물들이 강에 있어.
   ➡ _____

3. B. Allen씨는 휴가를 보내기 위해 도시로 여행을 가기로 결정했다.
   ➡ _____

4. 슬프게도 도시의 거리는 더럽고 시끄러웠다.
   ➡ _____

5. 심지어 차가 그를 칠 뻔 했다.
   ➡ _____

6. 그는 거기서 많은 어려움을 겪었다.
   ➡ _____

7. 도시에서의 며칠 후, 그는 그의 선택을 후회하고 고향으로 다시 돌아갔다.
   ➡ _____

Writing Workshop

1. 독서 감상문
   ➡ _____

2. 제목: Jonathan Livingston Seagull(갈매기의 꿈): 이야기
   ➡ _____

3. 작가: Richard Bach
   ➡ _____

4. 이 이야기는 Jonathan Livingston이라는 이름의 갈매기에 대한 것이다.
   ➡ _____

5. 그는 다른 갈매기들보다 더 잘 나는 것을 꿈꾼다.
   ➡ _____

6. 그의 목표에 도달하기 위해 그는 열심히 노력하고 비행을 연습한다.
   ➡ _____

7. 이 이야기가 내 자신의 믿음의 힘에 대해 배우도록 도와주었기 때문에 나는 이 이야기를 좋아한다.
   ➡ _____

8. 이 책은 내가 포기하지 않으면 내가 원하는 어떤 것이라도 할 수 있다고 말한다.
   ➡ _____

Into the World

1. 행복은 생각, 말, 행동이 조화를 이룰 때 찾아온다.– Mahatma Gandhi
   ➡ _____

2. 행복의 한쪽 문이 닫히면 다른 쪽 문이 열리게 된다.– Helen Keller
   ➡ _____

3. 행복은 준비된 것이 아니다. 행복은 당신 자신의 행동에서 비롯된다. – Dalai Lama XIV
   ➡ _____

※ 다음 영어를 우리말로 쓰시오.

01	competition	_____
02	fit	_____
03	hide	_____
04	crack	_____
05	rule	_____
06	miss	_____
07	home team	_____
08	anxious	_____
09	shorts	_____
10	determine	_____
11	pitch	_____
12	sometime	_____
13	dirt	_____
14	either	_____
15	stadium	_____
16	base	_____
17	batter	_____
18	international	_____
19	decide	_____
20	forget	_____
21	pet	_____

22	visiting team	_____
23	better	_____
24	ticket	_____
25	match	_____
26	order	_____
27	then	_____
28	vacation	_____
29	mean	_____
30	thunder	_____
31	past	_____
32	rock climbing	_____
33	support	_____
34	can't wait to 동사원형	_____
35	between A and B	_____
36	wait for	_____
37	be a big fan of	_____
38	hurry up	_____
39	look forward to (동)명사	_____
40	twice a week	_____
41	be excited about	_____
42	come back to	_____
43	in a hurry	_____

※ 다음 영어를 우리말로 쓰시오.

※ 다음 우리말을 영어로 쓰시오.

01	감추다, 숨기다		22	원정 팀
02	(부정문에서) ~도		23	반바지
03	티켓		24	과거
04	휴가		25	잊다
05	경기장		26	국제적인
06	(야구의) 루, 베이스		27	놓치다, 그리워하다
07	규칙		28	언젠가
08	방문하다		29	먼지
09	타자		30	획득하다, 사다
10	경기, 성냥		31	더 좋은, 더 나은
11	순서		32	(특정 스포츠 팀을) 응원하다
12	결정하다		33	그 뒤에, 그런 다음
13	투구		34	막 ~하려고 하다
14	암벽 등반		35	A와 B 사이에
15	의미하다		36	서둘러 ~하다
16	천둥		37	~의 열렬한 팬이다
17	찢어지는 듯한 소리		38	~을 몹시 기대하다
18	불안한		39	일주일에 두 번
19	대회		40	서둘러
20	맞다		41	~에 신나다, ~에 들뜨다
21	애완동물		42	~을 기대하다
			43	~을 기다리다

※ 다음 영영풀이에 알맞은 단어를 <보기>에서 골라 쓴 후, 우리말 뜻을 쓰시오.

1 _____ : to put something out of sight: _____

2 _____ : very nervous or worried about something: _____

3 _____ : to be the right size and shape for someone or something: _____

4 _____ : a sports team playing on its own ground: _____

5 _____ : the time before the moment of speaking or writing: _____

6 _____ : a throw of the ball for the batter to hit it: _____

7 _____ : relating to or involving different countries: _____

8 _____ : each corner of the square that makes a baseball diamond: _____

9 _____ : to decide or establish something conclusively: _____

10 _____ : a sports team playing on the competing team's field or court: _____

11 _____ : an event or contest in which people try to win something by defeating others: _____

12 _____ : the arrangement or disposition of people or things in a list from first to last: _____

13 _____ : the loud noise in the sky heard after a lightning flash during a storm: _____

14 _____ : used in a negative sentence to indicate a similarity with a statement just made: _____

15 _____ : the sudden loud explosive sound of something when it falls or bumps into itself or something else: _____

16 _____ : an athletic or sports ground used for playing and watching sports with rows of seats: _____

보기			
anxious	determine	home team	pitch
base	either	international	stadium
competition	fit	order	thunder
crack	hide	past	visiting team

※ 다음 우리말과 일치하도록 빈칸에 알맞은 말을 쓰시오.

해석

Listen & Speak 1 A

M: _____ _____ do you like? Soccer _____ basketball?

G: I like soccer _____. I play soccer _____ _____ _____.

M: 너는 어떤 운동을 좋아하니? 축구 아니면 농구?

G: 축구를 더 좋아해요. 저는 일주일에 두 번 축구를 해요.

Listen & Speak 1 B

1. G: What _____ you _____?

   B: _____ _____ _____ a world map.

   G: You _____ two countries. _____ _____ would you like _____ first? The U.S. _____ Mexico?

   B: I want _____ _____ the U.S. I'd _____ _____ see a basketball game there.

2. G: _____ _____ about _____ a pet. Do you _____ a pet?

   B: Yes, I do. I have a dog and a cat.

   G: _____ _____ you _____? _____ pet is _____ _____ me? A cat _____ a dog?

   B: _____ _____ _____ _____ _____ my house someday and _____ _____ my pets? Then you _____ _____.

1. G: 뭐 하고 있어?
   B: 세계 지도를 보고 있어.
   G: 두 나라에 표시를 했네. 어떤 나라를 먼저 방문하고 싶어? 미국 아니면 멕시코?
   B: 미국을 방문하고 싶어. 거기서 농구 경기를 보고 싶어.

2. G: 나는 애완동물을 기르는 것에 대해 생각 중이야. 넌 애완동물을 기르니?
   B: 응, 길러. 개와 고양이가 있어.
   G: 어떻게 생각해? 어떤 애완동물이 나에게 더 나아? 고양이 아니면 개?
   B: 어느 날 우리 집에 와서 내 애완동물과 놀아 보는 게 어때? 그런 다음 너는 결정할 수 있을 거야.

Listen & Speak 2 A

G: _____ you get the tickets?

B: Yes! I _____ _____ _____ _____ the game.

W: 너 티켓 구했니?
B: 응! 나는 경기를 빨리 보고 싶어.

Listen & Speak 2 B

1. G: Do you _____ _____ _____ my new mountain bike?

   B: Sure. _____ _____ you get it?

   G: Yesterday my father _____ _____ _____ _____. Can you _____ _____ _____ _____ this afternoon?

   B: Of _____. I _____ _____ _____ _____ it.

G: 내 새 산악 자전거를 보고 싶니?
B: 물론이지. 언제 생긴 거야?
G: 어제 아빠가 나에게 사 주셨어. 오늘 오후에 우리 집에 올래?
B: 당연하지. 나는 그것을 빨리 보고 싶어.

2. B: _____ _____ _____ we're going _____ _____ this weekend!

   G: Don't _____. I _____ _____.

   B: I'm _____ _____ going. _____ _____ _____.

3. G: Did you _____ _____ Jisu?

   B: What _____ her? She _____ _____ Canada.

   G: She _____ _____ to Korea last month. She _____ _____ _____ you.

   B: Oh, I _____ _____ _____ _____ her.

Real-Life Zone A

B1: Jiho, why are you in _____ _____ _____?

B2: Hi, Alex! I _____ _____ be home _____ 6:00. The game _____ the Thunders _____ the Cobras _____ at 6:00.

B1: Oh, are you a baseball fan? _____ _____ do you _____? The Cobras _____ the Thunders?

B2: The Cobras.

B1: Me, too! I don't want _____ _____ the game _____.

B2: _____ _____! We only have thirty minutes _____.

B1: Okay. _____ we can watch a game together _____.

B2: That's a great idea! How _____ _____ _____ _____ the next Cobras _____ _____ _____?

B1: Okay. They have a game next Saturday. We _____ _____ _____ _____ _____ _____ the game!

B2: That _____ great. _____ _____ _____ _____!

Wrap Up

B: Jimin, _____ _____ _____ _____ _____? Soccer _____ table tennis?

G: I love table tennis. _____ _____ you, Yunho?

B: I like soccer. I'm a _____ _____ _____ James Hood. He's a great soccer player.

G: Oh, really? There's a _____ _____ this weekend _____ Korea and Turkey. _____ you _____ _____ it?

B: Of course. I _____ _____ a ticket. _____ _____ _____ the game on Saturday. I _____ _____.

G: That's _____.

---

2. B: 이번 주말에 암벽 등반하러 가기로 한 거 잊지 마.

   G: 걱정 마. 잊지 않을게.

   B: 등반하러 가는 거 너무 신난다. 너무 기다려져.

3. G: 너 지수에 대해 들었니?

   B: 그녀에 대한 거 뭐? 그녀는 캐나다에 살고 있잖아.

   G: 지난달에 그녀는 한국에 돌아왔어. 너를 보고 싶어해.

   B: 오, 그녀를 빨리 보고 싶어.

B1: 지호야, 너 왜 그렇게 서두르니?

B2: 안녕, 알렉스! 나는 6시 전에 집에 있어야 해. 천둥 대 코브라의 경기가 6시에 시작돼.

B1: 오, 너 야구 팬이니? 어느 팀을 응원해? 코브라 아니면 천둥?

B2: 코브라.

B1: 나도야! 나도 이 경기를 놓치고 싶지 않아.

B2: 서둘러! 우리는 30분밖에 안 남았어.

B1: 알겠어. 언젠가 함께 경기를 볼 수도 있겠다.

B2: 좋은 생각이야! 다음 코브라 홈 경기를 함께 보러 가지 않을래?

B1: 좋아. 다음 주 토요일에 경기가 있어. 우리는 경기를 보면서 프라이드 치킨을 먹을 수 있어!

B2: 굉장해. 너무 기다려져!

B: 지민아, 너는 어떤 운동을 좋아하니? 축구 아니면 탁구?

G: 탁구를 좋아해. 윤호야, 너는 어때?

B: 축구가 좋아. 나는 제임스 후드의 열렬한 팬이야. 그는 위대한 축구 선수야.

G: 오, 정말? 이번 주말에 한국 대 터키의 축구 경기가 있어. 그것에 대해 들었니?

B: 물론이지. 나는 이미 표가 있어. 토요일에 경기를 보러 갈 거야. 너무 기다려져.

G: 환상적이다.

※ 다음 우리말에 맞도록 대화를 영어로 쓰시오.

Listen & Speak 1 A

M: _____

G: _____

Listen & Speak 1 B

1. G: _____

   B: _____

   G: _____

   _____

   B: _____

2. G: _____

   B: _____

   G: _____

   B: _____

Listen & Speak 2 A

G: _____

B: _____

Listen & Speak 2 B

1. G: _____

   B: _____

   G: _____

   B: _____

M: 너는 어떤 운동을 좋아하니? 축구 아니면 농구?

G: 축구를 더 좋아해요. 저는 일주일에 두 번 축구를 해요.

1. G: 뭐 하고 있어?

   B: 세계 지도를 보고 있어.

   G: 두 나라에 표시를 했네. 어떤 나라를 먼저 방문하고 싶어? 미국 아니면 멕시코?

   B: 미국을 방문하고 싶어. 거기서 농구 경기를 보고 싶어.

2. G: 나는 애완동물을 기르는 것에 대해 생각 중이야. 넌 애완동물을 기르니?

   B: 응, 길러. 개와 고양이가 있어.

   G: 어떻게 생각해? 어떤 애완동물이 나에게 더 나아? 고양이 아니면 개?

   B: 어느 날 우리 집에 와서 내 애완동물과 놀아 보는 게 어때? 그런 다음 너는 결정할 수 있을 거야.

W: 너 티켓 받았니?

B: 응! 나는 경기를 빨리 보고 싶어.

G: 내 새 산악 자전거를 보고 싶니?

B: 물론이지. 언제 생긴 거야?

G: 어제 아빠가 나에게 사 주셨어. 오늘 오후에 우리 집에 올래?

B: 당연하지. 나는 그것을 빨리 보고 싶어.

2. B: _____
   G: _____
   B: _____

3. G: _____
   B: _____
   G: _____
   B: _____

Real-Life Zone A

B1: _____
B2: _____
     _____
B1: _____
     _____
B2: _____
B1: _____
B2: _____
B1: _____
B2: _____
B1: _____
     _____
B2: _____

Wrap Up

B: _____
G: _____
B: _____
G: _____
B: _____
     _____
G: _____

2. B: 이번 주말에 암벽 등반하러 가기로 한 거 잊지 마.
   G: 걱정 마. 잊지 않을게.
   B: 등반하러 가는 거 너무 신난다. 너무 기다려져.

3. G: 너 지수에 대해 들었니?
   B: 그녀에 대한 거 뭐? 그녀는 캐나다에 살고 있잖아.
   G: 지난 달에 그녀는 한국에 돌아왔어. 너를 보고 싶어해.
   B: 오, 그녀를 빨리 보고 싶어.

B1: 지호야, 너 왜 그렇게 서두르니?
B2: 안녕, 알렉스! 나는 6시 전에 집에 있어야 해. 천둥 대 코브라의 경기가 6시에 시작돼.
B1: 오, 너 야구 팬이니? 어느 팀을 응원해? 코브라 아니면 천둥?
B2: 코브라.
B1: 나도야! 나도 이 경기를 놓치고 싶지 않아.
B2: 서둘러! 우리는 30분밖에 안 남았어.
B1: 알겠어. 언젠가 함께 경기를 볼 수도 있겠다.
B2: 좋은 생각이야! 다음 코브라 홈 경기를 함께 보러 가지 않을래?
B1: 좋아. 다음 주 토요일에 경기가 있어. 우리는 경기를 보면서 프라이드 치킨을 먹을 수 있어!
B1: 굉장해. 너무 기다려져!

B: 지민아, 너는 어떤 운동을 좋아하니? 축구 아니면 탁구?
G: 탁구를 좋아해. 윤호야, 너는 어때?
B: 축구가 좋아. 나는 제임스 후드의 열렬한 팬이야. 그는 위대한 축구 선수야.
G: 오, 정말? 이번 주말에 한국 대 터키의 축구 경기가 있어. 그것에 대해 들었니?
B: 물론이지. 나는 이미 표가 있어. 토요일에 경기를 보러 갈 거야. 너무 기다려져.
G: 환상적이다.

※ 다음 우리말과 일치하도록 빈칸에 알맞은 것을 골라 쓰시오.

1 A _____ at the _____ _____

A. Day   B. Stadium   C. Baseball

2 Today the Thunders _____ the Cobras _____ a _____.

A. game   B. have   C. and

3 Jihun's family _____ _____ the baseball _____.

A. at   B. is   C. stadium

4 Jihun: Jian, this is _____ _____ time to come to the baseball stadium, _____ _____?

A. isn't   B. first   C. it   D. your

5 Jian: Yes, I'm so _____. I _____ _____ _____ the game to start.

A. wait   B. for   C. excited   D. can't

6 Dad: Look, the players _____ _____ _____ now!

A. out   B. coming   C. are

7 Jian: _____ _____ is the Thunders?

A. team   B. which

8 Jihun: _____ there, _____ _____ base.

A. third   B. behind   C. over

9 They are _____ dark gray uniforms _____ they are the _____ team.

A. wearing   B. visiting   C. because

10 Jian: Does the visiting team _____ _____ a _____ color?

A. wear   B. always   C. dark

11 Jihun: Yes, _____'s the _____.

A. rule   B. that

12 _____ teams have _____ uniforms and _____ teams have _____ uniforms.

A. dark   B. bright   C. visiting   D. home

13 Jian: _____ is _____?

A. that   B. why

14 Mom: _____ is an _____ story _____ that.

A. about   B. interesting   C. there

15 In the _____, visiting teams could not _____ their uniforms after _____ game.

A. every   B. past   C. wash

16 So they started _____ dark colors to _____ the _____.

A. hide   B. dirt   C. wearing

17 Jian: Hahaha! That _____ a _____ _____!

A. idea   B. was   C. good

---

1 야구 경기장에서의 하루

2 오늘 천둥 대 코브라 게임이 있다.

3 지훈이네 가족은 야구 경기장에 있다.

4 지훈: 지안아, 네가 야구 경기장에 온 건 이번이 처음이야, 그렇지 않니?

5 지안: 응, 나 아주 흥분돼. 나는 경기가 빨리 시작했으면 좋겠어.

6 아빠: 봐, 선수들이 지금 나오고 있어!

7 지안: 어떤 팀이 천둥이야?

8 지훈: 저기, 3루 뒤.

9 그들은 원정 팀이기 때문에 어두운 회색 유니폼을 입고 있어.

10 지안: 원정 팀은 항상 어두운 색을 입어?

11 지훈: 응, 그게 규칙이야.

12 홈팀은 밝은 유니폼을 입고 원정팀은 어두운 유니폼을 입어.

13 지안: 왜?

14 엄마: 그것에 대한 흥미로운 이야기가 있단다.

15 과거에는 원정 팀이 매 경기 후 유니폼을 세탁할 수가 없었어.

16 그래서 그들은 때를 숨기기 위해 어두운 색을 입기 시작했지.

17 지안: 하하하! 좋은 생각이었네요!

18 The players are _____ _____.
   A. up   B. warming

19 Jian: Who's _____ _____ player?
   A. favorite   B. your

20 Jihun: _____ _____.
   A. 77   B. number

21 Jian: _____ _____ the number _____?
   A. what   B. mean   C. does

22 Jihun: Hmm…. Players _____ a number _____ _____ _____.
   A. they   B. choose   C. like

23 Dad: You _____ _____?
   A. what   B. know

24 In the past, the numbers were _____ _____ the players' _____ _____.
   A. order   B. by   C. determined   D. batting

25 Jihun: That means _____ were _____ players _____ number 77!
   A. with   B. there   C. no

26 Now, Jihun's favorite player _____ _____ _____ _____ bat.
   A. about   B. is   C. to

27 Jihun _____ _____.
   A. anxious   B. looks

28 Jian: Your _____ player is _____ _____.
   A. favorite   B. bat   C. at

29 Jihun: Yes. He _____ _____ 21 home _____ _____ this year.
   A. already   B. hit   C. has   D. runs

30 If he _____ one _____ today, he will _____ the home run leader this _____.
   A. more   B. season   C. hits   D. be

31 The _____ _____ _____ balls.
   A. misses   B. several   C. batter

32 Now he _____ a _____ _____.
   A. count   B. full   C. has

33 He is _____ _____ the next _____.
   A. pitch   B. for   C. waiting

34 Jihun: HOME _____! _____ RUN!
   A. RUN   B. HOME

35 _____! The ball _____ _____.
   A. fast   B. flies   C. crack

36 It _____ _____, going, going, _____!
   A. gone   B. going   C. is

18 선수들이 몸을 풀고 있다.

19 지안: 가장 좋아하는 선수가 누구야?

20 지훈: 77번.

21 지안: 그 숫자는 무엇을 의미해?

22 지훈: 음... 선수들이 원하는 번호를 선택해.

23 아빠: 그거 알아?

24 과거에는 번호가 선수들의 타순에 의해 결정되었단다.

25 지훈: 77번 선수가 없었다는 뜻이네요!

26 이제 지훈이의 가장 좋아하는 선수가 막 공을 치려고 한다.

27 지훈이는 불안해 보인다.

28 지안: 오빠가 가장 좋아하는 선수가 타석에 서네.

29 지훈: 응. 그는 올해 이미 21개의 홈런을 쳤어.

30 그가 오늘 하나를 더 치면, 그는 이번 시즌 홈런 리더가 될 거야.

31 타자는 여러 개의 공을 놓친다.

32 이제 그는 풀카운트가 되었다.

33 그는 다음 투구를 기다리고 있다.

34 지훈: 홈런! 홈런!

35 땅! 공은 빠르게 날아간다.

36 그것은 가고, 가고, 가고, 사라져 버렸다!

Step2

※ 다음 우리말과 일치하도록 빈칸에 알맞은 말을 쓰시오.

1 _____ _____ at the _____ _____

2 Today the Thunders and the Cobras _____ _____ _____.

3 Jihun's family _____ _____ the _____ _____.

4 Jihun: Jian, this is _____ _____ _____ to come to the baseball stadium, _____ _____?

5 Jian: Yes, I'm so _____. I _____ _____ _____ the game _____ _____.

6 Dad: Look, the players _____ _____ _____ now!

7 Jian: _____ _____ is the Thunders?

8 Jihun: _____ _____, _____ _____ _____ _____.

9 They _____ _____ dark gray uniforms _____ they are the _____ _____.

10 Jian: Does the _____ _____ always _____ _____ _____ _____?

11 Jihun: Yes, that's the _____.

12 Home teams _____ _____ _____ and visiting teams have _____ _____.

13 Jian: _____ is that?

14 Mom: _____ is _____ _____ _____ about that.

15 _____ _____ _____, visiting teams could not _____ _____ _____ _____ _____.

16 So they _____ _____ dark colors _____ _____ _____.

17 Jian: Hahaha! That was _____ _____ _____!

---

1 야구 경기장에서의 하루

2 오늘 천둥 대 코브라 게임이 있다.

3 지훈이네 가족은 야구 경기장에 있다.

4 지훈: 지안아, 네가 야구 경기장에 온 건 이번이 처음이야, 그렇지 않니?

5 지안: 응, 나 아주 흥분돼. 나는 경기가 빨리 시작했으면 좋겠어.

6 아빠: 봐, 선수들이 지금 나오고 있어!

7 지안: 어떤 팀이 천둥이야?

8 지훈: 저기, 3루 뒤.

9 그들은 원정 팀이기 때문에 어두운 회색 유니폼을 입고 있어.

10 지안: 원정 팀은 항상 어두운 색을 입어?

11 지훈: 응, 그게 규칙이야.

12 홈팀은 밝은 유니폼을 입고 원정팀은 어두운 유니폼을 입어.

13 지안: 왜?

14 엄마: 그것에 대한 흥미로운 이야기가 있단다.

15 과거에는 원정 팀이 매 경기 후 유니폼을 세탁할 수가 없었어.

16 그래서 그들은 때를 숨기기 위해 어두운 색을 입기 시작했지.

17 지안: 하하하! 좋은 생각이었네요!

18 The players _____ _____ _____.

19 Jian: Who's _____ _____ _____?

20 Jihun: _____ 77.

21 Jian: _____ _____ the _____ _____?

22 Jihun: Hmm…. Players _____ a number _____ _____.

23 Dad: _____ _____ _____?

24 In the past, the numbers _____ _____ _____ _____ _____ _____ _____.

25 Jihun: That means _____ _____ _____ players _____ number 77!

26 Now, Jihun's favorite player _____ _____ _____ bat.

27 Jihun _____ _____.

28 Jian: _____ _____ player is _____ _____.

29 Jihun: Yes. He _____ _____ 21 home runs already this year.

30 If he _____ _____ _____ today, he will be the home run leader _____ _____.

31 The batter _____ _____ _____.

32 Now he _____ _____ _____.

33 He is _____ _____ the _____ _____.

34 Jihun: _____! HOME RUN!

35 _____! The ball _____ _____.

36 It _____ _____, going, going, _____!

18 선수들이 몸을 풀고 있다.

19 지안: 가장 좋아하는 선수가 누구야?

20 지훈: 77번.

21 지안: 그 숫자는 무엇을 의미해?

22 지훈: 음... 선수들이 원하는 번호를 선택해.

23 아빠: 그거 알아?

24 과거에는 번호가 선수들의 타순에 의해 결정되었단다.

25 지훈: 77번 선수가 없었다는 뜻이네요!

26 이제 지훈이의 가장 좋아하는 선수가 막 공을 치려고 한다.

27 지훈이는 불안해 보인다.

28 지안: 오빠가 가장 좋아하는 선수가 타석에 서네.

29 지훈: 응. 그는 올해 이미 21개의 홈런을 쳤어.

30 그가 오늘 하나를 더 치면, 그는 이번 시즌 홈런 리더가 될 거야.

31 타자는 여러 개의 공을 놓친다.

32 이제 그는 풀카운트가 되었다.

33 그는 다음 투구를 기다리고 있다.

34 지훈: 홈런! 홈런!

35 땅! 공은 빠르게 날아간다.

36 그것은 가고, 가고, 가고, 사라져 버렸다!

※ 다음 문장을 우리말로 쓰시오.

1 A Day at the Baseball Stadium
➡ _____

2 Today the Thunders and the Cobras have a game.
➡ _____

3 Jihun's family is at the baseball stadium.
➡ _____

4 Jihun: Jian, this is your first time to come to the baseball stadium, isn't it?
➡ _____

5 Jian: Yes, I'm so excited. I can't wait for the game to start.
➡ _____

6 Dad: Look, the players are coming out now!
➡ _____

7 Jian: Which team is the Thunders?
➡ _____

8 Jihun: Over there, behind third base.
➡ _____

9 They are wearing dark gray uniforms because they are the visiting team.
➡ _____

10 Jian: Does the visiting team always wear a dark color?
➡ _____

11 Jihun: Yes, that's the rule.
➡ _____

12 Home teams have bright uniforms and visiting teams have dark uniforms.
➡ _____

13 Jian: Why is that?
➡ _____

14 Mom: There is an interesting story about that.
➡ _____

15 In the past, visiting teams could not wash their uniforms after every game.
➡ _____

16 So they started wearing dark colors to hide the dirt.
➡ _____

17 Jian: Hahaha! That was a good idea!
➡ _____

18 The players are warming up.
➡ _____

19 Jian: Who's your favorite player?
➡ _____

20 Jihun: Number 77.
➡ _____

21 Jian: What does the number mean?
➡ _____

22 Jihun: Hmm…. Players choose a number they like.
➡ _____

23 Dad: You know what?
➡ _____

24 In the past, the numbers were determined by the players' batting order.
➡ _____

25 Jihun: That means there were no players with number 77!
➡ _____

26 Now, Jihun's favorite player is about to bat.
➡ _____

27 Jihun looks anxious.
➡ _____

28 Jian: Your favorite player is at bat.
➡ _____

29 Jihun: Yes. He has hit 21 home runs already this year.
➡ _____

30 If he hits one more today, he will be the home run leader this season.
➡ _____

31 The batter misses several balls.
➡ _____

32 Now he has a full count.
➡ _____

33 He is waiting for the next pitch.
➡ _____

34 Jihun: HOME RUN! HOME RUN!
➡ _____

35 Crack! The ball flies fast.
➡ _____

36 It is going, going, going, gone!
➡ _____

※ 다음 괄호 안의 단어들을 우리말에 맞도록 바르게 배열하시오.

1 (Day / A / at / Baseball / the / Stadium)
➡ _____

2 (the / today / Thunders / and / Cobras / the / game. / a / have)
➡ _____

3 (family / Jihun's / at / is / baseball / stadium. / the)
➡ _____

4 (Jihun: / this / Jian, / is / first / your / to / time / come / to / baseball / the / it? / isn't / stadium,)
➡ _____

5 (Jian: / I'm / yes, / excited. / so // can't / I / for / wait / the / to / start. / game)
➡ _____

6 (Dad: / look, / players / the / coming / are / now! / out)
➡ _____

7 (Jian: / team / which / Thunders? / the / is)
➡ _____

8 (Jihun: / there, / over / base. / third / behind)
➡ _____

9 (are / they / dark / wearing / uniforms / gray / they / because / team. / visiting / the / are)
➡ _____

10 (Jian: / the / does / team / visiting / wear / always / color? / dark / a)
➡ _____

11 (Jihun: / that's / yes, / rule. / the)
➡ _____

12 (teams / home / bright / have / and / uniforms / teams / visiting / uniforms. / dark / have)
➡ _____

13 (Jian: / that? / is / why)
➡ _____

14 (Mom: / is / there / interesting / an / that. / about / story)
➡ _____

15 (the / in / past, / teams / visiting / not / could / wash / uniforms / their / game. / every / after)
➡ _____

16 (they / so / wearing / started / colors / dark / hide / dirt. / the / to)
➡ _____

17 (Jian: / hahaha! // was / that / idea! / good / a)
➡ _____

1 야구 경기장에서의 하루

2 오늘 천둥 대 코브라 게임이 있다.

3 지훈이네 가족은 야구 경기장에 있다.

4 지훈: 지안아, 네가 야구 경기장에 온 건 이번이 처음이야, 그렇지 않니?

5 지안: 응, 나 아주 흥분돼. 나는 경기가 빨리 시작했으면 좋겠어.

6 아빠: 봐, 선수들이 지금 나오고 있어!

7 지안: 어떤 팀이 천둥이야?

8 지훈: 저기, 3루 뒤.

9 그들은 원정 팀이기 때문에 어두운 회색 유니폼을 입고 있어.

10 지안: 원정 팀은 항상 어두운 색을 입어?

11 지훈: 응, 그게 규칙이야.

12 홈팀은 밝은 유니폼을 입고 원정팀은 어두운 유니폼을 입어.

13 지안: 왜?

14 엄마: 그것에 대한 흥미로운 이야기가 있단다.

15 과거에는 원정 팀이 매 경기 후 유니폼을 세탁할 수가 없었어.

16 그래서 그들은 때를 숨기기 위해 어두운 색을 입기 시작했지.

17 지안: 하하하! 좋은 생각이었네요!

18 (players / the / up. / warming / are)
➡ _____

19 (Jian: / your / who's / player? / favorite)
➡ _____

20 (Jihun: / 77. / number)
➡ _____

21 (Jian: / does / what / mean? / number / the)
➡ _____

22 (Jihun: / hmm.... // choose / players / number / a / like. / they)
➡ _____

23 (Dad: / what? / know / you)
➡ _____

24 (the / in / past, / numbers / the / determined / were / the / player's / by / order. / batting)
➡ _____

25 (Jihun: / means / that / were / there / players / no / 77! / number / with)
➡ _____

26 (now, / favorite / Jihun's / is / player / bat. / to / about)
➡ _____

27 (looks / Jihun / anxious.)
➡ _____

28 (Jian: / favorite / your / is / player / bat. / at)
➡ _____

29 (Jihun: / yes. // has / he / 21 / hit / home / already / runs / year. / this)
➡ _____

30 (he / if / hits / more / one / today, / will / he / the / be / run / home / season. / this / leader)
➡ _____

31 (batter / the / several / balls. / misses)
➡ _____

32 (he / now / a / has / count. / full)
➡ _____

33 (is / he / for / waiting / pitch. / next / the)
➡ _____

34 (Jihun: / RUN! / HOME / RUN! / HOME)
➡ _____

35 (crack! // ball / the / fast. / flies)
➡ _____

36 (is / it / going, / gone! / going, / going,)
➡ _____

18 선수들이 몸을 풀고 있다.

19 지안: 가장 좋아하는 선수가 누구야?

20 지훈: 77번.

21 지안: 그 숫자는 무엇을 의미해?

22 지훈: 음... 선수들이 원하는 번호를 선택해.

23 아빠: 그거 알아?

24 과거에는 번호가 선수들의 타순에 의해 결정되었단다.

25 지훈: 77번 선수가 없었다는 뜻이네요!

26 이제 지훈이의 가장 좋아하는 선수가 막 공을 치려고 한다.

27 지훈이는 불안해 보인다.

28 지안: 오빠가 가장 좋아하는 선수가 타석에 서네.

29 지훈: 응. 그는 올해 이미 21개의 홈런을 쳤어.

30 그가 오늘 하나를 더 치면, 그는 이번 시즌 홈런 리더가 될 거야.

31 타자는 여러 개의 공을 놓친다.

32 이제 그는 풀카운트가 되었다.

33 그는 다음 투구를 기다리고 있다.

34 지훈: 홈런! 홈런!

35 땅! 공은 빠르게 날아간다.

36 그것은 가고, 가고, 가고, 사라져 버렸다!

※ 다음 우리말을 영어로 쓰시오.

1 야구 경기장에서의 하루

➡ _____

2 오늘 천둥 대 코브라 게임이 있다.

➡ _____

3 지훈이네 가족은 야구 경기장에 있다.

➡ _____

4 지훈: 지안아, 네가 야구 경기장에 온 건 이번이 처음이야, 그렇지 않니?

➡ _____

5 지안: 응, 나 아주 흥분돼. 나는 경기가 빨리 시작했으면 좋겠어.

➡ _____

6 아빠: 봐, 선수들이 지금 나오고 있어!

➡ _____

7 지안: 어떤 팀이 천둥이야?

➡ _____

8 지훈: 저기, 3루 뒤.

➡ _____

9 그들은 원정 팀이기 때문에 어두운 회색 유니폼을 입고 있어.

➡ _____

10 지안: 원정 팀은 항상 어두운 색을 입어?

➡ _____

11 지훈: 응, 그게 규칙이야.

➡ _____

12 홈팀은 밝은 유니폼을 입고 원정팀은 어두운 유니폼을 입어.

➡ _____

13 지안: 왜?

➡ _____

14 엄마: 그것에 대한 흥미로운 이야기가 있단다.

➡ _____

15 과거에는 원정 팀이 매 경기 후 유니폼을 세탁할 수가 없었어.

➡ _____

16 그래서 그들은 때를 숨기기 위해 어두운 색을 입기 시작했지.

➡ _____

17 지안: 하하하! 좋은 생각이었네요!

➡ _____

18 선수들이 몸을 풀고 있다.

➡ _____

19 지안: 가장 좋아하는 선수가 누구야?

➡ _____

20 지훈: 77번.

➡ _____

21 지안: 그 숫자는 무엇을 의미해?

➡ _____

22 지훈: 음... 선수들이 원하는 번호를 선택해.

➡ _____

23 아빠: 그거 알아?

➡ _____

24 과거에는 번호가 선수들의 타순에 의해 결정되었단다.

➡ _____

25 지훈: 77번 선수가 없었다는 뜻이네요!

➡ _____

26 이제 지훈이의 가장 좋아하는 선수가 막 공을 치려고 한다.

➡ _____

27 지훈이는 불안해 보인다.

➡ _____

28 지안: 오빠가 가장 좋아하는 선수가 타석에 서네.

➡ _____

29 지훈: 응. 그는 올해 이미 21개의 홈런을 쳤어.

➡ _____

30 그가 오늘 하나를 더 치면, 그는 이번 시즌 홈런 리더가 될 거야.

➡ _____

31 타자는 여러 개의 공을 놓친다.

➡ _____

32 이제 그는 풀카운트가 되었다.

➡ _____

33 그는 다음 투구를 기다리고 있다.

➡ _____

34 지훈: 홈런! 홈런!

➡ _____

35 땅! 공은 빠르게 날아간다.

➡ _____

36 그것은 가고, 가고, 가고, 사라져 버렸다!

➡ _____

※ 다음 우리말과 일치하도록 빈칸에 알맞은 말을 쓰시오.

Real-Life Zone B

1. A: _____ _____ do you _____? Basketball _____ soccer?

2. B: I like basketball. I'm _____ _____ play it _____ my

   friends _____ _____. I _____ _____.

Writing Workshop

1. Abebe Bikila _____ _____

2. _____: _____ 7, 1932

3. _____: Ethiopia

4. Speciality: He _____ _____ _____ a marathon winner at the

   Rome and Tokyo _____ _____ _____.

5. When he was _____ _____ _____ the marathon in Rome, he

   _____ _____ that his shoes _____ _____ _____ well,

   so he _____ _____ _____ the race _____ _____.

6. He _____ _____ _____ the race, but he finished the race

   _____ _____ _____.

7. He was _____ _____ the greatest runners in the world, _____

   _____?

Wrap Up

1. Sarang _____ _____ _____ _____

2. Sarang Middle School Sports Day _____ _____ _____ on

   the school playing field _____ _____, _____ 15.

3. There _____ _____ _____ games _____ _____ baseball

   and soccer.

4. There _____ _____ be _____ _____.

5. It _____ _____ fun, _____ _____?

1. Abebe Bikila   마라톤 선수
2. 생일: 1932년 8월 7일
3. 국적: 에티오피아
4. 특별 사항: 그는 로마 국제 스포츠 대회와 도쿄 국제 스포츠 대회의 마라톤 우승자로 알려졌다.
5. 그가 로마에서 달리기를 준비하던 도중에 자신의 신발이 잘 맞지 않는다는 것을 알고 그는 신발을 신지 않고 달리기로 결심했다.
6. 그는 경주 도중에 통증을 느꼈지만 우승자로 경주를 끝마쳤다.
7. 그는 세계에서 가장 위대한 달리기 선수들 중의 한 명이었어, 그렇지 않니?

※ 다음 우리말을 영어로 쓰시오.

Real-Life Zone B

1. 너는 어떤 운동을 좋아하니? 농구 아니면 축구?

➡ _____

2. B: 농구를 좋아해. 이번 주말에 친구들이랑 농구를 할 거야. 너무 기다려져.

➡ _____

Writing Workshop

1. Abebe Bikila   마라톤 선수

➡ _____

2. 생일: 1932년 8월 7일

➡ _____

3. 국적: 에티오피아

➡ _____

4. 특별 사항: 그는 로마 국제 스포츠 대회와 도쿄 국제 스포츠 대회의 마라톤 우승자로 알려졌다.

➡ _____

_____

5. 그가 로마에서 달리기를 준비하던 도중에 자신의 신발이 잘 맞지 않는다는 것을 알고 그는 신발을 신지 않고 달리기로 결심했다.

➡ _____

_____

6. 그는 경주 도중에 통증을 느꼈지만 우승자로 경주를 끝마쳤다.

➡ _____

7. 그는 세계에서 가장 위대한 달리기 선수들 중의 한 명이었어, 그렇지 않았니?

➡ _____

Wrap Up

1. 사랑 중학교 운동회

➡ _____

2. 사랑 중학교 운동회가 학교 운동장에서 6월 15일 수요일에 열립니다.

➡ _____

3. 야구와 축구 같은 여러 가지 게임이 있을 것입니다.

➡ _____

4. 또한 탁구도 있을 것입니다.

➡ _____

5. 재미있게 들리지요, 그렇지 않나요?

➡ _____

MEMO

MEMO

영어 기출 문제집

적중100

1학기

정답 및 해설

시사 | 송미정

중 2

영어 기출 문제집

적중100

1학기

정답 및 해설

시사 | 송미정

중 2

Lesson 3

The School Club Activity Day

시험대비 실력평가 p.08

01 ①	02 ①	03 ①	04 ①
05 (n)eighbor	06 leader	07 ⑤	08 ④
09 who, can join			

01 둘은 반의어 관계이다. increase: 증가하다 decrease: 감소하다 difficult: 어려운 easy: 쉬운

02 bake: (빵 등을) 굽다 oven: 오븐 / 나는 오븐에 빵을 굽고 있다.

03 grow: (동식물을) 기르다 vegetables: 채소 / 그들은 채소를 재배하는 데 있어 유기농 방식을 사용한다.

04 opportunity: 기회 chance: 가능성, 기회 / 그것은 부유한 사람들이 어떻게 사는지 보여주는 귀중한 기회였다.

05 neighbor: 이웃 / 당신의 옆이나 근처에 사는 어떤 사람

06 leader: 지도자, 대표 / 그녀는 유럽에서 가장 강력한 국가의 지도자이다.

07 hold: (모임·식 등을) 개최하다

08 ① 십대들에게 가장 인기 있는 여가 시간 활동이 무엇입니까? ② 나는 정말 너의 요리가 그립다. ③ 그녀는 밝은 색들을 좋아하지 않는다. ④ note: 음, 음표 / 그는 단 하나의 음표도 읽지 못하지만, 피아노를 완벽하게 연주한다. ⑤ 한국은 이미 몇 개의 메달을 획득했다.

09 join: 참여하다, 가입하다

서술형 시험대비 p.09

01 (1) (g)et (2) (p)resent
02 have
03 How
04 (1) introduce (2) dolphins (3) doughnut (4) concert
05 (1) activity (2) neighborhood
06 (1) (c)lothes (2) introduce (3) interest (4) vegetables
07 If I join this club, I will practice very hard.

01 주어진 보기는 동의어 관계이다. happy: 행복한 pleased: 기쁜 (1) gain: 얻다, 입수하다 get: 얻다, 획득하다, 사다 (2) gift: 선물 present: 선물

02 have: 가지다 / 가지면 가질수록 더 갖고 싶다. have a great

time: 좋은 시간을 보내다 / 새 학기가 시작하기 전에 즐거운 시간을 보내라!

03 how: 어떻게 / 어떻게 제가 이 동아리에 가입할 수 있나요? how to+동사원형: ~하는 방법 / 나는 그것을 하는 방법을 배우고 싶다.

04 (1) introduce: 소개하다 (2) dolphin: 돌고래 (3) doughnut: 도넛 (4) concert: 연주회

05 (1) activity: 활동 / 어떤 종류의 동아리 활동을 좋아하세요? (2) neighborhood: 동네, (도시 내의 한 단위) 지역 / 이 근처 지역은 쇼핑하기에 아주 좋다.

06 (1) clothes: 옷, 의상 (2) introduce: 소개하다 (3) interest: 관심 (4) vegetables: 채소

07 join: 참여하다, 가입하다 club: 동아리 practice: 연습하다

교과서
Conversation

핵심 Check p.10~11

1 how to use
2 I want to learn how to take good pictures.
3 What do you, doing, free time / I enjoy listening to music
4 I enjoy riding a bike

교과서 대화문 익히기

Check(√) True or False p.12

(1) T (2) T (3) T (4) F (5) T (6) F

교과서 확인학습 p.14~15

Listen & Speak 1 A
know how to

Listen & Speak 1 B
1 heard you went to, How / I hope I can play / knew how to play the violin / good at
2 at, grew, myself, own / how to cook / taught

Listen & Speak 2 A
looking at, at night

Listen & Speak 2 B
1 Do you enjoy / love reading, about / reading / go,

the library

2 What did you do / made / Do you enjoy cooking / cook, cooking

3 Where, get / made it for me / designer / enjoys making clothes

Real-Life Zone A

the leader, interest / When did you start playing / how to play the violin when / experience playing / an orchestra when, elementary / volunteer to teach / Do you enjoy teaching / experience, enjoy working with / have

Wrap Up

look, delicious / made them myself, baking, going to / want to learn how to make / at / time / Sounds, See

---

시험대비 기본평가   p.16

01 ④   02 ①   03 ④   04 ①

01 여가 시간에 무엇을 즐기는지 묻고 대답하고 있다. 'I enjoy 동명사 ~.'를 사용해서 자신이 좋아하는 것을 표현할 수 있다.

02 종이 고양이를 만들 수 있는지 여부를 묻고 대답하고 있다. how to+동사원형: ~하는 방법, 어떻게 ~하는지

03 'Do you know how to+동사원형~?'을 이용해 상대방의 능력이나 무언가를 하는 방법에 대해 물을 수 있다.

04 할머니에게서 배웠다는 내용이 나왔으므로, 여자아이는 요리를 하는 방법을 알고 있다.

시험대비 실력평가   p.17~18

01 ①   02 ③   03 ②   04 ①
05 ⑤   06 (A)looking   (B)doing[to do]
07 ①   08 ⑤   09 ②   10 ③
11 (A) in a group (B) no experience
12 I started learning how to play the violin when I was ten.   13 ②

01 'How was it?'은 과거의 경험에 대한 느낌을 묻는 표현으로, 여기서는 유나의 바이올린 콘서트에 대한 느낌을 묻고 있고, 이에 대한 대답 'It was great.'으로 이어진다.

02 대화에서 (A)와 ③은 '~처럼'의 의미로 사용되었다. 이외의 보기는 '좋아하다'의 의미이다.

03 ② 남자아이는 자신이 바이올린을 잘 연주하지 못한다고 생각한다.

04 Do you know how to ~?: 어떻게 ~하는지 하니? how to+

동사원형: ~하는 방법, 어떻게 ~하는지. 스페인어를 하는 방법을 모른다는 말에, 상대방이 'Yes'라고 하고, 가르쳐 줄 수 있다고 말하므로, 상대방에게 스페인어를 말하는 법을 아느냐고 질문하는 것이 적절하다.

05 ⑤ Of course I am. → Of course I do.

06 enjoy는 동명사를 목적어로 취할 수 있고, love는 동명사와 to부정사를 둘 다 목적어로 취할 수 있다.

07 get: ~을 사다, ~을 얻다. 주어진 말의 it이 a pretty backpack을 가리키므로 ①이 적절하다.

08 문장의 끝에 오는 too는 '또한'의 의미로, 내용상 그녀는 훌륭한 디자이너이고, 또한 옷 만드는 것을 즐긴다는 말이 나와야 하므로, 'Yes, she is (a really good designer).'의 의미를 가진 ⑤가 적절하다.

09 ② 지윤이 가방을 만드는 방법을 안다는 내용은 언급되지 않았다.

10 주어진 문장의 We는 나눔 오케스트라를 의미하며, 자원봉사로 아이들을 가르친다는 내용이 나온 후, 다른 사람들을 가르치는 것을 즐기는지 묻는 것이 어울린다.

11 (A)가 있는 질문의 대답이 오케스트라의 멤버였다고 말하고 있으므로, 그룹으로 연주한 경험이 있느냐고 질문해야 한다. (B)가 있는 문장 다음에 But이라는 접속사가 있으므로 뒤의 내용과 반대 또는 대조되는 내용이 나와야 어울린다.

12 start+동명사 또는 to부정사: ~하는 것을 시작하다 how to+동사원형: ~하는 방법, 어떻게 ~하는지

13 케이트는 지금이 아니라 초등학교 때 오케스트라의 구성원이었다.

서술형 시험대비   p.19

01 (C) → (A) → (B)
02 (A) → (C) → (B)
03 at
04 me → myself
05 Do you know how to cook the vegetables (that) you grow
06 enjoyed do → enjoy doing
07 I didn't know you knew how to play the violin.
08 I'm not good at it yet

01 요리하기를 즐기는지 묻는 질문에 (C) 가끔 요리하기를 즐기고, 피자 만드는 법을 알고 있다고 대답한다. (A) 이에 상대방이 요리 동아리에 가입하는 것을 권유하자 (B) 생각해 보겠다고 대답한다.

02 드론을 샀는지 질문하자 (A) 사지는 않았고, 선물로 받았다고 대답하면서 드론을 사용하는 방법을 모른다고 얘기하며 상대방이 방법을 아는지 질문하자 (C) 모르지만 지나가 알 것이라고 대답한다. (B) 그러면, 지나에게 물어보겠다고 말한다.

03 look at: ~을 보다

04 grow의 목적어로 these vegetables가 왔으므로 목적어의 자리

3

에 들어갈 수 있는 me는 어울리지 않는다. 여기서는 내가 했다는 것을 강조하는 재귀대명사가 어울린다.

05 how to+동사원형: ~하는 방법, 어떻게 ~하는지 cook: 요리하다 grow: 기르다

06 'Do you ~?'로 질문하고 있으므로 현재형의 동사를 사용해야 한다. 또한, enjoy는 동명사를 목적어로 취한다.

07 know 다음에 접속사 that이 생략되었다. play the 악기 이름: ~을 연주하다

08 be good at: ~을 잘하다

교과서
Grammar

핵심 Check
p.20~21

1 (1) what to / what I should
　(2) where to meet / where I should meet
2 (1) who[that]　(2) which[that]

시험대비 기본평가
p.22

01 (1) eating → to eat　(2) go → to go
　(3) which → who[that]　(4) who → which[that]
02 ③, ④
03 (1) She didn't ask me what to do.
　(2) Mariel didn't know where to go.
　(3) Degas liked to paint dancers who were dancing.
　(4) He has the dog that barked at the girl yesterday.

01 (1), (2) '의문사+to부정사'가 문장 속에서 decide와 know의 목적어 역할을 하고 있다. (3) a man이 선행사이므로 which가 아니라 who나 that이 적절하다. (4) the movie가 선행사이므로 who가 아니라 which나 that이 적절하다.

02 ③ some pictures가 선행사이므로 who가 아니라 which나 that이 적절하다. ④ 'how to do'가 show의 목적어로 쓰여야 한다.

03 주격 관계대명사는 선행사가 사람이면 who나 that을 쓰고 사물이나 동물이면 which나 that을 쓴다.

시험대비 실력평가
p.23~25

01 ①　　**02** ②　　**03** ③　　**04** who → which 또는 that　　**05** ⑤　　**06** ④
07 ⑤　　**08** (1) which　(2) that　(3) that　(4) were

---

　(5) who　(6) who　(7) which was
09 I can't decide what to wear. / I can't decide what I should wear.
10 (1) ③, who[that]　(2) ③, which[that]
11 (1) how　(2) to spend　(3) what　(4) I should
　(5) how to read　　**12** ②　　**13** ①, ⑤
14 ①　　　　**15** (1) how they should[can] do
　(2) where I should put　(3) what I should do
16 ⑤　　　　**17** ③　　　　**18** ④
19 (1) where to buy　(2) which[that] have

01 do it이 나와 있으므로 목적어로 쓰일 수 있는 것은 적절하지 않으며 'why+to부정사'는 쓰지 않는다.

02 사람을 선행사로 하는 주격 관계대명사로는 that이나 who를 쓴다.

03 첫 문장에서는 the problem이 solve의 목적어로 있으므로 what이나 that은 적절하지 않다. 두 번째 문장에서는 the message가 선행사이므로 which나 that이 적절하다.

04 a party가 선행사이므로 who가 아니라 which나 that이 적절하다.

05 목적어 it이 있으므로 what이 아니라 how나 where 등이 나와야 한다.

06 주격 관계대명사는 선행사가 사람이면 who나 that을 쓰고 사물이나 동물이면 which나 that을 쓴다.

07 ① They went to the restaurant which[that] was famous for its traditional Korean food. ② I know a girl whose name is Karen. ③ Please let me know which way I should go. which가 way를 수식하도록 해야 한다. ④ Tom has a painting which was drawn by a famous artist.

08 (1) 선행사가 사물이므로 which가 적절하다. (2) 선행사가 '사람+동물[사물]'인 경우에는 반드시 관계대명사 that을 써야 한다. (3) 선행사가 사물이므로 that이 적절하다. (4) 주격 관계대명사의 선행사가 복수이므로 복수 동사가 적절하다. (5) a great novelist가 선행사로 사람이므로 who가 적절하다. (6) who를 목적격 whom 대신 쓸 수 있지만 whom을 who 대신 쓰지는 않는다. (7) 주격 관계대명사는 생략할 수 없으나 뒤에 분사나 부사구가 오는 경우 '주격 관계대명사+be동사'를 생략할 수 있으므로 which was를 쓰거나 which was를 생략한 형태로 써야 한다.

09 의문사+to부정사 = 의문사+주어+should+동사원형, what to wear: 무엇을 입을지

10 주격 관계대명사는 다음에 동사가 나오며 선행사가 사람이면 who나 that을, 사물이나 동물이면 which나 that을 쓴다.

11 (1) the machine이 목적어로 나와 있으므로 how가 적절하다. (2) '의문사+to부정사'가 적절하다. (3) why는 '의문사+to부정사'로 쓰이지 않는다. (4), (5) '의문사+to부정사'나 '의문사+주어+should+동사원형'이 적절하다.

12 주어진 문장과 ②번은 주격 관계대명사로 그 쓰임이 같다. ④번은 목적격 관계대명사이다.

13 go는 자동사로 목적어가 필요 없으므로 what은 적절하지 않고 'why+to부정사'는 쓰지 않는다.

14 주어진 문장과 ①번의 that은 주격 관계대명사이다. ② 접속사 ③ 지시대명사 ④ 지시형용사 ⑤ 지시부사

15 '의문사+to부정사'는 '의문사+주어+should/can+동사원형'으로 바꾸어 쓸 수 있다.

16 선행사가 사람이나 사물 또는 동물일 경우 모두 쓰일 수 있는 것은 that이다.

17 how to use: 어떻게 ~할지

18 an animal이 선행사이므로 which나 that을 써야 한다. ⑤번에서는 주격 관계대명사 that을 썼으므로 관계사절에서 주어로 쓰인 it을 삭제해야 한다.

19 (1) where to buy: 어디에서 살지 (2) 선행사가 사물이므로 which나 that을 쓴다.

서술형 시험대비
p.26~27

01 which → who[that], taught → (to) teach, using → to use

02 (1) who → which[that]
   (2) is running → (which[that] is) running
   (3) whom → who
   (4) is → are
   (5) who she teaches → who teaches

03 (1) how you should swim
   (2) Which movie we should watch
   (3) whom I should thank

04 (1) Here are two club leaders who[that] want students to join their clubs.
   (2) This is the tea which[that] is good for your health.
   (3) The movie which[that] was directed by James Cameron was interesting.
   (4) There are a boy and his dog that are running at the playground.
   (5) Do you know the girl (who is) dancing on the stage?

05 (1) You need to know how to play an instrument to join our club.
   (2) The old man didn't know how to use the smartphone.
   (3) When I should visit London has to be decided.
   (4) I don't know why I should go there.

06 (1) who is

   (2) which were

07 (1) We must learn how to speak English.
   (2) I don't know what to say to her.
   (3) Tell me where to park the car. 등 어법에 맞게 쓰면 정답

08 who[that] is reading a book

09 how to play

10 (1) Can you tell me how I can write an email in English?
   (2) I do not know what to do first.
   (3) Do you know that man who[that] is running along the river?

01 선행사가 people이므로 who나 that이 되어야 하며 helped의 목적격보어로 to부정사나 동사원형이 나와야 하고, '의문사(how)+to부정사'가 문장 속에서 teach의 직접목적어 역할을 하도록 하는 것이 적절하다.

02 (1) 선행사가 사물이므로 which나 that이 적절하다. (2) 주격 관계대명사는 생략할 수 없으나 뒤에 분사나 부사구가 오는 경우 '주격 관계대명사+be동사'를 생략할 수 있다. (3) 주격 관계대명사가 나와야 하므로 who나 that이 적절하다 who를 목적격 whom 대신 쓸 수 있지만 whom을 who 대신 쓰지는 않는다. (4) 주격 관계대명사절의 동사는 선행사의 수에 일치시킨다. (5) 관계대명사가 접속사와 대명사의 역할을 하므로 주어로 쓰인 she를 삭제해야 한다.

03 '의문사+to부정사'는 '의문사+주어+should/can+동사원형'으로 바꾸어 쓸 수 있다. 또한 의문사가 의문형용사로 쓰여 to부정사와의 사이에 명사가 올 수 있다.

04 선행사가 사람이면 who나 that을, 사물이나 동물이면 which나 that을, '사람+동물[사물]'이면 반드시 that을 쓴다. 주격 관계대명사는 생략할 수 없으나 뒤에 분사나 부사구가 오는 경우 '주격 관계대명사+be동사'를 생략할 수 있다.

05 (1) '의문사+to부정사'가 적절하다. (2) the smartphone이 목적어로 나와 있으므로 how가 적절하다. (3) '의문사+주어+should+동사원형'이 적절하다. (4) 'why+to부정사'는 쓰지 않는다.

06 주격 관계대명사는 생략할 수 없으나 뒤에 분사나 부사구가 오는 경우 '주격 관계대명사+be동사'를 생략할 수 있다.

07 '의문사+to부정사'는 문장 속에서 주어, 목적어, 보어 역할을 하는 명사구로 사용되어 '~해야 할지, ~하는 것이 좋을지'라는 뜻을 나타낸다.

08 the girl이 선행사이므로 who나 that을 이용한다.

09 피아노를 잘 친다는 대답으로 보아 'how to play the piano(피아노 치는 법)'가 적절하다.

10 (1) how+to부정사: 어떻게 ~할지 (2) what + to부정사: 무엇을 ~할지 (3) 주격 관계대명사는 선행사가 사람이면 who나 that을 쓴다.

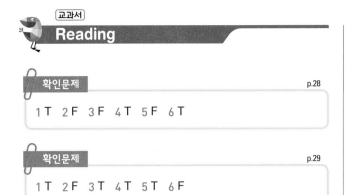

Reading

확인문제   p.29

1 T 2 F 3 T 4 T 5 T 6 F

교과서 확인학습 A   p.30~31

01 Why Don't You   02 Participating
in, to enjoy   03 How about   04 who want, to
join   05 what   06 Art Club
07 from   08 As, guess from
09 do volunteer work   10 participated in
11 On the dirty old walls, flying, jumping
12 As a result, into   13 to see,
thanked   14 don't have to   15 Anyone who
16 Come and be   17 Orchestra   18 the leader
19 playing music, came to school   20 those
21 play music for 22 how to play, a little bit
23 don't worry   24 practice hard, get better
25 also teach, as a service to
26 an eleven-year-old boy
27 At first, read a note
28 a simple song
29 Hearing him play, makes
30 By joining, have an opportunity
31 Come and join
32 for

교과서 확인학습 B   p.32~33

1 Why Don't You Join Our Club?
2 Participating in club activities is a great way to
enjoy your school life.
3 How about joining a club?
4 Here are two club leaders who want students to
join their clubs.
5 Let's listen to what they say.
6 The Picasso Art Club
7 Hi! I am Sora Kang from the Picasso Art Club.
8 As you can guess from the name of our club, we
paint.

9 We also do volunteer work from time to time.
10 Last summer, our club members participated in
the "Change Our Neighborhood" project.
11 On the dirty old walls of the buildings in our
neighborhood, we painted birds flying high in the
sky and dolphins jumping over blue waves.
12 As a result, the old neighborhood changed into a
bright and beautiful place.
13 The neighbors were happy to see our work and
thanked us.
14 You don't have to be a good painter.
15 Anyone who likes to paint can join.
16 Come and be a member of the Picasso Art Club.
17 The Boram Orchestra
18 Hi! I am Minsu Jang, the leader of the Boram
Orchestra.
19 Did you see several students playing music at the
main gate when you came to school today?
20 We were those students.
21 We play music for our friends every morning.
22 You need to know how to play an instrument a
little bit to join our club.
23 But don't worry if you don't play well.
24 We will practice hard and get better together.
25 We also teach children how to play musical
instruments as a service to our community.
26 I am teaching an eleven-year-old boy to play the
violin.
27 At first, he did not know how to read a note.
28 Now he can play a simple song.
29 Hearing him play the violin makes me very happy.
30 By joining our club, you can have an opportunity
to help others.
31 Come and join our club.
32 We are waiting for you.

시험대비 실력평가   p.34~37

01 (A)is (B)want (C)to join   02 ①, ③   03 two
club leaders   04 ③   05 ④
06 ⑤   07 to play → playing 또는 play
08 ③   09 준호   10 ②
11 잘하는 것: 공을 패스하는 것과 빨리 달리기
못하는 것: 공을 헤딩하는 것
12 will join → join   13 ②, ④

14 participating in   15 who 또는 that

16 ①   17 ④   18 ③

19 how to play 또는 to play   20 ②

21 ⑴ 매일 아침 친구들을 위해 음악을 연주한다. ⑵ 지역
사회를 위해 아이들에게 악기를 연주하는 법을 가르친다

22 ① joining → to join   23 ④   24 ⓐ득점,
ⓑ목표   25 ③   26 They will introduce
and sell books to people.   27 ③

01 (A) 동명사 'Participating'이 주어이므로 is가 적절하다. (B)
선행사가 'two club leaders'이므로 want가 적절하다. (C)
want+목적어+to부정사이므로 to join이 적절하다.

02 How about ~ing? = What about ~ing? = Why don't
you 동사원형?: ~하는 게 어때?

03 '두 명의 동아리 대표'를 가리킨다.

04 주어진 문장의 As a result에 주목한다. ③번 앞 문장의 결과를
가리키므로 ③번이 적절하다.

05 ⓐ와 ④번은 ~하다시피[~이듯이], ① 이유, ② (비례) ~함에
따라, ③ (자격 기능 등이) ~로(서), ④ (때) ~하고 있을 때, ~
하면서

06 ⑤그림 그리는 것을 좋아하는 사람은 누구라도 피카소 미술 동
아리의 회원이 될 수 있다.

07 지각동사 see의 목적격보어 자리에 to부정사를 쓸 수 없다.

08 동아리에 가입하려면 악기를 연주하는 '법'을 조금 알아야 한다
고 하는 것이 적절하다.

09 보람 오케스트라 동아리에 가입하려면 악기를 연주하는 법을 조금
알아야 한다고 했기 때문에, '능숙한 피아니스트는 아니지만 열심
히 피아노를 연습하는 준호'가 가입할 수 있다.

10 앞에 나오는 내용과 상반되는 내용이 뒤에 이어지므로
However가 가장 적절하다. ① 게다가, 더욱이, ③ 그러므로,
④ 비슷하게, ⑤ 예를 들어

11 '공을 패스하는 것'을 잘하고 '빨리 달린다.' 그러나, 나는 '공을
헤딩하는 법'을 모른다고 했다.

12 조건의 부사절에서는 현재시제가 미래시제를 대신한다.

13 ⓐ와 ①, ③, ⑤는 형용사적 용법, ② 부사적 용법, ④ 명사적
용법,

14 participating만 쓰면 틀림. join = participate in: ~에 참석
하다

15 선행사가 사람(two club leaders)이고 주어 자리이므로 주격
관계대명사 who 또는 that이 적절하다.

16 ⓐ from: (판단의 근거) ~로 (보아), ⓒ into: 상태의 변화를
나타냄

17 ④ 이웃 마을에 있는 건물들의 더럽고 오래된 벽에 그림을 그린
'결과', 오래된 마을이 밝고 아름다운 곳으로 바뀌었다고 하는 것
이 적절하다. ② 게다가, ⑤ 즉, 다시 말해

18 ⓓ와 ②, ④, ⑤번은 부사적 용법, ① 명사적 용법, ③ 형용사
적 용법

19 'teach+목적어+to부정사' 또는 'teach+목적어+의문사+to부
정사'

20 ⓑ와 ②번은 음, 음표, strike a note on a piano: 피아노로 어

떤 음을 치다, ① (기억을 돕기 위한) 메모, 기록 ③ (격식을 차
리지 않은 짧은) 편지, 쪽지, ④ 공책, ⑤ 주의하다, 유념하다,
주목하다

21 ⑴ 매일 아침 친구들을 위해 음악을 연주한다고 했다. ⑵ 민수
가 열한 살 소년에게 바이올린을 가르치고 있는 것처럼, 지역 사
회를 위해 아이들에게 악기를 연주하는 법을 가르친다

22 would like to부정사: ~하고 싶다

23 ④ 박 순호는 공을 헤딩하는 법을 모른다.

24 ⓐ make a goal: 득점하다, ⓑ goal(=aim, end, purpose):
목표

25 hold: 개최하다

26 사람들에게 책을 소개하고 팔 것이다.

27 ③ 전시회의 규모는 알 수 없다. ① 도서 전시회, ② 나눔중학
교, ④ 5월 5일 ⑤ 책을 사랑하는 사람

서술형 시험대비   p.38~39

01 (A)volunteer work   (B)painting   (C)painting

02 ⓐflying   ⓑjumping

03 need not 또는 don't need to

04 (A)a little   (B)eleven-year-old   (C)happy

05 unless

06 We also teach children how to play musical
instruments as a service to our community.

07 It changed into a bright and beautiful place.

08 must not → don't have to 또는 need not

09 Anyone who likes to paint can join.

10 악기를 연주하는 법을 조금 알아야 한다.

11 (A)worry   (B)get better

12 make → makes

01 피카소 미술 동아리는 미술 동아리이고 가끔 '자원봉사'도 한다.
'그림 그리는 것'을 좋아하는 사람은 누구나 동아리에 가입할 수
있고 '그림을 잘 그릴' 필요는 없다.

02 각각 뒤에서 앞의 명사를 수식하는 현재분사로 고치는 것이 적
절하다.

03 don't have to = need not = don't need to: ~할 필요가 없
다

04 (A) a little: '양'이나 '정도'가 조금, a few: '수'가 조금, a bit:
'정도'가 조금, (B) eleven-year-old가 boy를 수식하는 형용
사 역할을 하기 때문에 year에 s를 붙이지 않는 것이 적절하다.
(C) 목적격보어이므로 부사를 쓸 수 없고 형용사를 써야 한다.

05 if ~ not = unless

06 'as'를 보충하면 된다.

07 밝고 아름다운 곳으로 변했다.

08 여러분은 그림을 잘 그릴 '필요는 없다'고 해야 하므로 don't
have to나 need not으로 고치는 것이 적절하다. must not은
'금지'를 나타낸다.

09 anyone who: ~인 사람은 누구나

10 우리 동아리에 가입하기 위해서는 '악기 연주하는 법을 조금 알

아야 합니다.'라고 했다.

11 민수는 학생들에게 연주를 잘 못해도 그들이 열심히 연습하고 함께 '좋아질 것'이기 때문에 '걱정하지' 말라고 말한다.

12 동명사 Hearing이 주어이므로 단수 취급하여 makes로 고치는 것이 적절하다.

영역별 핵심문제
p.41~45

01 ② 02 ③ 03 ④

04 for 05 (1) (A)ctually (2) Where, to cook
(3) (o)pportunity 06 ② 07 ①

08 ⑤ 09 ⓐcooking ⓑcook ⓒcooking

10 ⑤ 11 ① 12 ③ 13 looking

14 looking at the stars 15 ①, ⑤

16 where to put 17 ② 18 (1) I can
get (2) to take (3) to look (4) which, to wear

19 (1) who (2) which 20 ⑤

21 (1) We are looking for volunteers.
(2) They are good at English.
(3) The friend lives in New Zealand.
(4) Chuck gave the present to her on her birthday.

22 ④

23 (1) She wants to see a movie which is interesting.
(2) Rose who works for a bank is Jake's best friend.
(3) James bought a new computer which is really nice.

24 several students playing music at the main gate when you came to school today 25 ①, ④

26 ① 27 ②, ⑤ 28 (A)Last summer (B) high (C)thanked 29 ③

30 sick children 31 magic 32 ②

33 ⑤

01 ②번은 반의어 관계이고 나머지는 동의어 관계이다. ① gift: 선물 present: 선물 ② dark: 어두운 bright: 밝은 ③ activity: 활동 action: 행동, 활동, 실행 ④ actually:실제로, 사실은 really: 정말로, 실제로 ⑤ enter: ~에 들어가다 join: 참여하다, 가입하다

02 be good at: ~을 잘하다 look for: ~을 찾다 participate in: ~에 참여하다

03 그 사람들 결혼 선물로 뭘 사줘야 할까요? get: ~을 사다, ~을 획득하다

04 ask for help: 도움을 청하다 thank for: ~에 대해 감사하다

05 (1) actually: 실제로, 사실은 (2) cook: 요리하다 (3) opportunity: 기회

06 enjoy는 동명사를 목적어로 사용할 수 있고, love는 동명사와 to부정사 둘 다 목적어로 사용할 수 있다. ⓐ to read → reading ⓔ to go → go 제안하는 말을 할 때 'Let's 동사원형 ~.'을 사용한다.

07 ① 소년의 취미가 무엇인지는 언급되지 않았다. ② 유미는 무슨

종류의 책을 읽기를 좋아하니? ③ 방과 후에 그들은 어디에 갈 계획입니까? ④ 유미는 읽는 것을 좋아하니? ⑤ 남자아이는 읽는 것을 좋아하니?

08 질문에 대한 대답에 made를 사용하였으므로, 과거의 일을 물어보는 질문이 어울린다. breakfast: 아침식사

09 ⓐ enjoy는 동명사를 목적어로 취한다. ⓑ cook: 요리사,; 요리하다 ⓒ cooking: 요리, 음식

10 but은 '그러나', '하지만'이라는 뜻으로 반대 또는 대조되는 말이 나와야 한다. 사람들과 일하는 것을 즐기며, 해보고 싶다는 말이므로, ⑤번이 어울린다.

11 interest: 관심

12 ⓒ that → when 여기서 when은 접속사로 '~할 때'의 의미이다.

13 enjoy는 동명사를 목적어로 취한다.

15 사람을 선행사로 하는 주격 관계대명사는 that이나 who를 쓴다.

16 where to put: 어디에 두어야 할지

17 ②번은 명사절을 이끄는 접속사이고 나머지는 모두 주격 관계대명사이다.

18 (1)~(3) 의문사+to부정사 = 의문사+주어+should/can+동사원형 (4) 의문대명사 which가 의문형용사로 쓰여 to부정사와의 사이에 명사가 올 수 있다.

19 선행사가 사람이면 who, 사물이면 which를 쓴다.

20 ⑤ the story가 목적어로 나와 있으므로 what을 how나 when, where 등으로 고치거나 the story를 삭제해야 한다.

21 관계대명사는 두 문장의 공통되는 명사나 대명사와 접속사의 역할을 하는 것이므로 관계사절에 공통되는 (대)명사를 원래대로 써준다.

22 ④번은 부정사의 형용사적 용법이고 나머지는 모두 명사적 용법으로 '의문사+to 부정사'로 쓰였다.

23 주격 관계대명사는 선행사가 사람이면 who나 that을 쓰고 사물이나 동물이면 which나 that을 쓴다.

24 '여러분들이 오늘 학교에 왔을 때 정문에서 음악을 연주하고 있던 몇 명의 학생들'을 가리킨다.

25 ⓑ와 ②, ③, ⑤번은 동명사, ①, ④번은 현재분사

26 '매일 아침' 연주한다.

27 ⓐ와 ①, ③, ④: 가끔, ② 항상 ⑤: 거의 ~ 않다

28 (A) '여름에'는 in summer라고 하지만, '지난여름에'는 전치사 in 없이 last summer라고 한다. (B) 하늘 '높이' 나는 새들이라고 해야 하므로 high가 적절하다. high: 높은; 높이, highly: 매우, 대단히, (C) were와 병렬구문을 이루도록 thanked라고 하는 것이 적절하다.

29 ③ Picasso Art Club은 그림 동아리이므로 '그림 그리는 것'을 좋아하는 사람은 누구나 가입할 수 있다고 하는 것이 적절하다.

30 '아픈 어린이들'을 가리킨다

31 Abracadabra 동아리는 '마술' 동아리이다. 5월 5일에 회원들이 한국 병원을 방문하여 아픈 어린이들에게 '마술'을 보여주고 '마술'하는 법을 가르쳐줄 것이다.

32 ⓐ와 ②번은 축제 마당, 풍물 장터, book fair: 도서 전시회 ① 공정한, ③ 금발의, ④ (수, 크기, 양이) 상당한, 제법 큰[많은], ⑤ (날씨가) 맑은 breezy: 산들바람이 부는

33 ⓑ look for: ~을 찾다, ⓒ sell은 'to'를 사용하여 3형식으로 고친다.

01 (p)ractice　　02 ④　　　　03 ④　　　　04 What
　　time　　05 join　　　　06 ③　　　　07 to play
08 (1) As a result　(2) At first, interested　(3) change
　　into　(4) let us know how to
09 (B) → (C) → (A)　　　　10 (B) → (A) → (C)
11 What do you enjoy doing when you have free time?
12 (1) Jisu asked her mother where to put the bag.
　　(2) Do you know what we should do next?
　　(3) I couldn't decide what to cook.
　　(4) There are a few girls who[that] are playing
　　　　basketball on the playground.
　　(5) Janet loves books which[that] have many
　　　　funny pictures.
　　(6) Linda and her dog that were crossing the
　　　　street were injured.　　13 ③
14 (1) get → to get
　　(2) what → how
　　(3) What he to eat → What to eat 또는 What he
　　　　should eat
　　(4) which → who[that]
　　(5) is standing → (who/[that] is) standing
　　(6) whom → who[that]
　　(7) is → are
　　(8) who he liked → who liked
15 ②, ⑤　　　16 to join　　　17 volunteer
18 we painted birds flying high in the sky and dolphins
　　jumping over blue waves　19 ①　　　20 ②
21 ④　　　　22 ②

01 주어진 단어는 동의어 관계이다. chief: 장, 우두머리 leader:
　　지도자, 대표 training: 훈련 practice: 연습
02 ① leader: 지도자, 대표 / 그는 음악 클럽의 지도자이다. ②
　　interest: 관심 / 오페라에 관심 있어요? ③ garden: 정원 / 그
　　집은 나무와 꽃이 있는 정원이 있다. ④ a little bit: 아주 조금 /
　　너는 조금 더 늦게 와도 된다. ⑤ drone: 무인 비행기 / 무인비행
　　기(드론)는 작은 원격 조정의 헬리콥터이다.
03 ⓐ, ⓑ, ⓒ는 cookies를 가리키며, ⓓ는 doughnuts를 가리킨다.
04 'At 2:00(2시에)'라는 시간 정보가 나왔으므로, What time(몇
　　시에)이 어울린다.
05 join: 참여하다, 가입하다 / 1. 조직, 사회, 그룹의 구성원이
　　되다 2. 다른 사람이 관련된 활동에 참여하기 시작하다. 위의 대
　　화에서는 2번의 의미로 사용되었다.
06 ①, ④ 여자아이는 어제 쿠키를 만들었다. ② 그들은 이번 주 토
　　요일에 여자아이 집에서 만날 것이다. ③ 남자아이가 무슨 음식
　　을 만들 수 있는지는 언급되지 않았다. ⑤ 여자아이는 이번 주
　　토요일에 도넛을 만들 것이다.
07 would like to+동사원형: ~하고 싶다 how to+동사원형: ~하
　　는 방법, 어떻게 ~하는지 play the 악기 이름: ~을 연주하다

08 (1) as a result: 결과적으로 (2) at first: 처음에 interested:
　　관심[흥미]이 있는 (3) change into: ~로 변화하다[바뀌다]
　　(4) let+목적어+동사원형: …가 ~하게 하다
09 주말에 무엇을 했는지 질문하자, (B) 가족을 위해 아침식사를 만
　　들었다고 대답한다. (C) 이어서 요리를 즐기는지 질문하자 (A)
　　요리를 즐기며, 자신은 좋은 요리사이고 가족들이 자신의 요리를
　　좋아한다고 대답한다.
10 예쁜 가방을 보고, 어디서 샀는지 질문하자 (B) 여동생이 만들어
　　주었다고 대답한다. (A) 여동생이 좋은 디자이너라고 칭찬하자,
　　(C) 동의하며, 옷을 만드는 것도 즐긴다고 말한다.
11 enjoy+동명사: ~하는 것을 즐기다 free time: 여가 시간
　　when:(접) ~할 때
12 (1)~(3) '의문사+to부정사'는 문장 속에서 주어, 목적어, 보
　　어 역할을 하는 명사구로 사용된다. (4)~(6) 주격 관계대명사
　　는 선행사가 사람이면 who나 that을 쓰고 사물이나 동물이면
　　which나 that을 쓴다. 선행사가 '사람+동물[사물]'인 경우에는
　　반드시 관계대명사 that을 써야 한다.
13 ③ '의문사+to부정사'가 주어 역할을 하고 있다.
14 (1) '의문사+to부정사'가 적절하다. (2) weight가 목적어로 나
　　와 있으므로 how가 적절하다. (3) '의문사+to부정사'나 '의문
　　사+주어+should+동사원형'이 적절하다. (4) 선행사가 사람
　　이므로 who나 that이 적절하다. (5) 주격 관계대명사는 생략
　　할 수 없으나 뒤에 분사나 부사구가 오는 경우 '주격 관계대명사
　　+be동사'를 생략할 수 있다. (6) 주격 관계대명사가 나와야 하
　　므로 who나 that이 적절하다. who를 목적격 whom 대신 쓸
　　수 있지만 whom을 who 대신 쓰지는 않는다. (7) 주격 관계대
　　명사절의 동사는 선행사(shoes)의 수에 일치시킨다. (8) 관계
　　대명사가 접속사와 대명사의 역할을 하므로 주어로 쓰인 he를
　　삭제해야 한다.
15 ⓐ와 ②, ⑤번은 동명사, 나머지는 다 현재분사
16 want+목적어+to부정사
17 volunteer: 자원봉사자, 그 일을 하기 원하기 때문에 그 일에
　　대한 보수 없이 일을 하는 사람
18 'high'를 보충하면 된다.
19 ① anyone who = whoever: ~인 사람은 누구나
20 주어진 문장의 those students에 주목한다. ②번 앞 문장의
　　several students를 받고 있으므로 ②번이 적절하다.
21 ⓐ와 ④ ~으로, ~로서, ① ~이므로, ~이기 때문에, ② ~하는대
　　로, ③ [보통 as … as ~로 형용사·부사 앞에서] ~와 같은 정도
　　로, ⑤ ~함에 따라, ~할수록
22 ② '처음에' 그는 음표를 읽는 법을 몰랐지만 이제 그는 간단한
　　노래를 연주할 수 있다고 하는 것이 적절하다. ① ③ 마침내, ④
　　그러므로, ⑤ 그 결과

01 (D) → (A) → (B) → (C)
02 Can you make a paper cat?
03 Do you know how to?
04 I will ask her for help.
05 (1) how to get (2) how to make (3) when to wake

9

(4) where to stop (5) what to do (6) Whom to meet

06 (1) Kay lives in a house which has a beautiful garden.

(2) Naomi who is standing over there is very beautiful.

07 They participated in the "Change Our Neighborhood" project.

08 As   09 that

10 (A)those (B)hard (C)play

11 they should

12 (A)leader (B) join

01 (D) 유미에게 책을 읽는 것을 즐기는지 질문하자, (A) 과학 책을 읽는 것을 좋아한다고 대답하면서 상대방은 어떤지 질문한다. (B) 상대방도 책을 읽는 것을 좋아한다고 대답하자 (C) 방과 후에 도서관에 가자고 제안한다.

02 'Do you know how to+동사원형 ~?' 또는 'Can you+동사원형 ~?'을 이용해 상대방의 능력이나 무언가를 하는 방법에 대해 물을 수 있다.

03 know: 알다 how to+동사원형: ~하는 방법, 어떻게 ~하는지 / 여기서 how to 뒤에 use it이 생략되어 있다.

04 will+동사원형: ~할 것이다 ask for help: 도움을 청하다

05 '의문사+to부정사'는 '의문사+주어+should/can+동사원형'으로 바꾸어 쓸 수 있다.

06 주격 관계대명사는 선행사가 사람이면 who나 that을 쓰고 사물이나 동물이면 which나 that을 쓴다.

07 피카소 미술 동아리 회원들은 지난여름 "우리 마을 바꾸기" 프로젝트에 참여했다.

08 as a result: 그 결과

09 주격 관계대명사 that이 적절하다.

10 (A) 뒤에 나오는 명사가 복수(students)이므로 지시형용사도 복수형인 those를 쓰는 것이 적절하다. (B) '열심히' 연습할 것이라고 해야 하므로 hard가 적절하다. hard: 열심히, hardly: 거의 ~ 않는, (C) 지각동사 hearing의 목적격보어 자리에 to부정사를 쓸 수 없으므로 play가 적절하다.

11 '의문사+to부정사'는 '의문사+주어+should+동사원형'으로 바꿔 쓸 수 있다. 아이들에게 악기를 연주하는 법을 가르치는 것이므로 they should로 고치는 것이 적절하다.

12 장 민수는 보람 오케스트라의 '회장'이고 동아리의 활동을 소개하면서 학생들에게 동아리에 '가입할' 것을 권한다.

창의사고력 서술형 문제
p.52

|모범답안|

01 (1) enjoy flying a drone.

(2) want to make a pizza.

02 (A) Name (B) FC Boram (C) passing (D) running

(E) heading (F) a good team player

03 (1) I don't know how to play the computer games.

(2) What to say is important to you.

(3) I'd like to know when to start.

(4) Let me know where to go.

(5) Tell me whom to find.

01 (1) enjoy는 동명사를 목적어로 사용한다. fly: (항공기·우주선·인공위성을) 조종하다, 날게 하다 drone: 무인 비행기 (2) want는 to부정사를 목적어로 사용한다. make: 만들다

단원별 모의고사
p.53~56

01 ③   02 ①   03 (1) interest (2) join

(3) neighbors (4) own

04 (p)ractice (h)old (n)eighborhood

(1) held (2) neighborhood (3) practice   05 ④

06 (A)them (B)I'm going (C)come   07 ②, ④

08 ⑤   09 drone   10 how to

11 ④ Of course not. → Of course.

12 (1) leader (2) orchestra   13 Thank you for your interest in our club.

14 (A) When did you start playing the violin?

(B) Do you have any experience playing in a group?

(C) Do you enjoy teaching others?   15 ①, ④

16 ②

17 (1) Tell me how to use this computer.

(2) He didn't know where[when/how] to go.

(3) Do you know how to swim? 또는 Do you know how I should swim?

(4) The doctors (who/[that] are) working in this hospital are very kind.

(5) Did you meet the girl that is wearing sunglasses?

(6) Mary has a cousin who[that] lives in Seoul.

(7) Melina took some pictures of her friends who were on a hiking trip.   18 ①, ④

19 ④   20 (A) to paint (B)a good painter

21 ③   22 ②, ④, ⑤

23 Hearing him play the violin makes me very happy.

01 walk: (사람·동물을) 걷게 하다

02 get: ~을 사다, ~을 획득하다.

03 (1) interest: 관심 (2) join: 참여하다, 가입하다 (3) neighbor: 이웃 one of 복수명사: ~ 중의 하나 (4) own: (소유격 다음에서 강조어로서) 자기 자신의, 직접 ~한

04 (1) hold: (모임·식 등을) 개최하다 / 회의, 파티, 선거 등을 특정한 장소 또는 특정한 시간에 갖다 / 그 회의가 이 호텔에서 개최될 것이다. (2) neighborhood: 동네, (도시 내의 한 단위) 지역 / 당신 주변의 지역이나 특정한 지역의 근처 또는 거기에 사는 사람들 / 이 동네에 좋은 중국집이 있나요? (3) practice: 연습; 연습하다 / 더 잘하기 위해서 규칙적으로 무엇인가를 하다

/ 나는 기타 연주를 연습할 필요가 있다.

05 주어진 문장에서 '네가 원한다면 우리 집에 와서 같이 해도 돼.'라는 내용이 나왔으므로, 남자아이가 도넛을 만드는 방법을 배우고 싶다고 하는 말 다음에 주어진 문장이 오고, 이후 시간 약속을 하는 말이 나오는 것이 흐름상 적절하다.

06 (A) 복수명사 cookies를 받기 때문에 them을 사용해야 한다. (B) this Saturday는 미래에 관한 시간 정보이기 때문에 'be going to 동사원형(~할 예정이다)'을 사용해야 한다. (C) should+동사원형: ~해야 한다

07 ② went → will go ④ cookies → doughnuts로 바꿔야 대화의 내용과 일치한다.

08 주어진 문장에서 She는 지나를 의미하므로 '아마도 지나는 어떻게 하는지 알 거야.'라는 문장 다음에 나와야 적절하다.

09 drone: 무인 비행기 / 조종사가 없지만 무선으로 작동되는 비행기

10 how to+동사원형: ~하는 방법, 어떻게 ~하는지

11 종이 고양이를 만드는 방법이 쉽다고 말하고 있으므로, 종이 고양이를 만드는 법을 알고 있다고 대답해야 적절하다.

12 (1) leader: 지도자, 대표 / 그룹, 조직, 국가 등을 총괄하거나 통제하는 사람 (2) orchestra: 오케스트라, 교향악단 / 많은 다른 종류의 악기를 연주하는 음악가와 지휘자에 의해 지휘되는 큰 규모의 집단

13 thank for: ~에 대해 감사하다 interest: 흥미

14 (A) when: 언제 start: 시작하다 play the 악기 이름: ~을 연주하다 (B) experience: 경험, 경력 (C) enjoy: 즐기다 teach: 가르치다

15 ① do의 목적어 it이 있으므로 what을 쓸 수 없다. ④ 'why+to부정사'는 사용하지 않는다.

16 Where are the pictures that were taken by Gibson? 주격 관계대명사의 선행사가 복수이므로 복수 동사를 써야 하며 '접속사+(대)명사의 역할을 하므로 주어로 쓰인 it을 삭제해야 한다.

17 (1) '의문사+to부정사'가 적절하다. (2) go는 자동사이므로 what과는 어색하며 how나 where 또는 when 등이 적절하다. (3) '의문사+to부정사'나 '의문사+주어+should+동사원형'이 적절하다. (4) 주격 관계대명사는 생략할 수 없으나 뒤에 분사나 부사구가 오는 경우 '주격 관계대명사+be동사'를 생략할 수 있다. (5) 관계대명사가 접속사와 대명사의 역할을 하므로 주어로 쓰인 she를 삭제해야 한다. (6) 주격 관계대명사절의 선행사가 사람이므로 who나 that을 써야 하며 동사는 선행사(a cousin)의 수에 일치시킨다. (7) 주격 관계대명사가 나와야 하므로 who나 that이 적절하다. who를 목적격 whom 대신 쓸 수 있지만 whom을 who 대신 쓰지는 않는다.

18 ⓐ와 ①, ④: 참가했다, ② 계획을 짰다, ③ 준비했다, ⑤ 돌보았다

19 ⓑ와 ①번은 현재분사, 나머지는 다 동명사이다. ② 전치사의 목적어, ③ 주어, talk behind somebody's back 남의 험담을 하다, ④ 목적어, ⑤ 보어

20 만약 당신이 '그림 그리는 것'을 좋아한다면 피카소 미술 동아리의 회원이 될 수 있지만 '그림을 잘 그릴' 필요는 없다.

21 ⓐ as: ~으로, ~로서 ⓓ By ~ing: ~함으로써

22 ⓑ와 ①, ③은 명사적 용법, ② 형용사적 용법, ④ 부사적 용법(목적), ⑤ 부사적 용법(정도)

23 동명사 Hearing을 주어로 사용하여 영작하면 된다.

The Two Roads

시험대비 실력평가
p.60

01 ②	02 ④	03 ②	04 ⑤
05 ①	06 ⑤		

07 (1) such (2) wide (3) (T)ake, away (4) go to
    (5) was (s)cared of (6) What if

01 silent(조용한)의 명사형은 silence이다. ① happy: 행복한 happiness: 행복 ③ sad: 슬픈 sadness: 슬픔 ④ kind:친절한 kindness: 친절 ⑤ dark: 어두운 darkness: 어두움

02 besides: 게다가 in addition: 더구나, 게다가 / 게다가 밖은 매우 춥다.

03 reply: 대답하다 answer: 답하다 / 나는 뭐라고 대답해야 할지 몰랐다.

04 look like+명사: ~처럼 보이다 / 그 옷을 입으니 완전히 다른 사람처럼 보여요.

05 break out: 발발하다 / 일부 사람들은 전쟁이 일어날 것을 우려하고 있다.

06 foreigner: 외국인 ① 그것은 긴 여행이었다. ② 그것에 대한 의견을 주시겠습니까? ③ 대부분의 십대들은 스트레스를 많이 받는다. ④ 갈매기들이 내 머리 위를 날고 있다. ⑤ 너의 삼촌은 외국인처럼 보인다.

07 (1) such: 너무나 ~한 (2) wide: 넓은 (3) take away: ~을 빼앗다 (4) go to the doctor: 병원에 가다 (5) be scared of: ~을 두려워하다 (6) What if 주어 동사 ~?: 만약 ~이라면 어떻게 될까?

서술형 시험대비
p.61

01 (d)arkness   02 get
03 take
04 (c)ub, (o)pinion, (t)hrone
    (1) throne (2) cubs (3) opinion
05 (1) foreign (2) scared (3) worried (4) good
06 (1) Who is your favorite character in this movie?
    (2) Have you ever been to India before?
    (3) I liked the last scene in that drama.

01 beautiful: (형) 아름다운 beauty: (명) 아름다움 / 형용사인 dark는 뒤에 ness를 붙여 명사가 된다. dark(어두운): darkness(어두움)

02 get+형용사: ~하게 되다 / 나는 노래하기 위해 무대에 설 때마다 긴장된다. get better: (병·상황 등이) 좋아지다 / 오늘은 날씨가 더 좋아질 거라고 하던데요.

03 take ~ for a walk: ~을 산책하러 데리고 가다 / 그는 그의 개들과 해안가를 따라 산책하는 것을 좋아한다. take away: 빼앗다 / 그들은 공기 중에서 나쁜 것들을 없애 준다.

04 cub: (곰, 사자 등의) 새끼 / 곰, 사자 또는 다른 포유류의 어린 새끼 opinion: 의견 / 어떤 것에 대한 생각이나 믿음 throne: 왕좌, 왕위 / 왕, 여왕 또는 황제가 앉는 장식용 의자 (1) 누가 왕위를 계승할 것인가? (2) 새끼 곰들은 사육사에 의해 보살핌을 받는다. (3) 우리는 고양이를 입양하는 것에 대해 다른 의견을 가지고 있다.

05 (1) foreign: 외국의 / 외국어를 배우는 가장 효과적인 방법은 무엇이냐? (2) be scared of: ~을 두려워하다 / 그 사람들도 치과의사를 무서워했다고 생각하니? (3) be worried about: ~에 대해 걱정하다 / 그의 가족들은 그의 나쁜 식습관 때문에 몹시 걱정했다. (4) be good at: ~을 잘하다 / 그는 어려운 수학 문제 푸는 것을 잘한다.

06 (1) character: 등장인물 (2) ever: 언제든, 한 번이라도 (3) scene: 장면

교과서 Conversation

핵심 Check
p.62~63

1 I'm, about / worry, can pass
2 (C) → (B) → (A)
3 (1) you think of (2) do you feel
4 (C) → (B) → (A) → (D)

교과서 대화문 익히기

Check(√) True or False
p.64

[1] T [2] F [3] T [4] T [5] F [6] T

교과서 확인학습 p.66~67

Listen & Speak 1 A

(w)orried about / Don't

Listen & Speak 1 B

1. Do you have, plans / to, (w)orried about / worry, won't
2. go / wrong / scared of / (f)riendly, looks scary because

Listen & Speak 1 C

1. I'm worried about / Don't worry
2. I'm worried about / You'll do great
3. I'm worried about my future. / worry, find something

Listen & Speak 2 A

What do you, of / like

Listen & Speak 2 B

1. saw / What did you think of it / (d)isappointed
2. What do you think of / think, (d)elicious / What
3. do you think of / happy that, myself

Listen & Speak 2 C

1. think of / looks light
2. What do you think / good on you

Real-Life Zone

who looked like / (h)ad / looked / were, to meet / comfortable / was worried about speaking, anymore / the hardest / What do you, (a)bout

시험대비 기본평가 p.68

01 ④   02 ①   03 ①

04 (C) → (A) → (B) → (D)

01 Don't worry.: 걱정하지 마. 걱정하는 상대방을 안심시키고 있는 표현이다.

02 be worried about: ~에 대해 걱정하다 / 여자아이가 날씨에 대해서 걱정하고 있으니 남자아이가 내일 제주도에 비가 내리지 않을 거라고 여자아이를 안심시키고 있다.

03 'What do you think of+명사?'는 '~에 대해 어떻게 생각해?'의 의미로, 무언가에 대하여 상대방의 의견을 물을 때 사용할 수 있다.

04 (C) 영화 '딸'을 보았느냐는 질문에 (A) 봤다고 대답한다. (B) 영화에 대한 상대방의 의견을 묻고 (D) 별로 좋지 않았다고 대답한다.

시험대비 실력평가 p.69~70

01 ④   02 ③   03 ②   04 ④

05 ⑤   06 ③   07 ①, ⑤   08 like

09 (A) who   (B) but   (C) when   10 ③

---

11 ①   12 (A) for   (B) of[about]

01 스마트폰에 대해 걱정하고 있는 상대방에게 근처에 서비스 센터가 있다고 안심시켜 준다.

02 Do you have any special plans for tomorrow?: 내일 특별한 계획이 있니? / 내일 계획에 대해서 묻자, 아침에 제주도에 갈 거라고 대답한다.

03 weather: 날씨에 대해 걱정하니까, 상대방이 제주도에 비가 내리지 않을 거라고 대답했다.

04 ① 여자아이는 내일 아침에 할 계획을 가지고 있다. ② 여자아이는 제주도의 날씨에 대해 걱정하고 있다. ③ 남자아이는 내일 제주도에 비가 올지 안 올지에 대해 알고 있다. ④ 남자아이는 내일 아침에 제주도에 갈 것이다. ⑤ 내일 제주도에 비가 내리지 않을 것이다.

05 만화책에 대한 의견을 묻는 말에, '네가 멋지다고 생각해.'는 어색하다.

06 be worried about: ~에 대해 걱정하다

07 What do you think of[about]+명사?: ~에 대해 어떻게 생각해?

08 look like+명사: ~처럼 보이다

09 (A) 선행사 someone을 수식하는 주격 관계대명사이다. 선행사가 사람이므로 which가 아닌 who가 적절하다. (B) 예전에는 영어로 말하는 것에 걱정했다는 내용과 더 이상은 걱정하고 있지 않다는 역접의 접속사로 연결하는 것이 적절하다. (C) when: (접) ~할 때

10 ① 여자아이가 영어를 말할 때 어떻게 느끼는가? ② 남자아이는 외국인과 무엇을 했는가? ③ 현재 남자아이가 걱정하는 것은 무엇인가? ④ 언제 여자아이가 남자아이를 보았는가? ⑤ 얼마나 자주 남자아이가 외국인을 만나는가?

11 주어진 문장의 it은 the book that I borrowed from the library(도서관에서 빌린 책)를 의미한다. 책을 봤는지 물어보는 질문에 무슨 책을 찾는지 물으며, 거실에서 책을 본 것 같다는 말이 어울리므로 ①에 주어진 문장이 들어가는 것이 적절하다.

12 (A) look for: ~을 찾다 (B) What do you think of[about]+명사?: ~에 대해 어떻게 생각해?

서술형 시험대비 p.71

01 will rain → won't rain

02 It's cool! → They're cool!

03 it gets easier and easier.

04 What do you think about me joining both of you for lunch?

05 (B) → (A) → (C)   06 (A) → (C) → (B)

01 내일 아침에 제주도에 가기 때문에 날씨를 걱정하고 있는 여자
아이에게 걱정하지 말라고 안심시키는 말과 내일 제주도에 비가
올 거라는 말은 어울리지 않는다.

02 These sunglasses는 복수 명사이므로 대명사 It이 아니라
They로 받는다.

03 get+형용사: ~하게 되다, 비교급 and 비교급: 점점 더 ~한[하
게]

04 What do you think of[about]+명사?: ~에 대해 어떻게 생
각해? join: 함께하다

05 학교 식당 음식에 대해 상대방의 의견을 묻자, (B) 식당 음식이
맛있다고 대답한다. (A) 이어서 최고의 품목이 무엇인지 질문하
니까 (C) 김밥이라고 대답한다.

06 걱정스러워 보인다며 무슨 일이 있는지 질문하자, (A) 빌린 책
을 찾을 수 없다며 본 적이 있는지 질문한다. (C) 어떤 책을 말
하는지 질문하고, 거실에서 '갈매기의 꿈'을 본 것 같다고 말한
다. (B) 그 책이 맞다고 얘기하며 감사를 표한다.

교과서
Grammar

핵심 Check
p.72~73

1 (1) has gone   (2) has played   (3) Have, watched
2 (1) If   (2) leave[start], won't be   (3) if[whether], will be

시험대비 기본평가
p.74

01 ③

02 (1) If school ends early
　　(2) won't attend the party if she is not invited

03 (1) play → played
　　(2) has met → met
　　(3) Does he have → Has he
　　(4) for → since
　　(5) will rain → rains
　　(6) don't turn → turn

01 ③ 'have gone to'는 '~에 가고 없다'는 결과를 나타내는 것으
로 3인칭만 주어로 쓸 수 있다. We have been to Seoul.로
고쳐야 한다.

02 (1) if는 '만약 ~한다면'이라는 뜻의 접속사이다. (2) 조건의 부
사절에서는 미래시제 대신에 현재시제를 쓴다.

03 (1) 현재완료는 'have[has]+과거분사'의 형태이다. (2) 현재
완료는 과거를 나타내는 어구와 함께 쓸 수 없다. (3) 현재완

료의 의문문은 have를 주어 앞으로 보낸다. (4) 현재완료에서
'since+시간 명사', 'for+기간 명사'를 쓴다. (5) 조건의 부사절
에서는 미래시제 대신에 현재시제를 쓴다. (6) unless는 'if ~
not'의 뜻이므로 don't를 삭제해야 한다.

시험대비 실력평가
p.75~77

01 ⑤　　　　02 ①　　　　03 ③　　　　04 ④
05 ②　　　　06 (1) has (2) visited (3) gone (4) went
　　(5) if (6) call　　　　07 ⑤
08 You'll miss the bus unless you walk more quickly. /
　 You'll miss the bus if you don't walk more quickly.
09 ①　　　　10 ②　　　　11 ④　　　　12 ③
13 ③, ⑤
14 (1) If my friend moves near my house, I can see
　　　her more often.
　　(2) You will be late unless you hurry up. / You will
　　　be late if you don't hurry up.
　　(3) Please let us know if you will come to the party
　　　tomorrow.
15 (1) Anna has loved Sam since she met him first.
　　(2) Mariel has lived in Tallinn for seven years.
16 ②, ④　　　17 ①　　　18 ③　　　19 ⑤

01 ⑤ 언제 컴퓨터를 샀는지 묻는 문장으로 특정한 과거의 한 시점
을 묻는 것이므로 현재완료가 아니라 과거시제가 되어야 한다.
보통 when은 현재완료와 쓰이지 않는다.

02 조건의 부사절을 이끄는 if가 적절하다. unless는 'if ~ not'의
뜻으로 문맥상 적절하지 않다.

03 현재완료의 의문문은 'have+주어+과거분사 ~?'이다.
'have[has] been to'는 '~에 가 본 적이 있다'는 경험을 나타내
고, 'have gone to ~'는 '가버리고 없다'는 뜻이므로 gone이
적절하다.

04 ④ unless = if ~ not이므로 If가 아니라 Unless가 되어야 한다.

05 긍정문이므로 already가 적절하다.

06 (1) 주어가 3인칭 단수이므로 has가 적절하다. (2) 현재완료는
'have[has]+과거분사'의 형태이다. (3) have[has] gone to
는 '~에 가고 없다'는 결과를 나타낸다. (4) 현재완료는 과거를
나타내는 어구와 함께 쓸 수 없다. (5) unless는 'if ~ not'이므
로 if가 적절하다. (6) 조건의 부사절에서는 미래시제 대신에 현
재시제를 쓴다.

07 ① Jenny raised a dog last year. ② Karen has been to
Malaysia three times. ③ Susan and I have been to
Paris. ④ Tom has studied English for ten years.

08 unless = if ~ not

09 현재완료형의 질문에 대한 답은 have 동사를 이용해 답한다.

10 ②번만 '~인지 아닌지'의 의미로 명사절을 이끄는 접속사로 쓰였다.

11 현재완료의 결과적 용법(…해서 (그 결과) 지금 ~하다)을 이용하여 과거에 우크라이나로 간 것이 아직도 거기에 있다는 현재의 결과를 나타내도록 한다.

12 조건의 부사절에서는 미래시제 대신에 현재시제를 쓰므로 앞에는 meet, 뒤에는 내용에 맞게 will give를 쓴다.

13 ③번은 계속 용법, ⑤번은 경험 용법, 나머지는 모두 완료 용법으로 쓰였다.

14 (1) 조건의 부사절에서는 미래시제 대신에 현재시제를 쓴다. (2) unless는 'if ~ not'의 뜻으로 보통 not과 함께 쓰이지 않는다. (3) if가 명사 역할을 하는 경우로 미래를 나타낼 때에는 미래 시제를 써야 한다.

15 (1) 처음 만났을 때 사랑에 빠져 지금도 사랑하고 있으므로 현재완료의 계속적 용법으로 나타낸다. (2) 7년 전에 살기 시작해서 아직도 살고 있으므로 현재완료의 계속적 용법으로 나타낸다.

16 의미상 ②, ④가 적절하다. unless = if ~ not, immediately: 즉시 take time: 천천히 하다

17 ①과 <보기>는 '경험' 용법이다. ②, ⑤ 결과 용법 ③ 계속 용법 ④ 완료 용법

18 조건의 부사절에서는 미래시제 대신에 현재시제를 쓰며 unless는 'if ~ not'의 뜻으로 not과 함께 쓰이지 않는다.

19 현재완료의 의문문은 'Have[Has]+주어+과거분사 ~?'로 나타낸다. 'have[has] been to'는 '~에 가 본 적이 있다'는 경험을 나타내고, 'have gone to ~'는 '~에 가고 (지금) 없다'는 결과를 나타낸다.

서술형 시험대비 p.78~79

01 (1) Have you read *Charlie and the Chocolate Factory* already?
   (2) Jina has experienced a lot while traveling.
   (3) Don't open a shop unless you know how to smile.
   (4) Why don't you eat some snacks if you are hungry?

02 naming → named, help → helped, unless → if

03 (1) |예시답| I have cooked ramyeon many times.
   (2) |예시답| I have never experienced skiing up to now.

04 (1) Sophia has lost her cap.
   (2) I have visited Paris twice.

05 (1) then → 삭제 또는 You had a lot of trouble then.
   (2) since → for (3) been → gone (4) will go → go
   (5) Unless → If

06 (1) Jason has eaten Korean food.
   (2) Mankind has existed for thousands of years.
   (3) If it rains, I will take an umbrella with me.
   (4) Don't miss your classes unless it is really important.

07 (1) Stephanie hasn't used her computer for 3

years. / Has Stephanie used her computer for 3 years?
   (2) You haven't seen it before. 또는 You have never seen it before. / Have you seen it before?

08 (1) If (2) Unless

09 (1) has rained (2) has gone (3) has broken

01 (1) 현재완료의 '완료' 용법 (2) while 다음에 '주어+be동사'가 생략된 형태이다. (3) unless = if ~ not, how to smile: 웃는 법 (4) Why don't you ~?: ~하는 게 어때?

02 Louis라고 이름이 지어진 것이므로 named, 현재완료는 'have[has]+과거분사'의 형태, unless는 'if ~ not'이므로 의미상 if가 적절하다.

03 현재완료의 '경험' 용법을 이용하여 쓴다.

04 (1) 현재완료의 '결과' 용법을 이용한다. (2) 현재완료의 '경험' 용법을 이용한다.

05 (1) 현재완료는 과거를 나타내는 어구와 함께 쓸 수 없다. then은 '그때'라는 뜻으로 과거를 나타내는 말이다. (2) 현재완료에서 'since+시간 명사', 'for+기간 명사' (3) have[has] been to는 '~에 가 본 적이 있다'는 경험을 나타내고, have[has] gone to는 '~에 가고 없다'는 결과를 나타내므로 have gone to로 고쳐야 한다. (4) 조건의 부사절에서는 미래시제 대신에 현재시제를 쓴다. (5) unless는 'if ~ not'이므로 if가 적절하다.

06 (1) 현재완료의 '경험' 용법을 이용한다. (2) 현재완료의 '계속' 용법을 이용한다. (3) 조건의 부사절에서는 미래 시제 대신에 현재 시제를 쓴다. (4) unless는 'if ~ not'이므로 단어 수에 맞추어 unless를 쓴다. mankind: 인류

07 현재완료의 부정문은 'have[has]+not[never]+과거분사'로, 의문문은 'Have[Has]+주어+과거분사 ~?'로 나타낸다.

08 명령문, and ~: '~해라, 그러면'(= If ~), 명령문, or ~: '~해라, 그렇지 않으면'(= If not ~ = Unless ~)

09 (1) 현재완료의 '계속' 용법을 이용한다. (2), (3) 현재완료의 '결과' 용법을 이용한다.

교과서
Reading

확인문제 p.80

1 T 2 F 3 F 4 T 5 T 6 F

확인문제 p.81

1 T 2 F 3 F 4 T

02 went on   03 in front of

04 said, into, across   05 her cubs

06 Take, run up   07 find happiness

08 go and find   09 How can we know

10 What if   11 Besides, away from

12 Instead of   13 How, if

14 went their own way

15 went into, swam across   16 There was

17 sleeping   18 took her cubs

19 took him to, made   20 as a king

21 broke out, lost his throne   22 on the road

23 talked about, for the last   24 I was right

25 have lived   26 have had

27 regret my choice

28 nothing, something to remember

1 The Two Brothers

2 Two brothers went on a journey.

3 They found a rock in front of a forest.

4 It said, "Go into the forest and swim across the river.

5 There you will find a bear and her cubs.

6 Take the bear cubs and run up the mountain.

7 There you will find happiness."

8 The younger brother said, "Let's go and find happiness together."

9 "No," said the older brother. "How can we know this is true?

10 What if the river is too wide?

11 Besides, will it be easy to take the cubs away from their mother?

12 Instead of finding happiness, we can be killed!"

13 The younger brother replied, "How can we know if we don't try?"

14 They separated, and they both went their own way.

15 The younger brother went into the forest and swam across the river

16 There was the bear.

17 She was sleeping.

18 He took her cubs and ran up the mountain.

19 When he reached the top, some people took him to their city and made him their king.

20 There he lived as a king for five years.

21 Then a war broke out, and he lost his throne.

22 He was on the road again.

23 One day, the two brothers met again and talked about their lives for the last five years.

24 The older brother said, "I was right.

25 I have lived quietly and well.

26 You were once a king, but you have had a lot of trouble."

27 The younger brother answered, "I don't regret my choice.

28 I may have nothing now, but I will always have something to remember."

01 ③   02 a rock   03 ④   04 ⑤

05 ④   06 ②   07 ③   08 ②, ③

09 ①   10 ②   11 ②, ④   12 ⑤

13 flying better than others 14 ①, ④ / ②, ③, ⑤

15 own beliefs

16 He was on the road again.   17 ②, ⑤

18 something → nothing, nothing → something

19 named   20 (A) others (B) hard (C) learn

21 ③   22 ③   23 ③, ⑤

24 In fact, As a matter of fact

25 You look like a traveler, not a king now.

01 ⓐ go on a journey: 여행을 떠나다, ⓑ swim across: ~을 헤엄쳐 건너다

02 '바위'를 가리킨다.

03 ④ '곰 새끼들'을 데리고 산 위로 뛰어 올라가라고 되어 있다.

04 주어진 문장의 replied에 주목한다. ⑤번 앞 문장의 형의 말에 대해 대답한 것이므로 ⑤번이 적절하다.

05 ⑤번은 현재분사이고 ⓐ와 나머지는 모두 동명사이다.

06 ② 동생은 "우리가 시도하지 않으면 어떻게 알 수 있어?"라고 말했다.

07 ③은 '형'을 가리키고, 나머지는 다 '동생'을 가리킨다.

08 ⓐ와 ①, ④, ⑤ 형용사적 용법, ② 부사적 용법, ③ 명사적 용법

09 ① 어떤 사람들이 왜 그를 그들의 왕으로 만들었는지는 대답할 수 없다. ② Because a war broke out. ③ He has lived quietly and well. ④ They talked about their lives for the last five years. ⑤ No.

10 동생은 "함께 가서 행복을 찾자. 우리가 시도하지 않으면 어떻게 알 수 있어?"라고 말했고, 형은 "싫어."라고 말했기 때문

에, 제목으로는 '행복을 향한 두 가지 선택들'이 적절하다. ④ doubtful: 확신이 없는, 의심[의문]을 품은, response: 반응, ⑤ put ~ into practice: 실천하다

11 ⓐ와 ①, ③, ⑤는 명사적 용법, ② 형용사적 용법, ④ 부사적 용법

12 ⑤ 도전적인, ① 부정적인, ② 이기적인, ③ 후한, 너그러운, ④ 수동적인, 소극적인

13 '남들(다른 갈매기들)보다 더 잘 나는 것'을 가리킨다.

14 ⓑ와 ①, ④번은 명사절을 이끄는 접속사, ⓒ와 ②, ③, ⑤번은 관계대명사

15 위의 독서 감상문을 쓴 사람이 이 책을 좋아하는 이유는 이 책이 '자기 자신의 믿음'의 힘에 대해 배우도록 도와주었기 때문이다.

16 on the road: 여행 중인, (살 수 있는 집이 없이) 이리저리 옮겨 다니는

17 ⓑ와 ②, ⑤번은 계속 용법, ① 완료 용법, ③ 결과 용법, ④ 경험 용법

18 나는 지금 '아무것도' 없지만 언제까지나 기억할 '어떤 것'이 있다고 하는 것이 적절하다.

19 A named[called] B: B라고 일컫는[불리는] A

20 (A) '남들(다른 갈매기들)보다'라고 해야 하므로 others가 적절하다. the other: 둘 중 나머지 하나, (B) '열심히' 일한다고 해야 하므로 hard가 적절하다. hardly: 거의 ~ 않는, (C) help+목적어+원형(혹은 to부정사)이기 때문에 learn이 적절하다.

21 위 글은 '독서 감상문'이다. ① 수필, ② 전기, ④ 일기, ⑤ (신문·잡지의) 글, 기사

22 ⓐ와 ④, ⑤번은 계속 용법, ① 완료 용법, ② 경험 용법, ③ 결과 용법

23 ⓑ와 ①, ②, ④: (오랜만에 만났을 때) 어떻게 지내셨어요? How have you been? = What have you been up to? = What have you been doing? = How have you been getting along? ③ 처음 뵙겠습니다. ⑤ 컨디션이 어때요?

24 Actually: 실제로, In fact, As a matter of fact를 쓰면 된다.

25 앞 문장에서 형이 한 말을 가리킨다.

---

(4) 행복을 찾는 대신에, 자신들이 죽을 수 있기 때문이다.

08 unless we try

09 for

10 I may have nothing now, but I will always have something to remember.

11 (A) quietly and well　(B) as a king

12 flying

13 anything

---

01 What if: ~이라면 어찌 되는가?, ~이라면 어쩌지?

02 '형'은 동생과 함께 가지 '않는' 것을 선택했고, '동생'은 혼자 숲에 들어가서 강을 헤엄쳐 건너 새끼 곰을 데리고 산을 '뛰어 올라갔다.'

03 그들은 '헤어졌고' 둘 다 자신의 길을 갔다라고 해야 하므로 separated로 고쳐야 한다. separate: 갈라지다, 헤어지다, unite: (다른 사람들과) 연합하다

04 (A) reach는 타동사로 전치사 없이 바로 목적어를 써야 하므로 reached가 적절하다. (B) 전쟁이 '일어났다'고 해야 하므로 broke가 적절하다. break out: 발발[발생]하다, (C) 동사(lived)를 꾸며주므로 부사 quietly가 적절하다.

05 그는 '왕좌'를 잃었다, throne: 왕위, 왕좌, 왕

06 우리는 '죽을 수 있어'라고 해야 하므로 수동태로 쓰는 것이 적절하다.

07 "No," 다음에 형이 한 말을 쓰면 된다.

08 unless = if ~ not

09 지난 5년 '동안'이라고 해야 하므로 for가 적절하다. for+숫자, during+특정 기간

10 'nothing'을 보충하면 된다.

11 지난 5년 동안 형은 '조용히 잘' 살아 왔고, 동생은 '왕으로' 살았다.

12 practice는 목적어로 동명사를 취한다.

13 이 책에 따르면, 만약 내가 포기하지 않으면 내가 원하는 '어떤 것'이라도 할 수 있다. give up = stop trying to do something

---

서술형 시험대비　p.90~91

01 What if

02 (A) older　(B) not　(C) younger　(D) ran

03 united → separated

04 (A) reached　(B) broke　(C) quietly

05 throne

06 kill → be killed

07 (1) 이것이(앞에 나온 내용이) 사실인지 알 수 없기 때문이다.

　　(2) 강이 너무 넓을 수도 있기 때문이다.

　　(3) 곰 새끼들을 엄마에게서 빼앗는 것이 쉽지 않을 수도 있기 때문이다.

영역별 핵심문제　p.93~97

01 (1) unfriendly　(2) happiness　　　02 ③

03 ①

04 (1) The king ruled his country for a long time.

　　(2) Thank you for your support.

05 ④　　　　06 ④　　　　07 ①

08 (A) great (B) that

09 about the painting, painted herself, the colors

10 (A) What　(B) What　　　11 ④

12 I was worried about speaking in English before, but not anymore.　　　13 ①

14 If you are Spring people　15 ⑤　　　16 ①

17 ④	18 ③	19 ⑤
20 founded → found		21 cubs
22 On the mountain		23 In addition 24 ②
25 25	26 ①	27 ④ 28 ②
29 ⑤	30 ②	31 ④

01 (1) 반의어 관계이다. noisy: 시끄러운 quiet: 조용한 friendly: 친절한 unfriendly: 불친절한, 쌀쌀맞은 (2) 형용사와 명사의 관계이다. popular: 인기 있는 popularity: 인기 happy: 행복한 happiness: 행복

02 character는 '성격'이라는 뜻도 있지만, ③에서는 '등장인물'의 의미로 사용되었다. ①이 상점의 전 품목이 세일이에요! ② 나는 그 신문에서 그의 작품을 논평했다. ③ 처음에 그녀는 가장 중요한 인물인 신데렐라의 배역을 원했다. ④ 베스트셀러의 제목이 뭔가요? ⑤ 그들은 지난달에 헤어졌다.

03 correct: 올바른 / 잘못을 가지고 있지 않은

04 (1) rule: 지배하다 (2) support: 지지; 지지하다

05 'What do you think of/about ~?', 'What's your opinion of/about/on ~?', 'What's your view on ~?', 'How do you feel about ~?', 'How do you like ~?' 등은 의견을 묻는 말이다. ④ 너는 무엇을 하고 싶니?

06 많이 가지면 가질수록 더 많이 원한다는 말에, 상대방이 걱정된다는 말은 어색하다.

07 역사 수업에 대한 의견을 묻는 말에, 나한테는 어렵다고 대답한다. ① 나에게 어려워. ② 너에게 잘 어울려. ③ 네가 좋아하니 기뻐. ④ 좋은 생각이야. ⑤ 가볍고 빨라 보여.

08 (A) look+형용사: ~하게 보이다 (B) happy 다음에 '주어+동사'가 있으므로 접속사인 that을 사용해야 한다.

09 그들은 여자아이가 직접 그린 그림에 대해 이야기하고 있다. 남자아이는 그 그림의 색을 좋아한다. talk about: ~에 대해 이야기하다 painting: 그림 color: 색깔

10 (A) What do you think of/about+명사?: ~에 대해 어떻게 생각해? (B) what: 무엇 / 최고의 품목이 뭐라고 생각하니?

11 외국인처럼 보이는 사람과 같이 있는 것을 보았다는 말에, (C) 그렇다고 대답하며, 외국인과 점심을 같이 먹었다고 대답한다. (B) 좋은 시간을 보내고 있었던 것처럼 보인다는 말에 (A) 그렇다고 말하며, 한 달에 두 번 만나서 점심을 먹는다고 대답한다. (D) 여자아이는 외국인과 좀 더 편하게 이야기하고 싶은 자신의 소망을 말한다.

12 be worried about: ~에 대해 걱정하다 not anymore: 더 이상 않는

13 since(~한 이래로)는 보통 현재완료와 함께 많이 쓰인다. 이때 since절에는 과거 시제가 많이 쓰인다.

14 그림의 내용에 맞게 if를 이용하여 조건절을 쓴다.

15 ⑤번은 '결과' 용법이지만 나머지는 '계속' 용법이다.

16 '~한다면'이라는 조건과 '~인지 아닌지'를 나타낼 수 있는 if가 적절하다.

17 ⓐ have met → met ⓓ have gone to → have been to

18 ③번은 명사절을 이끌어 '~인지 아닌지'의 뜻으로 쓰였고 나머지는 모두 부사절을 이끌어 '만약 ~한다면'으로 쓰였다.

19 현재완료는 과거를 나타내는 어구와 함께 쓸 수 없다.

20 바위를 '발견했다'라고 해야 하므로 find의 과거형인 found로 고쳐야 한다. found - founded: 설립하다

21 cub: (곰·늑대·사자 등의) 새끼, the young: 새끼들(the+형용사 = 복수 보통명사)

22 '산에서'를 가리킨다.

23 besides = in addition: 게다가

24 ② 모험하지 않으면 얻는 것도 없다. "우리가 시도하지 않으면 어떻게 알 수 있어?"라는 말은 행동으로 옮겨 실천할 것을 뜻한다. ① 돌다리도 두들겨 보고 건너라. ③ 엎질러진 우유를 놓고 울어봐야 소용없다. ④ 말하기는 쉬워도 실천하기는 어렵다. ⑤ 쥐구멍에도 볕들 날이 있다.

25 총 20명의 학생들 중에서 5명의 학생들이 친구와 이야기할 때 행복하다고 했으므로 '25'퍼센트에 해당한다.

26 ①은 의문부사(언제), 나머지는 모두 접속사(때)

27 맛있는 음식을 먹을 때 행복한 학생은 3명이고 수학에서 좋은 점수를 받을 때 행복한 학생은 2명이므로, 맛있는 음식을 먹을 때 행복한 학생의 수가 더 '많다.'

28 ⓐ와 ②, ③은 부사적 용법, ①, ⑤ 명사적 용법, ④ 형용사적 용법

29 ⑤ Jonathan이 언제 나는 연습을 하는지는 대답할 수 없다. ① *Jonathan Livingston Seagull* ② Richard Bach. ③ A seagull named Jonathan Livingston. ④ Flying better than others.

30 그는 그곳에서 많은 문제를 겪었다고 했으므로 자신의 선택을 '후회했다'고 하는 것이 적절하다. ① 받아 주다, 수락하다, ③ 개선하다, 향상시키다, ④ 달성하다, 성취하다, ⑤ 거절하다

31 여행가기로 결정할 때는 '기대에 찬' 심경이었다가 '실망하게' 되었다. disappointed: 실망한, expectant; 기대에 찬, frightened: 겁먹은, 무서워하는

단원별 예상문제   p.98~101

01 ① 02 look, on 03 about / are, at

04 (1) bigger and bigger (2) (H)appiness

05 ② 06 (C) → (D) → (A) → (B) 07 ③

08 ⑤ 09 character 10 ④ 11 ③

12 What do you think of our school cafeteria food?

13 (1) They have sold all the books.

(2) Mina has been to the flea market once.

(3) I have lived in Paris since I was born.

(4) The train has already departed from the station.

(5) If it is sunny tomorrow, we will go to the beach.

(6) I wonder if the dress will look good on you.

14 (1) gone → been (2) has → did (3) for → since

(4) lived → has lived　(5) will push → push

15 will it be easy to take the cubs away from their mother?

16 ④	17 ①	18 ⑤	19 ③, ⑤
20 ②	21 a war broke out		22 ④
23 ③	24 is his friend → his friend is		

25 How about reading it?

01 ① have, have a good time: 좋은 시간을 보내다 / 휴가 잘 보내셨어요? ② ruled, rule: 지배하다 / 로마는 500년 이상 동안 세계를 지배했다. ③ reply, reply: 대답하다 / 그녀에게 직업을 물어봤지만 그녀는 대답하지 않았다. ④ support, support: 지지; 지지하다 / 너는 그녀의 선택을 존중하고 지지해야 한다. ⑤ regret, regret: 후회하다 / 나는 그렇게 부주의했던 것이 후회스럽다.

02 look good (on 사람): (~에게) 잘 어울리다

03 be worried about: ~에 대해 걱정하다 be good at: ~을 잘하다

04 (1) 비교급 and 비교급: 점점 더 ~한[하게] (2) happiness: 행복

05 'I think I should study harder to get good grades.'는 '나는 좋은 성적을 얻기 위해 더 열심히 공부해야 한다고 생각한다.'의 의미로 수학에 대한 걱정을 해결하기 위해 할 수 있는 일이다.

06 (C) 내일의 계획을 물어보고 (D) 아침에 제주도에 갈 거라고 대답하며 날씨를 걱정하자, (A) 내일 제주도에는 비가 내리지 않는다고 걱정하지 말라고 안심시킨다. (B) 비가 오지 않는다는 말에 좋아한다.

07 ⓐ first ⓑ wrong ⓒ friendly ⓓ scary ⓔ big / 남자아이는 개를 무서워해 여자아이가 먼저 들어가기를 원했다.

08 주어진 문장은 '이미 두 번 읽었어요.'란 의미로 책을 읽어 봤는지 물어보는 질문의 대답으로 어울린다.

09 character: 등장인물 / 영화, 책 또는 연극에 있는 인물

10 by the way: 그런데(대화에서 화제를 바꿀 때 씀)

11 ① 여자아이는 '갈매기의 꿈'을 몇 번 읽었는가? ② 그들은 무슨 관계인가? ③ 여자는 '갈매기의 꿈'에서 어떤 등장인물을 좋아하는가? ④ 처음에, 왜 여자아이가 걱정스러워 보였는가? ⑤ 여자아이는 도서관에서 무슨 책을 빌렸는가?

12 What do you think of/about+명사?: ~에 대해 어떻게 생각해?

13 (1) 현재완료의 '결과' 용법을 이용한다. (2) 'have[has] been to'는 '~에 가 본적이 있다'는 경험을 나타낸다. (3) 현재완료의 '계속' 용법을 이용한다. (4) 현재완료의 '완료' 용법을 이용한다. (5) 조건의 부사절에서는 미래시제 대신에 현재시제를 쓴다. (6) if절이 명사 역할을 하는 경우도 있으며, 미래를 나타낼 때 미래시제를 써야 한다. look good on: ~에게 잘 어울리다

14 (1) have[has] been to는 '~에 가 본 적이 있다'는 경험을 나타내고, have[has] gone to는 '~에 가고 없다'는 결과를 나

타내므로 have been to로 고쳐야 한다. (2) '시장에서 기술이 활용 가능한 때는 언제였습니까?'라는 질문으로 when이 과거의 어느 시점인지를 묻는 의문사로 쓰여 현재완료와는 쓸 수 없다. (3) 현재완료에서 'since+시간 명사', 'for+기간 명사' (4) until now로 보아 현재완료가 적절하다. (5) 조건의 부사절에서는 미래시제 대신에 현재시제를 쓴다.

15 가주어 'it'을 보충하면 된다.

16 ④ 행복을 찾는 '대신에', 우리는 죽을 수 있어! ① ~ 외에도, ② ~와 함께, ③ ~ 때문에, ⑤ ~에 더하여

17 ① ~인지(ask, know, find out, wonder 등의 동사 뒤에 쓰여 두 가지 이상의 가능성 중 하나를 도입할 때 씀). ⓒ와 나머지는 모두 '만약'의 뜻으로 조건절을 이끈다.

18 주어진 문장은 "너는 한때 왕이었지만 많은 어려움을 겪었다."는 형의 말에 대한 동생의 대답이므로 The younger brother answered 다음인 ⑤번이 적절하다.

19 ⓐ와 ③, ⑤ ~에 도착하다, ① start from: ~를 떠나다, ② leave for: ~로 떠나다, ④ contact: 접촉하다, 연락을 취하다

20 이 글에서 형은 '자신의 선택이 옳았다'고 말하고 동생은 '자신의 선택을 후회하지 않는다'고 말하므로, 제목으로는 '나는 내 선택에 만족해!'가 적절하다. ③ get along with: ~와 잘 지내다, ④ quarrel: 다툼, ⑤ harmonious relations: 의좋은 사이

21 break out: 발발[발생]하다

22 ⓑ와 ④번은 (추측을 나타내어) ~일지[할지]도 모르다, 아마 ~일[할] 것이다, ①과 ⑤ (허락을 나타내어) ~해도 되다[좋다], ② ~하기 위하여, ③ (기원을 나타내어) ~이기를 (빌다)

23 ③ 만족한, ① 지루한, ② 후회하는, ④ 실망한, ⑤ 불안해하는, 염려하는

24 understands의 목적어에 해당하므로 간접의문문의 순서(의문사+주어+동사)로 고치는 것이 적절하다.

25 Why don't you 원형? = How about ~ing?: ~하는 게 어때?

서술형 실전문제　p.102~103

01 ⑤ excited → disappointed

02 ① think with → think of[about] ⑤ painted it mine → painted it myself

03 (1) I'm (a)nxious　(2) I'm (c)oncerned

04 (1) for　(2) before　(3) since

05 (1) has lived　(2) has gone to
　(3) have visited, three times

06 (1) If you finish your report by 6, you can play the computer games.
　(2) If you don't work hard, you won't overcome your weakness. (또는 Unless you work hard, you won't overcome your weakness.)

07 ② If I meet Suji, I will give her this letter.

08 older → younger

09 choice

10 내가 옳았다. / 나는 내 선택을 후회하지 않는다.

11 (A) How　(B) Besides　(C) if

12 Instead of finding happiness, we can be killed!

13 ⓑ the bear　ⓒ The younger brother

01 영화가 어땠는지 의견을 묻는 질문에 별로 좋지 않았다는 내용과 영화를 재미있게 봤다는 내용은 일치하지 않으므로 어울리지 않는다.

02 ① What do you think of/about+명사?: ~에 대해 어떻게 생각해? ⑤ 주어가 직접 했다는 사실을 강조하기 위해 재귀대명사를 사용한다.

03 'be worried about ~.', 'be anxious about ~.', 'be concerned about ~.' 모두 걱정을 표현하는 말이다.

04 (1) 현재완료에서 'since+시간 명사', 'for+기간 명사' (2) ago는 현재완료와 함께 사용할 수 없으나 before는 사용할 수 있다. (3) since(~이래로)는 보통 현재완료와 함께 많이 쓰인다. 이때 since절에는 과거시제가 많이 쓰인다.

05 (1) 현재완료의 '계속' 용법을 이용한다. (2) 현재완료의 '결과' 용법을 이용한다. (3) 현재완료의 '경험' 용법을 이용한다.

06 명령문, + and ~: '~해라, 그러면'(= If ~), 명령문, + or ~: '~해라, 그렇지 않으면'(= If not ~ = Unless ~)

07 조건의 부사절에서는 미래시제 대신에 현재시제를 쓴다.

08 왕좌를 잃고 다시 길바닥에 나앉은 사람은 '형'이 아니라 '동생'이다.

09 앞에 소유격이 있으므로 명사로 쓰는 것이 적절하다.

10 형의 생각: "나는 조용히 잘 살았어."라고 말하면서 자신이 옳았다고 했다. 동생의 생각: "나는 지금 아무것도 없지만 언제까지나 기억할 것이 있어."라고 말하면서 자신의 선택을 후회하지 않는다고 했다.

11 (A) '어떻게' 알 수 있어?'라고 해야 하므로 How가 적절하다. (B) '게다가'라고 해야 하므로 Besides가 적절하다. beside: ~ 옆에, (C) '우리가 시도하지 않으면'이라고 해야 하므로 if가 적절하다.

12 Instead of 뒤에 동명사로 써야 하고, 수동태(be killed)를 사용하는 것이 적절하다.

13 ⓑ는 '곰'을, ⓒ는 '동생'을 가리킨다.

창의사고력 서술형 문제　p.104

|모범답안|

01 I'm worried that I can't finish reading these books.

02 (1) If it is sunny tomorrow, I will go hiking.

(2) If I go to Jejudo, I'll swim in the sea.

(3) If you know the result, please let me know.

(4) If you exercise hard, you will become healthy.

03 (A) who　(B) character　(C) how　(D) such

(E) Why don't you

01 be worried about: ~에 대해 걱정하다 finish: 끝내다 do great: 잘하다

단원별 모의고사　p.105~108

01 ①　　02 about, to, for, at　　03 ③

04 ④　　05 ⑤

06 What do you think of this painting?　　07 worried

08 ④　　09 I'm scared of your dog.　10 ⑤

11 ⑤　　12 nervous　13 ③　　14 ③

15 ②

16 (1) have you started → did you start

(2) was → have been

(3) since → for

(4) will sleep → sleep

(5) Unless she doesn't wear → Unless she wears

(또는 Unless → If)

17 (1) Judy has been in her friend's house for two hours.

(2) Someone has taken away my umbrella.

18 ②　　19 ③　　20 ⑤　　21 ④

22 ②　　23 remember　24 ①

01 ①은 반의어 관계이다. 이외의 보기는 동의어 관계이다. ① separate: 헤어지다 unite: 통합하다 ② disappointed: 실망한, 기대에 어긋난 discouraged: 낙담한 ③ character: 등장인물 role: 배역 ④ happiness: 행복 pleasure: 즐거움, 기쁨 ⑤ correct: 올바른 right: 바른, 옳은

02 be worried about: ~에 대해 걱정하다 have to 동사원형: ~해야 한다 take ~ for a walk: ~을 산책하러 데리고 가다 at night: 밤에

03 ① scary: 무서운 / 이 큰 집에서 혼자 있는 것은 무섭다. ② nervous: 불안한 / 나는 시험 전에 정말 불안하다. ③ correct: 올바른 / 올바른 날짜와 시간을 선택하세요. ④ noisy: 시끄러운 / 나는 시끄러운 곳에서는 일에 집중할 수 없다. ⑤ comfortable: 편안한 / 그것은 사람들을 더 행복하고 더 편안하게 해줍니다.

04 ④는 never에 대한 영영풀이다 ever: 언제든, 한 번이라도 (at any time 언제든지) ① support: 지지 / 어렵거나 불행한 시기 동안 누군가에게 주어지는 도움, 격려 또는 위로 ② reply: 대답하다 / 어떤 것에 응답하여 무언가를 말하거나 쓰다 ③ teenager: 십대 / 13살에서 19살 사이의 사람 ⑤ separate: 헤어지다 / 따로 이동하다

05 'You'll find something you like to do. (네가 하고 싶은 것을 발견할 거야)'는 미래에 대해 걱정하고 있을 때 위로로 할 수 있는 말이다.

06 What do you think of/about+명사?: ~에 대해 어떻게 생각해?

07 be worried about: ~에 대해 걱정하다

08 (B) 아침에 제주도에 가기 때문에 날씨를 걱정하고 있는 여자아이에게 남자아이는 비가 안 온다고 안심시키는 것이 적절하다. (C) That's good to hear.: 그거 반가운 소리다.

09 be scared of: ~을 두려워하다

10 개가 커서 무섭게 보인다는 말이므로 이유를 나타내는 because가 어울린다.

11 주어진 문장에서 that은 the first time을 의미한다. 처음이 지나고 점점 쉬워진다는 것이므로 ⑤가 적절하다.

12 nervous: 불안한 / 일어나고 있는 일 또는 일어날 수도 있는 일에 대해서 걱정하고 염려하는

13 ⓐ look worried ⓑ that I borrowed ⓒ Have you seen ⓓ have you read ⓔ What did you think

14 주어진 문장과 ③번은 부사절을 이끌고 있으나 나머지는 명사절을 이끌고 있다.

15 ② 현재완료는 과거를 나타내는 어구와 함께 쓸 수 없다.

16 (1) 현재완료는 과거의 특정 시점을 나타내는 when과는 함께 쓰이지 않는다. (2) 7월 1일에 도착해서 7월 10일인 오늘까지 있으므로 현재완료의 '계속' 용법으로 나타내는 것이 적절하다. (3) 현재완료에서 'since+시간 명사', 'for+기간 명사' (4) 조건의 부사절에서는 미래시제 대신에 현재시제를 쓴다. (5) unless = if ~ not

17 (1) 현재완료의 '계속', (2) '결과' 용법을 이용한다.

18 동생의 말에 "싫어,"라며 여러 이유를 말하고 있으므로 '의심이 많다'고 하는 것이 적절하다. doubtful: 확신이 없는, 의심[의문]을 품은, ① 긍정적인, ③ 활동적인, ④ 자신감 있는, ⑤ 근면한, 성실한

19 추가하는 내용이 뒤에 이어지므로 Besides(게다가)가 가장 적절하다. ① 그러나, ② 그러므로, ④ 예를 들어, ⑤ 다시 말해

20 ⓑ와 ⑤번은 가주어, ① 그것(앞에 이미 언급되었거나 현재 이야기되고 있는 사물·동물을 가리킴), ②와 ④ 비인칭 주어, ③ 가목적어

21 ⓐ take 사람 to 장소: ~을 …로 데리고 가다, ⓒ talk about ~: ~에 대해 이야기하다

22 ⓑ와 ②번은 '~으로, ~로서(전치사)', ① (비례) ~함에 따라, ~할수록, ③ ~이므로, ~이기 때문에, ④ ~와 같이, ~하는 대로, ⑤ (보통 as ... as ~로 형용사·부사 앞에서) ~와 같을 정도로 statesman: 정치가

23 그 당시에는 그가 아무것도 없을지 모르지만, 언제까지나 '기억할' 거리가 있을 것이기 때문이다.

24 ① 동생이 '정상'에 도착했을 때, 어떤 사람들이 그를 자기들 도시로 데려가서 그들의 왕으로 만들었다.

Lesson 5

We Love Baseball

시험대비 실력평가
p.112

01 ⑤　　　02 I was about to call you when you called me.　03 ①　　04 support, (1) 응원하다
(2) 지원하다 (3) 지원, 후원　05 ④　　06 ③
07 ④

01 ⑤를 제외한 나머지는 동사와 동사의 행위를 하는 사람이다. 반면에 'cook'은 '요리하다'이나 'cooker'는 '요리 기구'라는 뜻이며, 요리사는 'cook'이다.

02 be about to: 막 ~하려는 참이다

03 order: 순서 / 그 문제들을 다른 순서로 살펴보자. ② class: 학급, 반 ③ lesson: 수업, 강의 ⑤ nature: 자연

05 in a hurry: 서둘러 / 이 일이 급하지 않기 때문에 서둘러 하지 않아도 된다. in the past: 과거에 / 과거에 의사들은 그 이유를 몰랐었습니다.

06 <보기>의 miss는 '놓치다'의 의미로 사용했다. ③은 '그리워하다'의 의미로 사용되었고 나머지는 '놓치다'의 의미로 사용되었다. ① 나는 영화의 시작 부분을 놓치는 걸 싫어한다. ② 내년에는 이 신나는 축제를 놓치지 마세요. ③ 저는 여러분이 학창시절(학교 생활)을 그리워할 것이라고 확신합니다. ④ 과학을 배우고 경험할 수 있는 이번 기회를 놓치지 마세요! ⑤ 그 경기를 놓치다니 애석합니다.

07 thunder: 천둥 / 폭풍우 동안 번개가 번쩍인 후에 들리는 하늘에서 나는 큰 소리

서술형 시험대비
p.113

01 (1) batter　(2) writer　02 can't wait
03 (1) stadium　(2) home team　(3) thunder　(4) match
04 Why　05 come　06 up
07 (1) a big fan of　(2) at bat　(3) is about to
(4) over there　(5) twice a week　(6) like to

01 주어진 보기는 동작과 동작의 행위자의 관계이다. act: 연기하다 actor: 배우 (1) bat: 공을 치다 batter: 타자 (2) write: 쓰다 writer: 작가

02 be looking forward to ~: ~을 기대하다, can't wait for ~: ~을 몹시 기대하다

03 (1) stadium: 경기장 / 이 경기장은 정말 거대해, 그렇지 않니? (2) home team: 홈팀 / 홈팀이 3대 0으로 원정 팀을 이겼다. (3) thunder: 천둥 / 경보음이 천둥 소리와 같다. (4) match: 경기 / 스페인 팀이 축구 경기에서 이기고 있어.

04 why don't we ~?: ~하는 게 어때?(제안, 권유) Why not?: 좋아.

05 come back to: ~으로 돌아오다, come out: 나오다

06 hurry up: 서두르다 / 서둘러 줄 수 있나요? 시간이 별로 없어요. warm up: (스포츠나 활동 전에) 몸을 천천히 풀다, 준비 운동을 하다 / 무거운 역기를 들기 전에 준비운동을 해라.

07 (1) be a big fan of: ~의 열렬한 팬이다 (2) at bat: 타석에 서서 (3) be about to 동사원형: 막 ~하려고 하다 (4) over there: 저기 (5) twice a week: 일주일에 두 번 (6) would like to 동사원형: ~하고 싶다

교과서
Conversation

핵심 Check
p.114~115

1 Which, or fish / meat
2 Which do you like better, dogs or cats
3 (B) → (D) → (A) → (C)
4 I can't wait for the trip. / I can't wait to take the trip.
5 can't , to

교과서 대화문 익히기

Check(√) True or False
p.116

1 F　2 T　3 F　4 T

교과서 확인학습
p.118~119

Listen and Speak 1 A

Which sport, or / more, twice, week

Listen and Speak 1 B

1 doing / I'm, at / Which country, or / to visit, like to
2 I'm thinking, getting, have / What, Which, better, or / Why don't, play with, can decide

Listen and Speak 2 A

Did / can't wait to watch

Listen and Speak 2 B

1 want to see / When did / bought it for me, come / can't wait to see

2 forget that / won't forget / excited, I can't wait

3 about, in / came, wants to see / can't wait to see

Real-Life Zone A

such / before, between, starts / Which team, support / miss, either / Hurry, left / sometime / about going to / while watching / I can't wait

Wrap Up

which sport do you like, or / about / big fan of / between, Have / I'm going to see, can't wait / fantastic

---

시험대비 기본평가　　　　　　　　　p.120

| 01 ③ | 02 ② | 03 ②, ④ | 04 ④ |

01　I can't wait.: 너무 기다려져.(희망, 기대 표현하기)

02　빈칸 다음에 일주일에 두 번 축구를 한다는 말로 보아 농구보다 축구를 더 좋아하는 것을 유추할 수 있다.

03　피터팬 아니면 마지막 잎새라는 말과 피터팬을 좋아한다는 말로 보아, 둘 중에 어느 것을 좋아하는지를 묻는다는 것을 유추할 수 있다. Which do you prefer?: 어느 것을 더 선호하니? Which story book do you like?: 너는 어떤 이야기책을 좋아하니?

04　'더 좋아하는 것에 대해 말할 때는 'I like A.', 'I like A better[more] (than B).'로 말할 수 있다.

시험대비 실력평가　　　　　　　　　p.121~122

01 ②	02 ④	03 ③	04 ④
05 ④	06 ④	07 I can't wait to see it.	
08 ②	09 ①	10 I'm going to go surfing.	

01　주어진 문장은 개와 고양이가 있다는 의미인데, 이것은 'Do you have a pet?(넌 애완동물을 기르니?)'의 대답이 될 수 있다. 그러므로 ②의 위치가 적절하다.

02　④의 문장은 '너의 애완동물과 놀 것이 매우 기다려져.'라는 기대의 말인데, 남자아이가 자신의 집에 와서 애완동물과 놀아 보는 것을 제안하기 전에 여자아이가 미리 말한 것이므로 어색하다.

03　③ 여자아이가 개와 고양이 중 어떤 동물을 더 좋아하는지는 대화에서 언급되어 있지 않다. ① 남자아이는 애완동물을 기르는가? ② 왜 남자아이는 여자아이에게 자신의 집에 오라고 제안을 하는가? ③ 어떤 동물을 여자 아이가 더 좋아하는가? 개 아니면 고양이? ④ 얼마나 많은 개를 남자아이는 기르고 있는가? ⑤ 어

떤 종류의 애완동물을 남자아이는 가지고 있는가?

04　무엇을 하고 있는지 묻는 질문에 (C) 지도를 보고 있다고 대답한다. (A) 두 나라에 표시한 것을 얘기하면서, 어느 나라를 먼저 방문하고 싶은지 묻자, (B) 미국을 방문하고 싶다고 대답하고 미국에서 농구 경기를 보고 싶다는 말을 한다.

05　선호에 대해 묻고 있는 질문에, 어느 것을 더 좋아한다는 답이 아닌 'Of course I do.(물론 나도 그래.)'는 어울리지 않는다.

06　'주어진 문장은 '오늘 오후에 우리 집에 올래?'라고 제안하는 말이다. 이에 대해 상대방이 거절이나 수락하는 것이 어울리므로, 'Of course.(당연하지.)'의 수락의 답과 연결될 수 있는 ④의 위치가 적절하다.

07　I can't wait: 너무 기다려져 'I can't wait.' 뒤에는 'for+ 명사'나 'to+동사원형'을 덧붙여 어떤 것을 기대하는지 쓸 수 있다.

08　지호에게 왜 그렇게 서두르는지 질문하자 (B) 천둥 대 코브라 경기가 6시에 시작한다며 6시 전에 집에 있어야 한다고 대답한다. (C) 코브라와 천둥 팀 중 어느 팀을 응원하는지 질문하자 (A) 코브라라고 대답한다. (D) 상대방도 코브라 팀을 응원한다고 말하며, 자신도 그 경기를 놓치고 싶지 않다고 말한다.

09　① 다음 코브라 홈 경기가 몇 시에 시작하는가? ② 경기를 보면서 그들은 무엇을 먹을 수 있는가? ③ 다음 코브라 홈 경기가 언제 있는가? ④ 그들은 어느 팀을 더 좋아하는가, 코브라 아니면 천둥? ⑤ 지금은 몇 시인가?

10　be going to 동사원형: ~할 것이다. 빈칸 다음에 서핑을 하러 가는 것이 기다려진다는 말을 했으므로 방학에 서핑을 하러 갈 것이다.

서술형 시험대비　　　　　　　　　p.123

01 (A) that (B) about　02 forget

03 He can't wait to go rock climbing this weekend.

04 (C) → (A) → (B)　05 (A) → (C) → (B)

06 (A) Have (B) have

07 to see the game on Saturday

01　(A) 다음에 주어와 동사가 나와 있으므로 접속사인 that이 어울린다. (B) be excited about: ~에 신나다, ~에 들뜨다

02　대화의 흐름상 이번 주말에 암벽 등반하러 가기로 한 것을 잊지 않겠다고 말하는 것이 어울린다.

03　be looking forward to (동)명사: ~을 기대하다 can't wait to 동사원형: ~을 기대하다

04　지수에 대해서 들었는지 물어보는 질문에 (C) 그녀에 대한 뭐를 얘기하는 것인지 질문하며 그녀가 캐나다에 살고 있다고 말한다. (A) 그녀가 한국에 돌아왔으며, 그녀가 상대방을 보고싶어 한다는 것을 전해 준다. (B) 이에, 그녀를 빨리 보고 싶다고 기대를 표현하는 말을 한다.

05 테니스와 야구 중 어떤 운동을 하는 것을 좋아하는지 질문하자 (A) 테니스 치는 것을 좋아한다고 대답한다. (C) 오늘 오후에 같이 테니스를 칠 것을 제안하자. (B) 수락의 대답을 한다.

06 Have you heard about ~?: ~에 대해 들어본 적 있니? (현재 완료의 경험적 용법) have: 가지다

07 'I can't wait.' 뒤에는 'to+동사원형'을 덧붙여 어떤 것을 기대 하는지 쓸 수 있다.

교과서
Grammar

핵심 Check
p.124~125

1 (1) don't (2) he (3) doesn't (4) didn't

2 (1) to (2) in

시험대비 기본평가
p.126

01 ④   02 ③

03 (1) was cleaned   (2) was written

　(3) doesn't she   (4) can he

04 (1) built → was built   (2) Dorothy → she

01 능동태를 수동태로 만들 때는 수동태 문장의 주어 자리에는 능 동태 문장의 목적어가 오고, 동사를 'be+pp'로 바꾸고 by 다음 에는 능동태 문장의 주어를 목적격으로 쓴다.

02 앞 문장에 일반동사가 사용되고 현재시제이므로 do를 사용하 며, 앞 문장이 긍정이므로 부정으로 쓰고, 인칭대명사 주어 they 를 써야 하며, 축약형으로 쓴다.

03 (1) 수동태는 'be+pp'의 형태이다. (2) 책 이름은 단수로 취급 한다. (3), (4) 부가의문문은 앞의 문 장이 긍정이면 부정으로 하고 부정이면 긍정으로 한다. be동사나 조동사가 있으면 그 be 동사나 조동사를 이용하고 일반동사일 경우는 do/does/did를 이용한다. 반드시 축약형을 사용해야 하고 주어는 인칭대명사로 바꿔 주어야 한다는 것에 주의해야 한다.

04 (1) 다리가 건설되는 것이므로 수동태가 적절하다. (2) 부가의 문문에서 주어는 인칭대명사로 바꿔 주어야 한다는 것에 주의해 야 한다.

시험대비 실력평가
p.127~129

01 ⑤   02 ②

03 (1) to (2) for (3) of (4) doesn't (5) isn't 04 ④

05 ③   06 ①   07 ④   08 ⑤

09 ③   10 ②   11 ①   12 ②

13 (1) Was this letter delivered by David?

　(2) My uncle's house was destroyed by the flood.

　(3) The table is made of wood.

　(4) The teenagers will travel to Europe, won't they?

　(5) Let's go to play tennis, shall we?

14 (1) doesn't she   (2) didn't you   (3) can she

　(4) was he   (5) will[won't] you   (6) shall we

15 (1) chosen to → chosen for

　(2) is reduced → reduces

　(3) be appeared → appear

　(4) didn't Mina → didn't she

　(5) will you → won't you

　(6) does she → is she

16 ②   17 will be held

01 The dirt가 숨겨지는 것이므로 수동태가 적절하다.

02 부가의문문은 앞의 문장이 긍정이면 부정으로 하고 부정이 면 긍정으로 한다. be동사나 조동사가 있으면 그 be동사나 조동사 를 이용하고 일반동사일 경우는 do/does/did를 이용한다. 반 드시 축약형을 사용해야 하고 주어는 인칭대명사로 바꿔 주어야 한다는 것에 주의해야 한다.

03 직접목적어를 주어로 한 수동태에서 간접목적어 앞에 (1) give 는 전치사 to를, (2) make는 전치사 for를, (3) ask는 전치사 of를 쓴다. (4), (5) 부가의문문은 앞의 문장이 긍정이면 부정으 로, be동사나 조동사가 있으면 그 be동사나 조동사를 이용하고 일반 동사일 경우는 do/does/did를 이용한다.

04 ④ A nice pen was given to me by Emily. ③ 능동태의 주 어가 명확하지 않을 경우 생략할 수 있다.

05 ① isn't she ② isn't she ④ wasn't she ⑤ didn't she

06 4형식의 직접목적어를 주어로 하는 수동태에서 make는 간접목 적어 앞에 for를 쓰는 동사이다. 또한 make, buy, read, write 등은 직접목적어를 주어로 하는 수동태만 가능하다

07 have가 일반동사 '먹다'의 뜻으로 쓰였으므로 do로 받는다. 앞 이 과거이고 긍정이므로 didn't가 적절하다.

08 능동태의 목적어로 쓰인 the numbers를 주어로 하고 동사를 'be+pp' 형태인 'were determined'로 한 후 일반주어인 they 를 'by them'으로 쓰거나 생략한다. by the players' batting order는 부사구로 쓰인 것이므로 그대로 둔다.

09 일반동사 긍정이므로 do를 이용하여 부정으로하고 대명사 주어 she를 쓴다.

10 ② 수동태는 'be+과거분사'이다.

11 ①번은 be동사가 쓰였으므로 wasn't he를 쓰지만, 나머지는 일반동사의 과거형이므로 didn't he를 써야 한다.

12 be filled with: ~로 가득 차다, be pleased with: ~로 기뻐하다

13 (1), (2) 편지가 배달되고 집이 무너지는 것이므로 수동태가 적 절하다. (3) be made of: ~로 만들어지다(물리적 변화) (4) 조

동사 will이 있으므로 won't를 쓰고 주어로 대명사 they를 쓴
다. (5) Let's의 부가의문문은 shall we이다.

14 부가의문문은 앞의 문장이 긍정이면 부정으로 하고 부정이면 긍
   정으로 한다. be동사나 조동사가 있으면 그 be동사나 조동사를
   이용하고 일반동사일 경우는 do/does/did 를 이용한다. 축약형
   을 사용해야 하고 주어는 인칭대명사로 바꿔 주어야 준다. 또한
   명령문의 부가의문문은 will you? 나 won't you?를 쓰고 권유
   문(Let's ~)의 경우에는 shall we?를 쓴다.

15 (1) choose는 직접목적어를 주어로 한 수동태에서 간접목적어
   앞에 for를 쓴다. (2) my stress가 목적어이므로 능동태가 적
   절하다. (3) appear는 자동사이므로 수동태로 쓰이지 않는다.
   (4), (5), (6) 부가의문문은 앞의 문장이 긍정이면 부정으로 하
   고 부정이면 긍정으로 한다. be동사나 조동사가 있으면 그 be동
   사나 조동사를 이용하고 일반동사일 경우는 do/does/did를 이
   용 한다. 축약형을 사용해야 하고 주어는 인칭대명사로 바꿔 주
   어야 준다.

16 그가 준비하는 것이므로 능동태 'was preparing'이 적절하다.

17 시제가 미래(next week)이므로 'will be+pp' 형태가 적절하다.

서술형 시험대비 p.130~131

01 (1) The big house is cleaned by Tino on Sundays.
   (2) They will hold Sarang Middle School Sports
       Day on the school playing field on Wednesday,
       June 15.
   (3) Delicious spaghetti was made for Judy by
       Jonathan.
   (4) Are you satisfied with your job as a tour guide?
   (5) By whom was Water Lilies painted in 1906?
   (6) He will be made to take part in the science
       camp by Cathy.
   (7) The animals are being looked after by them.

02 didn't he

03 (1) aren't they   (2) can he   (3) did he   (4) is she
   (5) doesn't it   (6) will[won't] you   (7) shall we

04 (1) was repaired   (2) was bought for
   (3) are made   (4) was made to

05 doesn't she   06 was painted

07 (1) The pens were bought by the boy. 또는 The boy
       bought the pens.
   (2) Soy sauce is made from soy beans and salt.
   (3) Jack wrote Cloe a letter. 또는 A letter was
       written to Cloe by Jack.
   (4) Vivian was heard to open the window by her
       son.

---

   (5) Samgyupsal will be cooked for Emma by her
       husband next weekend.
   (6) By whom was this table made?

08 (1) My bike was stolen last Friday.
   (2) These cookies were made by my mom.
   (3) His house is filled with books.
   (4) Jenny wasn't at the party last night, was she?
   (5) Let's talk about our favorite sport, shall we?

01 (1) 수동태는 능동태의 목적어를 주어로 하고 동사는 'be+pp'
   로 바꾸고 능동태의 주어를 'by+목적격'으로 바꾸어 쓴다. (2)
   미래 시제의 수동태는 'will be+과거분사'이다. (3) make는
   직접목적어를 주어로 하는 수동태만 가능하며 수동태에서 간접
   목적어 앞에 for를 쓴다. (4) be satisfied with: ~에 만족하다
   (5) 의문대명사 who가 whom으로 바뀌는 것에 주의한다. 전
   치사 by를 문장 뒤로 보내 Who[Whom] was Water Lilies
   painted in 1906 by?로 바꿔 쓸 수도 있다. (6) 목적격보어가
   원형부정사인 경우, 수동태 문장에서는 to부정사로 바뀐다. (7)
   구동사의 수동태는 구동사를 하나의 동사처럼 취급한다. after
   나 by를 빠뜨리지 않도록 주의한다.

02 과거시제이며 일반동사 긍정이므로 didn't를 쓰고 인칭대명사
   he가 적절하다.

03 부가의문문은 앞의 문장이 긍정이면 부정으로 하고 부정이면 긍정
   으로 한다. be동사나 조동사가 있으면 그 be동사나 조동사를 이용
   하고 일반동사일 경우는 do/does/did 를 이용한다. 반드시 축약
   형을 사용해야 하고 주어는 인칭대 명사로 바꿔 주어야 준다. 또한
   명령문의 부가의문문은 will you?나 won't you?를 쓰고 권유문
   (Let's ~)의 경우에는 shall we?를 쓴다.

04 (1), (2), (3) 컴퓨터나 스마트폰이 만들어지고 책이 구매되어
   지는 것이므로 수동태가 적절하다. buy는 간접목적어 앞에 전
   치사 for를 쓴다. (4) 목적격보어가 원형부정사인 경우, 수동태
   문장에서는 to부정사로 바뀐다.

05 앞 문장이 긍정이고 현재이며 일반동사가 사용되었으므로
   doesn't she가 적절하다.

06 샤갈의 '나와 마을'이란 작품이 샤갈에 의해 그려진 것이므로 수
   동태가 적절하다.

07 (1) The pens를 주어로 하면 수동태가, The boy를 주어로 하
   면 능동태가 적절하다. (2) be made of: ~로 만들어지다(물리
   적 변화), be made from: ~로 만들어지다(화학적 변화) (3)
   write는 직접목적어를 주어로 하는 수동태만 가능하다. (4) 목
   적격보어가 원형부정사인 경우, 수동태 문장에서는 to부정사로
   바뀐다. (5) cook은 직접목적어를 주어로 한 수동태에서는 간
   접목적어 앞에 for를 쓰며 next weekend가 있으므로 미래서
   체인 'will be+과거분사'로 써야 한다. (6) 수동태에서 능동태
   의 주체가 'by+목적격'이 되므로 'By whom'으로 시작되는 의
   문문이 적절하다.

08 (1), (2) 수동태는 '주어+be동사+동사의 과거분사+by+행위자'의 형식이다. 행위자가 중요치 않거나 확실하지 않은 경우 'by+행위자'는 생략한다. (3) be filled with: ~로 가득 차다 (4) wasn't가 있고 주어가 Jenny이므로 was she?를 쓴다. (5) 권유문(Let's ~)의 부가의문문은 shall we?이다.

교과서 Reading

확인문제
p.132

1 T 2 F 3 T 4 F 5 T 6 F

확인문제
p.133

1 T 2 F 3 T 4 F 5 T 6 F

교과서 확인학습 A
p.134~135

01 Baseball Stadium　　02 have a game
03 is at　　04 your first time, isn't it
05 can't wait for　06 are coming out
07 Which team　08 behind third base
09 visiting team　10 wear a dark color
11 rule
12 have bright uniforms　13 Why
14 interesting story
15 wash their uniforms　16 to hide the dirt
17 a good idea　18 warming up　19 favorite player
20 Number　21 What, mean
22 choose, they like　　23 what
24 by the players' batting order　25 no, with
26 Is about to　27 anxious　28 at bat
29 has hit　30 hits one more　31 misses
32 a full count　33 next pitch　35 Crack, flies
36 gone

교과서 확인학습 B
p.136~137

1 A Day at the Baseball Stadium
2 Today the Thunders and the Cobras have a game.
3 Jihun's family is at the baseball stadium.
4 Jihun: Jian, this is your first time to come to the baseball stadium, isn't it?

5 Jian: Yes, I'm so excited. I can't wait for the game to start.
6 Dad: Look, the players are coming out now!
7 Jian: Which team is the Thunders?
8 Jihun: Over there, behind third base.
9 They are wearing dark gray uniforms because they are the visiting team.
10 Jian: Does the visiting team always wear a dark color?
11 Jihun: Yes, that's the rule.
12 Home teams have bright uniforms and visiting teams have dark uniforms.
13 Jian: Why is that?
14 Mom: There is an interesting story about that.
15 In the past, visiting teams could not wash their uniforms after every game.
16 So they started wearing dark colors to hide the dirt.
17 Jian: Hahaha! That was a good idea!
18 The players are warming up.
19 Jian: Who's your favorite player?
20 Jihun: Number 77.
21 Jian: What does the number mean?
22 Jihun: Hmm.... Players choose a number they like.
23 Dad: You know what?
24 In the past, the numbers were determined by the players' batting order.
25 Jihun: That means there were no players with number 77!
26 Now, Jihun's favorite player is about to bat.
27 Jihun looks anxious.
28 Jian: Your favorite player is at bat.
29 Jihun: Yes. He has hit 21 home runs already this year.
30 If he hits one more today, he will be the home run leader this season.
31 The batter misses several balls.
32 Now he has a full count.
33 He is waiting for the next pitch.
34 Jihun: HOME RUN! HOME RUN!
35 Crack! The ball flies fast.
36 It is going, going, going, gone!

시험대비 실력평가
p.138~141

01 ④　　02 ②, ⑤　　03 ③　　04 bright
05 Home teams have bright uniforms and visiting

teams have dark uniforms. 06 ②

07 ①　　　　　08 without

09 (A) to run　(B) to run　(C) during

10 ④　　　　　11 ⑤

12 The players are warming up.

13 과거: 선수의 타순이 7번째였다.

현재: 선수가 좋아하는 숫자인 7을 등번호로 선택한 것이다.

14 ②　　　　　15 home run leader　　　16 ④

17 ③　　　　　18 wasn't she　　　19 ②

20 ②　　　　　21 Who do you think will win?

22 22nd　　　23 do　　　24 ②　　　25 ⑤

26 How → What

27 In the past, catchers stood about one meter behind home base and stopped the ball.

---

01 동의를 구하거나 사실을 확인하기 위해 '~해. 그렇지?'라고 되묻는 부가의문문 문장은 앞 문장이 긍정이면 부정으로 만든다. This는 it으로 바꾸는 것이 적절하다.

02 ⓐ와 ②, ⑤번: 형용사적 용법, ①, ④: 명사적 용법, ③: 부사적 용법

03 지안이가 야구 경기장에 온 건 이번이 처음이다.

04 dark의 반의어가 알맞다

05 '홈팀은 밝은 유니폼을 입고 원정 팀은 어두운 유니폼을 입는 것'을 가리킨다.

06 '때'를 숨기기 위해 어두운 색을 입기 시작했다고 하는 것이 적절하다. ① (정형화된) 양식, 패턴, 무늬

07 ⓐ be known as: ~로 알려져 있다, ⓒ as the winner: 우승자로서

08 신발이 잘 맞지 않아서 '신발을 신지 않고(신발 없이)' 달리기로 결정했다고 하는 것이 적절하다.

09 (A) prepare는 목적어로 to부정사를 취하므로 to run이 적절하다. (B) decide는 목적어로 to부정사를 취하므로 to run이 적절하다. (C) 'during+기간을 나타내는 명사', 'while+주어+동사'이므로 during이 적절하다.

10 '도쿄'가 아니라 '로마'에서 신발을 신지 않고 달렸다.

11 ⓐ by: [척도·표준을 나타내어] …에 의거하여, …에 따라, by the batting order: 타순에 의해, ⓑ with number 77: 77번을 가진

12 warm up: (스포츠나 활동 전에) 몸을 천천히 풀다[준비 운동을 하다]

13 현재는 선수들이 좋아하는[원하는] 번호를 선택하지만, 과거에는 번호가 선수들의 타순에 의해 결정되었다.

14 ⓐ와 ①, ②, ④번은 완료 용법, ③ 계속 용법, ⑤ 결과 용법

15 지훈이의 가장 좋아하는 선수가 마침내 홈런을 쳤기 때문에 그는 이번 시즌 '홈런 리더'가 될 것 같다.

16 ④ 지훈이의 가장 좋아하는 선수가 오늘 몇 개의 파울 볼을 쳤는지는 대답할 수 없다. ① Jihun's favorite player. ② 21

---

home runs. ③ Yes. ⑤ Yes. / inning: (야구에서 9 =회 중의 한) 회

17 (A) 어렸을 때 학교 최고의 '아마추어' 골프 선수였다. (B) 1996년에 '프로' 골프 선수가 되었다. ② mature: 성숙한, immature: 미숙한, ④ expert: 전문가

18 부가의문문은 앞 문장이 긍정이면 부정으로 만든다.

19 골프를 시작한 나이는 알 수 없다. ① 프로 골프선수, ③ 1996년, ④ 1998년부터 2016년까지, ⑤ 2007년 11월

20 ⓐ와 ②번: 차례, ① 돌다, ③ (어떤 것이 다른 방향을 향하도록) 돌리다, 뒤집다, ④ (차량의) 방향 전환, ⑤ (…한 상태로) 변하다

21 Who를 맨 앞에 쓰는 것이 적절하다.

22 그는 올해 이미 21개의 홈런을 쳤다고 했으므로, 22번째 홈런을 친 것이다. twenty-second도 가능하다.

23 play를 받는 대동사 'do'를 쓰는 것이 적절하다.

24 A: newscaster(뉴스 프로 진행자) - B: 스포츠 기자의 관계이다.

25 위 글은 '스포츠 뉴스 대본'이다. ① 요약, 개요, ② (신문, 잡지의) 글, 기사, ③ 수필, ④ (책, 연극, 영화 등에 대한) 논평 [비평], 감상문

26 think의 목적어로 'What'을 쓰는 것이 적절하다.

27 앞 문장의 내용을 가리킨다. 과거에 포수들은 홈 베이스의 약 1미터 뒤에 서서 공을 잡았다.

서술형 시험대비

01 (1) wait　(2) dying

02 They are wearing dark gray uniforms because they are the visiting team.

03 (A) never　(B) excited

04 원정 팀은 항상 어두운 유니폼을 입는 것

05 in order / so as / in order that, might[could] / so that might[could]

06 take a shower → wash their uniforms

07 Players choose a number that[which] they like.

08 4

09 과거에는 번호가 선수들의 타순에 의해 결정되었는데, 한 팀의 야구선수는 9명이기 때문이다.

10 (A) has hit　(B) hits

11 Your favorite player is at bat.

12 Jihun's favorite player

---

01 I can't wait: 기다리기 힘들 정도로, 무엇인가를 너무나 하고 싶을 때 쓸 수 있는 표현, I'm dying to 부정사(for 명사): 몹시 …하고 싶어 하는, …하고 싶어 못 견디는

02 'visiting'을 보충하면 된다.

27

p.145~149

03 지안이는 전에 야구 경기장에 온 적이 '결코' 없어서 그녀는 아주 '흥분된다.'

04 바로 다음 문장의 내용을 쓰면 된다.

05 목적(~하기 위하여)을 나타내는 부사적 용법의 to부정사는 in order to, so as to, in order that ~ may[can], so that ~ may[can]로 바꿀 수 있다.

06 과거에는 원정 팀이 매 경기 후 '유니폼을 세탁할 수' 없었기 때문에 그들은 때를 숨기기 위해 어두운 색을 입기 시작했다. take a shower: 샤워를 하다

07 목적격 관계대명사 that[which]이 생략되어 있다.

08 과거에는 번호가 선수들의 타순에 의해 결정되었다고 했기 때문에 '4'번이라고 하는 것이 적절하다.

09 한 팀의 야구선수는 9명이므로, 등번호도 9번까지만 있었을 것이다.

10 (A) already가 있으므로 현재완료가 적절하다. (B) 조건의 부사절에서는 현재가 미래를 나타낸다.

11 at bat 타석에 서서

12 '지훈이의 가장 좋아하는 선수'를 가리킨다.

영역별 핵심문제

01 ④ 02 ④ 03 miss

04 ④ 05 ②

06 Which sport do you like? Soccer or table tennis?

07 ticket 08 ④

09 Which baseball player do you like?

10 more than Daniel Parker 11 ③

12 I'm looking forward to seeing it.

13 ④ 14 ③

15 (1) At last the thief was caught by the police last Saturday.

(2) We don't know exactly when the accident happened.

(3) Delicious galbitang is being made for him by Anna.

(4) Your love can be shown to your partner by saying "I love you."

(5) Mariel was seen to go out with her friend by Andy.

(6) The festival was put off by the city on account of the bad weather.

(7) She didn't say good-bye, did she?

(8) She can play soccer very well, can't she?

(9) Tino is wearing a blue shirt, isn't he?

(10) The hotel where we stayed was near the city hall, wasn't it?

16 (1) Tino likes eating ice cream, doesn't he?

(2) It was an interesting movie, wasn't it?

17 ②

18 (1) Where was your dog found yesterday?

(2) French is spoken in many countries in Africa. (

(3) Mr. Park goes shopping every Sunday, doesn't he?

19 (A) can't (B) is (C) visiting 20 ②

21 the Thunders 22 ③ 23 ②

24 ⑤ 25 ② 26 ③ 27 ⑤

28 gone 29 batting

30 it falls to the ground → it flies fast (and is gone)

01 ④ order: 순서 / 술을 섞을 때는 순서를 지키는 것이 중요합니다.

02 anxious: 불안한 ① excited: 신난, 흥분한 ② pleased: 기쁜 ③ bored: 지루한 ④ nervous: 불안한 ⑤ interested: 관심 있는, 흥미 있는

03 miss: 놓치다 / 타자는 여러 개의 공을 놓쳤다. 나는 이 경기를 놓치고 싶지 않아.

04 while+동사ing: ~하는 동안

05 축구와 탁구 중에 어떤 것을 좋아하는지 묻는 질문에 여자아이는 탁구를 좋아한다고 대답하고, 상대방은 어떤지 물어보는 질문이 들어가야 남자아이가 축구를 좋아한다고 대답할 수 있으므로 주어진 문장의 위치는 ②가 적절하다.

06 which 명사 do you like? A or B?: 어떤 ~을 좋아하니? A 아니면 B?

07 ticket: 티켓 / 어느 장소에 들어가기 위해 또는 어떤 것을 하기 위해 당신이 돈을 지불했다는 것을 보여 주는 공식적인 종이나 카드

08 ⓐ I looked at → I'm looking at ⓑ What country → Which country ⓒ would you like to visiting → would you like to visit ⓔ I'd like to seeing → I'd like to see

09 Which 명사 do you like?: 어떤 ~을 좋아하니?

10 더 좋아하는 것에 대해 말할 때는 'I like A.', 'I like A better[more] than B.' 또는 'I prefer A to B.'로 표현한다. 이때 비교대상이 되는 'than B'나 'to B'는 생략할 수 있다.

11 남자아이가 'When did you get it?(언제 생긴 거야?)'으로 물었으므로 때에 대한 정보를 대답해야 한다. ⓒYesterday my father bought it for me.

12 can't wait to 동사원형: ~하기를 기대하다, be looking forward to 동명사: ~하기를 기대하다

13 ① James teaches math, doesn't he? ② She was great, wasn't she? ③ The door was opened by Tom. ⑤ The wall will be painted by the painters tomorrow.

14 첫 문장은 집이 청소하는 것이 아니라 청소되는 것이므로 수동태로 쓰인 is cleaned가, 두 번째 문장은 앞에 일반동사가 쓰였고 현재시제이며 긍정이므로 doesn't를 쓰고 주어가 Jejudo이므로 주어를 대명사 it으로 받는 것이 적절하다.

15 (1) 도둑이 경찰에 잡힌 것이므로 수동태 (2) happen은 자동사이므로 수 동태로 쓰이지 않는다. (3) 직접목적어를 주어로 한 수동태에서 make는 간접목적어 앞에 for를 쓴다. (4) 조동사가 있는 문장의 수동태는 '조동사 (7)~(10) 부가의문문은 앞의 문장이 긍정이면 부정으로 하고 부정이면 긍정 으로 한다. be동사나 조동사가 있으면 그 be동사나 조동사를 이용하고 일반 동사일 경우는 do/does/did를 이용한다. 반드시 축약형을 사용해야 하고 주어는 대명사로 바꿔 주어야 한다.

16 부가의문문은 '평서문(긍정문 또는 부정문)+반대 상황의 의문문'의 형태를 갖는다.

17 be interested in: ~에 흥미가 있다 be covered with: ~로 덮여 있다 be satisfied with: ~에 만족하다 be pleased with: ~로 기뻐하다 be filled with: ~로 가득 차다

18 (1), (2) 개가 발견되고 프랑스어가 말해지는 것이므로 수동태로 쓴다. (3) Mr. Park이 주어이므로 대명사 he로 받고 일반동사, 현재시제, 긍정이므로 doesn't를 쓴다.

19 (A) I can't wait: 기다리기 힘들 정도로, 무엇인가를 너무나 하고 싶을 때 쓸 수 있는 표현, (B) 'Which team'이 주어이므로 is가 적절하다. (C) visiting team: 원정 팀

20 ⓐ와 ②번: 형용사적 용법, ①, ④: 부사적 용법, ⑤ 명사적 용법

21 '천둥 팀'을 가리킨다.

22 과거에는 원정 팀이 매 경기 후 유니폼을 세탁할 수가 없었기 때문에 때를 숨기기 위해 어두운 색을 입기 시작했다는 말이 뒤에 나오므로, 홈팀은 '밝은' 유니폼을 입고 원정 팀은 '어두운' 유니폼을 입는다고 하는 것이 적절하다.

23 ⓒ와 ①, ④번은 동명사, 나머지는 다 현재분사

24 ⑤ 지안이는 그것이 '좋은' 생각이라고 말한다.

25 ⓐ와 ②번: 순서, ① (상품의) 주문, ③ 명령[지시]하다, ④ 정돈[정리](된 상태), ⑤ 주문하다

26 ③ 지훈이가 그 선수를 왜 좋아하는지는 대답할 수 없다., ① They are warming up. ② Number 77. ④ It means that the player likes the number 77. ⑤ They were determined by the players' batting order.

27 (A) at bat 타석에 서서, (B) wait for: ~을 기다리다

28 공이 '사라져 버렸다'고 해야 홈런을 치는 것이 된다.

29 be about to 동사원형 = be on the point of ~ing: 막 ~하려는 참이다

30 공이 땅에 떨어지는 것이 아니라, 빠르게 날아가서 사라진다.

단원별 예상문제   p.150~153

01 ③
02 (1) first base (2) competition (3) either (4) orders
03 (A) to take (B) wait   04 ③, ⑤   05 ④
06 ③   07 ②   08 ⓐ in ⓑ and ⓒ up
09 Which country would you like to visit first? The U.S. or Mexico?   10 ②
11 There's a soccer match this weekend between Korea and Turkey.
12 ③   13 ①
14 (1) will be read to his son by Simon tonight
(2) was fixed by Peter this morning
15 (1) didn't she (2) can't they (3) was it   16 isn't it
17 (A) excited (B) to start (C) third base   18 ⑤
19 ②   20 wash their uniforms, to hide
21 ②, ③, ④   22 It is 77.   23 ①, ④   24 ②

01 at bat: 타석에 서서 / 내가 아주 좋아하는 선수가 타석에서 있다. be about to 동사원형: 막 ~하려고 하다 / 영화가 막 시작하려 하고 있다. twice a week: 일주일에 두 번 / 그는 또한 일주일에 두 번 영어 수업을 듣는다.

02 (1) base: (야구의) 루, 베이스 (2) competition: 대회 (3) either: (부정문에서) ~도 (4) order: 순서

03 (A) take a boat ride: 보트를 타다 be going to 동사원형: ~할 것이다 (B) can't wait to 동사원형: ~을 기대하다

04 ① hide: 감추다, 숨기다 / 딸이 반지를 침대 밑에 숨겼다. ② fit: 맞다 / 헬멧이 잘 맞는지 확인하는 것을 잊지 마세요. ③ either: (부정문에서) ~도 / 그는 못 가고, 나도 못 간다. ④ decide: 결정하다 / 무엇을 먹을지 결정하는 것은 쉽지 않다. ⑤ support: (특정 스포츠 팀을) 응원하다 / 당신은 어느 팀을 응원하나요?

05 ④번은 visiting team(원정 팀: 경쟁하는 팀의 경기장이나 코트에서 경기를 하는 스포츠 팀)에 대한 설명이다.

06 주어진 문장에서 the game은 천둥 대 코브라의 경기를 의미한다. 지호가 그 경기를 보러 서둘러 집에 가고 있는 상황에서 알렉스가 놓치고 싶지 않다고 얘기하고 있다.

07 support: (특정 스포츠 팀을) 응원하다

08 ⓐ in a hurry: 서둘러 ⓑ between A and B: A와 B 사이에 ⓒ hurry up: 서두르다

09 would like to 동사원형: ~하고 싶다 visit: 방문하다

10 ② 남자아이는 멕시코에서 무엇을 하고 싶은가?

11 there is 단수명사: ~가 있다 between A and B: A와 B 사이에

12 ③ 윤호는 이번 주말의 축구 경기에 대해 들었다.

13 수동태 문장에서 행위자가 중요치 않거나 확실하지 않은 경우 'by+행위자'는 생략한다.

14 능동태의 목적어가 주어 자리에 있으므로 수동태로 쓴다.

15 부가의문문은 몰라서 질문하는 것이 아니고 상대방의 동의를 구하거나 사실을 확인하기 위해 사용된다.

16 동의를 구하거나 사실을 확인하기 위해 '~해, 그렇지?'라고 되묻는 부가의문문 앞 문장이 긍정이면 부정으로 만든다. This는 it으로 바꾸는 것이 적절하다.

17 (A) 감정을 나타내는 동사는 수식받는 명사가 감정을 느끼게 되

29

는 경우에 과거분사를 써야 하므로 excited가 적절하다. (B) to start가 wait의 목적어이고, for the game은 to start의 의미상의 주어이다. (C) '3루'라고 해야 하므로 third base가 적절하다. three bases: 세 개의 루

18 원정 팀의 선수들이 어두운 회색 유니폼을 입고 있는 이유는 대답할 수 없다. ① The Thunders and the Cobras do. ② At the baseball stadium. ③ No. ④ She feels so excited.

19 이 글은 '원정 팀이 어두운 유니폼을 입게 된' 이유에 관한 글이다. strong points: 강점, weak points: 약점

20 과거에는 원정 팀이 매 경기 후 '유니폼을 세탁할 수'가 없었기 때문에 그들은 때를 '숨기기 위해' 어두운 색을 입기 시작했다.

21 ⓐ와 ①, ⑤: 부사적 용법(목적), ②, ④: 명사적 용법, ③ 형용사적 용법

22 ③ 'Players choose a number they like.'라고 했기 때문에, 지훈이가 가장 좋아하는 77번 선수가 좋아하는 숫자는 '77'이다.

23 ⓐ와 ①, ④: (이야기 첫 머리에서) 재미있거나 놀라운 의견·소식 등을 말하려 할 때 씀. '저 있잖아, 내 이야기 들어봐'라는 뜻. ②, ⑤: 그것에 대해 어떻게 생각해? ③ 어떻게 (요리 를) 해드릴까요?

24 '지훈'이가 가장 좋아하는 선수가 77번 선수이다.

서술형 실전문제
p.154~155

01 will → won't
02 can → can't
03 I'm looking forward to watching the game.
04 (1) What was cooked for her family by her last night?
(2) Kimdaesung built Dabotap in the eighth century.
(3) Kevin waters the plants every morning.
(4) Some flowers were given (to) me by my friend two days ago. 또는 I was given some flowers by my friend two days ago.
05 (1) The light bulb was invented by Edison. 또는 Edison invented the light bulb.
(2) A dress was made for Sue by her mom.
(3) You aren't paying attention, are you?
(4) You forgot to bring your umbrella, didn't you?
06 (A) excited (B) wearing
07 I can't wait for the game to start.
08 they are the visiting team
09 has come → has never come
10 (A) warming (B) Who's (C) what
11 A number they like is chosen by players. 또는 A number players like is chosen by them.
12 they determined the numbers by the players'

batting order.
13 In the past, the numbers were determined by the players' batting order.

01 암벽 등반하러 가기로 한 것을 잊지 말라는 말에 걱정하지 말라며 잊을 거라고 말하는 것은 어색하고 잊지 않을 것이라고 말하는 것이 어울린다. won't = will not: ~하지 않을 것이다

02 볼링과 야구 중 어떤 운동을 좋아하는지 묻는 질문에, 야구를 좋아한다며 이번 주말에 친구들이랑 야구를 하러 간다는 대답을 했는데 'I can wait.(나는 기다릴 수 있어.)'라는 말은 어색하다. I can't wait: 너무 기다려져

03 I can't wait to 동사원형.: ~하는 것이 너무 기다려져 = I'm looking forward to 동명사.

04 (1) 의문문의 수동태는 능동태의 의문문을 평서문으로 바꾼 후 이것을 수동태로 고치고, 다시 의문문으로 바꾸면 쉽다. (4) 4형식 문장의 수동태는 간접목적어와 직접목적어 각각을 주어로 하는 수동태가 가능하며 직접목적어를 주어로 한 수동태에서 give 동사는 간접목적어 앞에 전치사 to를 쓴다. 이 때의 to는 생략되기도 한다.

05 (1) 전구가 무엇을 발명할 수는 없으므로 수동태로 쓰거나 목적어로 쓰여야 한다. (2) make는 간접목적어를 주어로 하 는 수동태로 쓰이지 않는다. 수동태에서 간접목적어 앞에 for을 쓰며 능동태(Her mom made Sue a dress.)로 고쳐도 좋다. (3) be동사가 쓰이고 있으므로 are you가 되 어야 한다. (4) 일반동사의 과거시제가 쓰이고 있으므로 did 를 써야 하고, 긍정이므로 부정으로 써야 하며 반드시 축약 형 didn't로 써야 함에 유의한다.

06 (A) 지안이가 흥분을 느끼는 것이므로 과거분사 excited가 적절하다. (B) 선수들이 유니폼을 입고 있는 것이므로 현재 분사가 적절하다.

07 I can't wait: 기다리기 힘들 정도로, 무엇인가를 너무나 하고 싶을 때 쓸 수 있는 표현.

08 '그들은 원정 팀이기' 때문에 어두운 회색 유니폼을 입고 있다. the Thunders가 팀 선수들을 가리키고 있기 때문에 복수로 취급하는 것이 직질하다.

09 지안이가 야구 경기장에 온 건 이번이 처음이라고 했기 때문에 has 'never' come으로 고쳐야 한다.

10 (A) warm up: (스포츠나 활동 전에) 몸을 천천히 풀다, 준비운동 을 하다, 현재진행형으로 써야 하므로 warming이 적절하다. (B) 가장 좋 아하는 선수가 '누구야'?라고 해야 하므로 Who's가 적절하다. whose: 누 구의, (C) You know what?: (이야기 첫 머리에서) 재미있거나 놀라운 의 견·소식 등을 말하려 할 때 씀.

11 능동태의 목적어인 a number they like를 주어로 하여 수동태로 바꾼다.

12 by the players' batting order가 행위자를 나타내는 것이 아니 고 야구팀의 감독이나 팀 관계자들이 선수들의 타순에 의거하여 선수들의 번호를 결정한 것이므로 they를 주어로 하여 고쳐야 한다.

13 앞 문장의 내용을 가리킨다.

|모범답안|

01 (1) The dress was chosen for her by her mom.

(2) Lots of money is donated to charity by me.

(3) Lights should be turned off when you leave the room.

(4) Chicken soup was made for him by her.

(5) *Romeo and Juliet* was written by Shakespeare.

02 (A) amateur   (B) professional

(C) LPGA Tours   (D) World Golf Hall of Fame

01 ①

02 (c)ompetition, (c)rack, (p)ast, (h)ide

(1) hide   (2) cracks   (3) competition   (4) past

03 (1) over there   (2) in a hurry

(3) come out   (4) waiting for

04 ④   05 more[better] than the red ones

06 I prefer the green ones to the red ones.

07 ⑤   08 ②   09 (A) starts (B) either

(C) left   10 team   11 ②

12 more → better   13 ④   14 ③

15 (1) from → of

(2) William was bought a new computer
    → A new computer was bought for William

(3) are taken place → take place

(4) don't → aren't

(5) can't → will 또는 won't

16 ②

17 (1) don't you   (2) isn't she   (3) wasn't he

(4) doesn't he   (5) won't you   (6) didn't you

(7) will[won't] you   (8) shall we

18 ③   19 The Cobras.

20 wearing dark colors to hide the dirt   21 ④

22 the numbers were determined by the players' batting order

23 (A) players   (B) like

01 decide: 결정하다 determine: 결정하다 / 가격은 수요와 공급에 의해 결정된다.

02 (1) hide: 감추다, 숨기다 / 보이지 않는 곳에 무언가를 두다 / 그 개는 어제 뼈다귀를 땅속에 숨겼다. (2) crack: 찢어지는 듯한[날카로운] 소리 / 어떤 것이 떨어지거나 자체로 또 는 다른 것과 부딪칠 때 나는 갑작스러운 큰 폭발음 / 밤새 큰 천둥 소리가 울렸다. (3) competition: 대회 / 사람들이 다른 사람들을 물리침으로써 어떤 것을 얻으려고 하는 행사 나 경기 / 경쟁이 심해지고 있다. (4) in the past: 과거에 past: 과거 / 말하거나 쓰는 순간 이전의 시간 / 과거에 사람들은 말을 타고 여행을 다녔다.

03 (1) over there: 저기 (2) in a hurry: 서둘러 (3) come out: 나오다 (4) wait for: ~를 기다리다

04 go+동사ing: ~하러 가다 go surfing: 서핑하러 가다 go swimming: 수영하러 가다 play+운동 이름: ~하다 play soccer: 축구를 하다 play tennis: 테니스를 치다

05 더 좋아하는 것에 대해 말할 때는 'I like A.', 'I like A better[more] than B.' 이때 비교 대상이 되는 'than B'는 생략할 수 있다.

06 prefer A (to B): B보다 A를 더 좋아하다

07 다음 코브라 홈 경기를 함께 보자고 제안하고 있으므로 'Okay. (좋아.)'라고 수락하는 것이 어울린다.

08 어떤 팀을 더 응원하는지 선호를 묻는 문장이 나와야 하므로 의문사 'Which'로 질문해야 한다. support: (특정 스포츠 팀을) 응원하다

09 (A) The game이 문장의 주어로 3인칭 단수이기 때문에 동사에 s를 붙여야 한다. (B) either는 부정문에서 '~도'의 의미로 사용된다. (C) thirty minutes를 수식하므로 수동의 의미로 '남겨진'의 의미인 left가 어울린다.

10 team: 팀 / 다른 모임의 사람들에 대항해서 운동이나 경기를 함께 하는 사람들의 모임

11 ② watched → will watch 대화의 내용상 그들은 다음 코브라 홈 경기를 함께 보러 갈 것이다.

12 어떤 동물이 나에게 더 나은지 질문하고 있으므로, more(더 많은)보다 good의 비교급인 better(더 좋은)가 내용상 어 울린다.

13 ① Cheesecake is baked for Scott every day. ② Mr. Lee wrote a letter. ③ My computer was fixed by my brother. ⑤ You have a pen, don't you?

14 ③ The plan was given up because of the heavy costs (by them). give up을 한 단어처럼 취급해야 한다.

15 (1) be made of: ~로 만들어지다(물리적 변화) be made from: ~로 만들어지다(화학적 변화) (2) buy는 간접목적어를 주어로 수동태를 만들 수 없으며 수동태로 바뀔 때 간접목적어 앞에 for를 쓴다. (3) take place는 자동사로 쓰이므로 수동태로 쓰이지 않는다. (4) 긍정의 현재시제 be동사가 쓰이고 있으므로 'be동사+n't'로 부가의문문을 만들어야 한다. (5) 명령문이므로 부가의문문은 'will you?'나 'won't you?'로 써야 한다.

16 ②번은 과거 동사로 쓰였고 나머지는 과거분사로 수동태를 만들고 있다.

17 부가의문문은 앞의 문장이 긍정이면 부정으로 하고 부정이면 긍

정으로 한다. be동사나 조동사가 있으면 그 be동사나 조동사를 이용하고 일반동사일 경우는 do/does/did를 이용한다. 반드시 축약형을 사용해야 하고 주어는 대명사로 바꿔 주어야 준다. 또한 명령문의 부가의문문은 will you?나 won't you?를 쓰고 권유문(Let's ~)의 경우에는 shall we?를 쓴다.

18 ⓐ와 ①, ④번은 현재분사, 나머지는 다 동명사

19 '코브라'가 홈팀이다.

20 '때를 숨기기 위해 어두운 색을 입기 시작한 것'을 가리킨다.

21 어떤 팀이 처음으로 어두운 유니폼을 입기 시작했는지는 대답할 수 없다.

22 'by'를 보충하면 된다. by: [척도·표준을 나타내어] …에 의거하여, …에 따라

23 요즘은 '선수들' 자신에 의해 번호가 선택되는데, 그것은 그들이 '좋아하는' 숫자이다.

교과서 파헤치기

Lesson 3

1 bright, 밝은　2 grow, 자라다　3 a bit, 조금, 약간
4 practice, 연습하다　5 walk, (동물을) 걷게 하다
6 bake, (빵 등을) 굽다　7 drone, 무인 비행기
8 join, 가입하다　9 neighbor, 이웃　10 garden, 정원
11 musical instrument, 악기　12 leader, 지도자, 대표
13 opportunity, 기회　14 hold, (모임·식 등을) 개최하다
15 orchestra, 오케스트라, 교향악단　16 club, 동아리

01 연주회	02 (동식물을) 기르다, 자라다
03 실제로, 사실은	04 조금, 한 조각(가지), 부분
05 옷, 의상	06 기회　07 밝은, 똑똑한
08 돌고래	09 초등학교　10 악기
11 요리하다; 요리사	12 여가 시간
13 (모임·식 등을) 개최하다	14 참여하다, 가입하다
15 쉬운　16 이웃	17 정문
18 오케스트라, 교향악단	19 소개하다
20 자기 자신의　21 정원	22 채소
23 도서관　24 선물; 참석한	25 봉사하다
26 경험, 경력　27 몇몇의	28 음, 음표
29 활동　30 지도자, 대표	
31 관심; ~의 관심[흥미]을 끌다	32 연습; 연습하다
32 동네, (도시 내의 한 단위) 지역	33 요리, 음식
34 결과적으로　35 ~하는 것을 즐기다	
36 ~을 찾다　37 ~하고 싶다	38 ~에 참여하다
39 ~로 변화시키다[바꾸다]	40 도움을 청하다
41 ~을 잘하다　42 ~하는 방법	

01 doughnut	02 experience	03 drone
04 present	05 practice	06 activity
07 cooking	08 interest	09 fly
10 service	11 several	12 neighborhood
13 get	14 leader	15 library
16 club	17 however	18 volunteer
19 note	20 project	21 Spanish
22 walk	23 actually	24 opportunity
25 hold	26 introduce	27 actually
28 bright	29 clothes	30 grow
31 hold	32 neighbor	33 main gate
34 vegetable	35 change into	36 a little bit
37 fall into	38 as a result	39 participate in
40 get better	41 thank for	42 ask for help
43 watch out (for)		

Listen & Speak 1 A

know how to make / course, easy

Listen & Speak 1 B

1 heard you went to, How / I hope I can play, like her someday / knew how to play the violin / not good at, yet
2 Look at, grew, myself, own garden / how to cook, grow, too / taught me

Listen & Speak 2 A

looking at, at night / love doing

Listen & Speak 2 B

1 Do you enjoy reading / love reading, about / reading, too / let's go, the library
2 What did you do / made breakfast / Do you enjoy cooking / good cook, cooking
3 Where, get / made it for me / really good designer / enjoys making clothes, too

Real-Life Zone A

the leader, Thank, for your interest / to meet / When did you start playing / how to play the violin when / experience playing / Actually, an orchestra when, elementary school / volunteer to teach, Do you enjoy teaching others / experience, enjoy working with, like to try / have, playing, Welcome to

Wrap Up

look, delicious / made them myself, baking, going to, this Saturday / want to learn how to make, Is, difficult / at all, join me / What time should / At / Sounds, See, then

Listen & Speak 1 A

A: Do you know how to make a paper cat?
B: Of course. It's easy.

Listen & Speak 1 B

1 G: I heard you went to Yuna's violin concert yesterday. How was it?

B: It was great. I hope I can play the violin like her someday.

G: I didn't know you knew how to play the violin

B: I can, but I'm not good at it yet.

2 G: Look at these pictures. I grew these vegetables myself. I have my own garden.

B: Cool! Do you know how to cook the vegetables you grow, too?

G: Yes, my grandmother taught me.

Listen & Speak 2 A

A: Do you enjoy looking at the stars at night?

G: Yes, I love doing that.

Listen & Speak 2 B

1 B: Do you enjoy reading books, Yumi?

G: Yes, I love reading science books. How about you?

B: I love reading books, too.

G: Then, let's go to the library after school today.

2 G: What did you do on the weekend, Minsu?

B: I made breakfast for my family.

G: Do you enjoy cooking?

B: Yes, I'm a good cook! My family loves my cooking.

3 B: Jiyun, that's a pretty backpack! Where did you get it?

G: My sister made it for me.

B: Wow! She's a really good designer.

G: Yes, she is. And she enjoys making clothes, too .

Real-Life Zone A

B: Hello, Kate. I'm Hamin, the leader of the Nanum Orchestra. Thank you for your interest in our club.

G: Hi. Nice to meet you.

B: You play the violin? When did you start playing the violin?

G: I started learning how to play the violin when I was ten.

B: Do you have any experience playing in a group?

G: Yes. Actually, I was a member of an orchestra when I was in elementary school.

B: Great. We also volunteer to teach children. Do you enjoy teaching others?

G: I have no experience teaching others. But I enjoy working with people, so I'd like to try.

B: Good. I think we'll have a great time playing together. Welcome to the Nanum Orchestra.

Wrap Up

B: These cookies look so delicious. Did you make them?

G: Yes. I made them myself yesterday. I enjoy baking.

I'm going to make doughnuts this Saturday.

B: Oh, I want to learn how to make doughnuts. Is it difficult?

G: Not at all. You can come to my house and join me if you want.

B: Thanks, Bora. What time should I come?

G: At 2:00.

B: Sounds good. See you then.

본문 TEST Step 1 p.09~10

01 Why Don't, Join

02 Participating, way, life   03 How, joining

04 are, leaders who, join   05 Let's, to what

06 Art Club   07 from, Art Club

08 As, guess from, paint

09 volunteer work, to

10 Last, participated in, Change

11 dirty, flying, jumping, waves

12 As, into, bright, place

13 neighbors, to, thanked   14 don't have to

15 Anyone, paint, join

16 Come, be, member

17 Boram Orchestra

18 leader of, Orchestra

19 several, playing, main gate   20 were those

21 play, for, every

22 need, how, little bit   23 worry if, play

24 practice, get better

25 musical instruments, service, community

26 teaching, eleven-year-old, play 27 At, how, note

28 can, simple song

29 Hearing, play, makes

30 By joining, opportunity, others

31 Come, join, club   32 waiting for

본문 TEST Step 2 p.11~12

01 Why Don't You Join

02 Participating in club activities, to enjoy

03 How about joining

04 Here are, who want, to join   05 Let's, to what

06 Art Club   07 from, Art Club

08 As, can guess from, paint

09 do volunteer work from, to

10 Last, participated in, Change, Neighborhood

11 On the dirty old walls, painted, flying, jumping over blue waves
12 As a result, changed into, beautiful place
13 were happy to see, thanked
14 don't have to, painter
15 Anyone who likes to, join
16 Come and be   17 Orchestra
18 the leader of
19 see, playing music, main gate, came to school
20 were those   21 play music for
22 how to play, a little bit to join
23 don't worry if, don't
24 practice hard, get better
25 also teach, how to, as a service to
26 teaching an eleven-year-old boy
27 At first, how to read a note
28 can play a simple song
29 Hearing him play, happy
30 By joining, have an opportunity, to help others
31 Come and join   32 waiting for

17 보람 오케스트라
18 안녕하세요! 저는 보람 오케스트라의 회장 장민수입니다.
19 오늘 학교에 왔을 때 정문에서 음악을 연주하는 몇 명의 학생들을 보았습니까?
20 우리가 그 학생들이었습니다.
21 우리는 매일 아침 친구들을 위해 음악을 연주합니다.
22 우리 동아리에 가입하기 위해서는 악기 연주하는 법을 조금 알아야 합니다.
23 그러나 여러분이 연주를 잘 못한다고 해서 걱정하지 마세요.
24 우리는 열심히 연습하고 함께 좋아질 것입니다.
25 우리는 지역 사회에 대한 봉사로 아이들에게 악기를 연주하는 법도 가르칩니다.
26 저는 열한 살 소년에게 바이올린을 가르치고 있습니다.
27 처음에 그는 음표를 읽는 법을 알지 못했습니다.
28 이제는 간단한 노래도 연주할 수 있습니다.
29 그가 바이올린을 연주하는 걸 듣는 것은 저를 매우 행복하게 합니다.
30 우리 동아리에 가입함으로써, 여러분은 다른 사람들을 도울 수 있는 기회를 가질 수 있습니다.
31 와서 우리 동아리에 가입하세요.
32 우리는 여러분을 기다리고 있습니다.

1 우리 동아리에 가입하는 게 어때?
2 동아리 활동에 참여하는 것은 학교생활을 즐기는 좋은 방법이에요.
3 동아리에 가입하는 게 어떤가요?
4 여기 학생들이 그들의 동아리에 가입하기를 원하는 두 명의 동아리 대표가 있어요.
5 그들이 하는 말을 들어 봅시다.
6 피카소 미술 동아리
7 안녕하세요! 저는 피카소 미술 동아리의 강소라입니다.
8 우리 동아리의 이름에서 추측할 수 있듯이, 우리는 그림을 그립니다.
9 우리는 가끔 자원봉사도 합니다.
10 지난여름, 우리 동아리 회원들은 "우리 마을 바꾸기" 프로젝트에 참여했습니다.
11 우리 마을에 있는 건물의 더럽고 오래된 벽에 하늘 높이 나는 새들과 푸른 파도 위로 점프하는 돌고래들을 그렸습니다.
12 결과적으로, 오래된 마을은 밝고 아름다운 곳으로 바뀌었습니다.
13 이웃들은 우리의 작품을 보고 행복해 했고 고마워했습니다.
14 여러분은 그림을 잘 그릴 필요는 없습니다.
15 그림 그리는 것을 좋아하는 사람은 누구나 가입할 수 있습니다.
16 와서 피카소 미술 동아리의 회원이 되세요.

1 Why Don't You Join Our Club?
2 Participating in club activities is a great way to enjoy your school life.
3 How about joining a club?
4 Here are two club leaders who want students to join their clubs.
5 Let's listen to what they say.
6 The Picasso Art Club
7 Hi! I am Sora Kang from the Picasso Art Club.
8 As you can guess from the name of our club, we paint.
9 We also do volunteer work from time to time.
10 Last summer, our club members participated in the "Change Our Neighborhood" project.
11 On the dirty old walls of the buildings in our neighborhood, we painted birds flying high in the sky and dolphins jumping over blue waves.
12 As a result, the old neighborhood changed into a bright and beautiful place.
13 The neighbors were happy to see our work and thanked us.
14 You don't have to be a good painter.

15 Anyone who likes to paint can join.

16 Come and be a member of the Picasso Art Club.

17 The Boram Orchestra

18 Hi! I am Minsu Jang, the leader of the Boram Orchestra.

19 Did you see several students playing music at the main gate when you came to school today?

20 We were those students.

21 We play music for our friends every morning.

22 You need to know how to play an instrument a little bit to join our club.

23 But don't worry if you don't play well.

24 We will practice hard and get better together.

25 We also teach children how to play musical instruments as a service to our community.

26 I am teaching an eleven-year-old boy to play the violin.

27 At first, he did not know how to read a note.

28 Now he can play a simple song.

29 Hearing him play the violin makes me very happy.

30 By joining our club, you can have an opportunity to help others.

31 Come and join our club.

32 We are waiting for you.

After You Read

1. leader, community center

2. started teaching, how to play

3. how to read a note

4. hope to join, main gate

Writing Workshop

1. Middle School Club

2. Name

3. Student Name

4. to Join, would like to

5. good at passing, running

6. how to head, so

7. become, who

8. Goals, join, practice, hard

Real Life Zone

1. would like

2. how to play

3. lots of, playing

4. enjoys working

5. Let's, welcome, to

After You Read

1. Today, Minsu, the leader of the Boram Orchestra, came to community center.

2. He started teaching me how to play the violin last month.

3. At first, I didn't know how to read a note.

4. I hope to join the Boram Orchestra and play the violin at the main gate when I become a middle school student.

Writing Workshop

1. Boram Middle School Club Membership Form

2. • Name of Club: FC Boram

3. • Student Name: Sunho Park

4. • Why You Want to Join the Club: I love soccer and would like to join FC Boram.

5. I am good at passing the ball and running fast.

6. However, I don't know how to head the ball, so I want to learn how to do that.

7. I want to become a soccer player who can make wonderful heading goals.

8. • Your Goals: If I join this club, I will practice very hard and become a good team player!

Real Life Zone

1. I would like to introduce our new orchestra member, Kate.

2. She knows how to play the violin.

3. She also has lots of experience playing in a group.

4. And she said she enjoys working with people.

5. Let's all welcome her to the Nanum Orchestra.

Lesson 4

12 title, 제목   13 seagull, 갈매기   14 nervous, 불안한

15 support, 지지. 후원   16 review, 감상문, 논평

단어 TEST Step 1   p.21

01 게다가	02 올바른	03 대답하다
04 언제든, 한 번이라도		05 등장인물
06 지배하다	07 장면	08 친절한
09 행복	10 갈매기	11 품목
12 시끄러운	13 지지; 지지하다	14 제목
15 편안한	16 함께 하다	17 그러한, 너무나 ~한
18 왕좌, 왕위	19 여행	20 근처에
21 외국의	22 헤어지다	23 감상문, 논평
24 학교 식당	25 날씨	26 (곰, 사자 등의) 새끼
27 실망한, 기대에 어긋난		28 불안한
29 외국인	30 의견	31 후회하다
32 무서운	33 십 대	34 넓은
35 ~에 대해 걱정하다		
36 (병·상황 등이) 나아지다		37 (~에게) 잘 어울리다
38 ~을 빼앗다	39 ~을 두려워하다	40 ~처럼 보이다
41 ~을 잘하다	42 그런데	
43 만약 ~이라면 어떻게 될까?		

단어 TEST Step 2   p.22

01 nervous	02 reply	03 separate
04 weather	05 scene	06 cub
07 review	08 foreign	09 journey
10 such	11 teenager	12 support
13 friendly	14 besides	15 happiness
16 item	17 character	18 seagull
19 join	20 nearby	21 opinion
22 regret	23 comfortable	24 noisy
25 throne	26 rule	27 disappointed
28 scary	29 foreigner	30 school cafeteria
31 title	32 wide	33 correct
34 ever	35 break out	36 not anymore
37 by the way	38 try to+동사원형	39 be worried about
40 look like+명사	41 be scared of	42 get better
43 go into		

단어 TEST Step 3   p.23

1 separate, 헤어지다   2 journey, 여행   3 happiness, 행복

4 besides, 게다가   5 noisy, 시끄러운   6 character, 등장인물

7 rule, 지배하다   8 cub, (곰, 사자 등의) 새끼

9 foreign, 외국의   10 reply, 대답하다   11 teenager, 십대

대화문 TEST Step 1   p.24~25

Listen & Speak 1 A

worried about / Don't worry, do fine

Listen & Speak 1 B

1 Do you have, special plans / going to, worried about / Don't worry, won't rain

2 can, go into / What's wrong / scared of / friendly, just looks scary because

Listen & Speak 1 C

1 I'm worried about / Don't worry, going to

2 I'm worried about / worry, You'll do great

3 I'm worried about my future / worry, find something, like to do

Listen & Speak 2 A

What do you think of / look like

Listen & Speak 2 B

1 Did, watch / saw, last Saturday / What did you think of it / disappointed, wasn't, good

2 What do you think of / think, delicious / What, best item / like, the best

3 do you think of / looks great / happy that, painted, myself

Listen & Speak 2 C

1 What, think of / looks light, fast

2 What do you think / look good on you

Real-Life Zone

who looked like / had / looked like, were having / were, try to meet twice / wish, could feel, comfortable / was worried about speaking, anymore / get, nervous, try to speak / the hardest, gets easier, easier / What do you, about, both of / great idea

대화문 TEST Step 2   p.26~27

Listen & Speak 1 A

B: I'm worried about the math test.

W: Don't worry. You'll do fine.

Listen & Speak 1 B

1 B: Do you have any special plans for tomorrow?

G: I'm going to Jejudo in the morning. But I'm worried about the weather.

B: Don't worry. It won't rain on Jejudo tomorrow.

G: Oh, that's good to hear.

2 B: Jina, can you go into your house first?

G: Why? What's wrong?

B: I'm scared of your dog.

G: Don't worry. He's a friendly dog. He just looks scary because he's so big.

Listen & Speak 1 C

1 A: I'm worried about your health.

B: Don't worry. I'm going to the doctor tomorrow.

2 A: I'm worried about the speech contest.

B: Don't worry. You'll do great.

3 A: I'm worried about my future.

B: Don't worry. You'll find something you like to do.

Listen & Speak 2 A

B: What do you think of these sunglasses?

G: They're cool! You look like a movie star.

Listen & Speak 2 B

1 G: Did you watch the movie, *The Daughter*?

B: Yes, I saw it last Saturday.

G: What did you think of it?

B: I was disappointed. It wasn't very good.

2 B: What do you think of our school cafeteria food?

G: I think the cafeteria food is delicious.

B: What do you think is the best item?

G: I like the Gimbap the best.

3 G: What do you think of this painting?

B: It looks great. I like the colors.

G: I'm happy that you like it. I painted it myself.

Listen & Speak 2 C

1 A: What do you think of my bike?

B: It looks light and fast.

2 A: What do you think of these shoes?

B: They look good on you.

Real-Life Zone

G: I saw you with someone who looked like a foreigner yesterday.

B: Yes. We had lunch together.

G: You looked like you were having a good time.

B: We were. We try to meet twice a month for lunch.

G: I wish I could feel more comfortable talking with a foreigner.

B: I was worried about speaking in English before, but not anymore.

G: I get really nervous when I try to speak in English.

B: Well, the first time is the hardest. After that, it gets easier and easier.

G: What do you think about me joining both of you for lunch?

B: That's a great idea.

01 Two Brothers   02 went on, journey

03 found, front of   04 said, into, across

05 find, her cubs   06 Take, run up   07 find happiness

08 go, find, together   09 How can, true

10 What if, wide   11 Besides, away from

12 Instead, finding, killed   13 replied, if, try

14 went, own way

15 went into, swam across   16 There was

17 was sleeping   18 took, ran up

19 reached, took, made   20 lived as, for

21 broke out, lost   22 on, road

23 One, met, for, last   24 older, right

25 have lived, well   26 once, had, lot

27 younger, regret, choice

28 nothing, something to remember

01 Two Brothers   02 went on, journey

03 found, in front of

04 said, Go into, swim across

05 will find, her cubs   06 Take, run up

07 will find happiness

08 Let's go and find happiness together

09 older brother, How can we know, true

10 What if, too wide

11 Besides, easy to take, away from

12 Instead of finding, be killed

13 replied, How, if, don't try

14 separated, both went their own way

15 went into, swam across   16 There was

17 was sleeping   18 took her cubs, ran up

19 reached the top, took him to, made

20 lived as a king for

21 broke out, lost his throne

22 was on the road

23 One day, talked about, lives for the last

24 I was right   25 have lived quietly, well

26 once, have had a lot of trouble

27 younger brother, regret my choice

28 nothing, will always have something to remember

1 두 형제

2 두 형제는 여정을 떠났다.

3 그들은 숲 앞에서 바위를 발견했다.

4 거기에 쓰여 있었다. "숲에 들어가 강을 헤엄쳐 건너시오.

5 당신은 거기에서 곰과 새끼들을 발견할 것입니다.

6 곰 새끼들을 데리고 산 위로 뛰어 올라가시오.

7 거기에서 당신은 행복을 찾을 수 있을 것입니다."

8 동생이 말했다. "함께 가서 행복을 찾자."

9 "싫어." 형은 말했다. "이것이 사실인지 우리가 어떻게 알 수 있어?

10 강이 너무 넓으면 어쩌지?

11 게다가, 곰 새끼들을 엄마에게서 빼앗는 것이 쉬울까?

12 행복을 찾는 대신에, 우리는 죽을 수 있어!"

13 동생은 대답했다. "우리가 시도하지 않으면 어떻게 알 수 있어?"

14 그들은 헤어졌고, 둘 다 자신의 길을 갔다.

15 동생은 숲에 들어가서 강을 헤엄쳐 건넜다.

16 곰이 있었다.

17 그녀는 자고 있었다.

18 그는 새끼들을 데리고 산을 뛰어 올라갔다.

19 그가 정상에 도착했을 때, 어떤 사람들이 그를 자기들 도시로 데려가서 그들의 왕으로 만들었다.

20 그곳에서 그는 5년간 왕으로 살았다.

21 그런 다음 전쟁이 일어났고, 그는 왕좌를 잃었다.

22 그는 다시 길바닥에 나앉았다.

23 어느 날, 두 형제는 다시 만났고 지난 5년 동안의 그들의 삶에 대해 이야기했다.

24 형은 말했다. "내가 옳았어.

25 나는 조용히 잘 살았어.

26 너는 한때 왕이었지만 많은 어려움을 겪었지."

27 동생은 대답했다. "나는 내 선택을 후회하지 않아.

28 나는 지금 아무것도 없지만 언제까지나 기억할 어떤 것이 있어."

from their mother?

12 Instead of finding happiness, we can be killed!"

13 The younger brother replied, "How can we know if we don't try?"

14 They separated, and they both went their own way.

15 The younger brother went into the forest and swam across the river.

16 There was the bear.

17 She was sleeping.

18 He took her cubs and ran up the mountain.

19 When he reached the top, some people took him to their city and made him their king.

20 There he lived as a king for five years.

21 Then a war broke out, and he lost his throne.

22 He was on the road again.

23 One day, the two brothers met again and talked about their lives for the last five years.

24 The older brother said, "I was right.

25 I have lived quietly and well.

26 You were once a king, but you have had a lot of trouble."

27 The younger brother answered, "I don't regret my choice.

28 I may have nothing now, but I will always have something to remember."

본문 TEST Step 4- Step 5 p.34~37

1 The Two Brothers

2 Two brothers went on a journey.

3 They found a rock in front of a forest.

4 It said, "Go into the forest and swim across the river.

5 There you will find a bear and her cubs.

6 Take the bear cubs and run up the mountain.

7 There you will find happiness."

8 The younger brother said, "Let's go and find happiness together."

9 "No," said the older brother, "How can we know this is true?

10 What if the river is too wide?

11 Besides, will it be easy to take the cubs away

구석구석지문 TEST Step 1 p.38

Before You Read

1. There, filled with, across

2. watch out, are

3. chose, go on journey

4. Sadly, dirty, noisy

5. almost hit

6. lots of trouble

7. After a few days, regretted, went back

Writing Workshop

1. Book Review

2. Title

3. Writer

4. is about, named

5. flying better than others

6. To reach, practices flying

7. because, helped me learn

8. that, anything that, give up

Into the World

1. when, think, say, in harmony

2. When, closes, another

3. something ready-made, comes from

구석구석지문 TEST Step 2   p.39

Before You Read

1. A. There is a box filled with gold behind a tree across the river.

2. But watch out! Dangerous animals are in the river.

3. B. Mr. Allen chose to go on journey to the city for his vacation.

4. Sadly the city streets were dirty and noisy.

5. A car even almost hit him.

6. He had lots of trouble there.

7. After a few days in the city, he regretted his choice and went back to his hometown.

Writing Workshop

1. A Book Review

2. Title : *Jonathan Livingston Seagull: a story*

3. Writer : Richard Bach

4. This story is about a seagull named Jonathan Livingston.

5. He dreams of flying better than others .

6. To reach his goal, he works hard and practices flying.

7. I like this story because it has helped me learn about the power of my own beliefs.

8. The book says that I can do anything that I want if I do not give up.

Into the World

1. Happiness is when what you think , what you say , and what you do are in harmony.
   - Mahatma Gandhi

2. When one door of happiness closes, another opens. - Helen Keller

3. Happiness is not something ready-made. It comes from your own actions. - Dalai Lama XIV

Lesson 5

단어 TEST Step 1   p.40

01 대회	02 맞다	03 감추다, 숨기다
04 찢어지는 듯한[날카로운] 소리		05 규칙
06 놓치다, 그리워하다		07 홈팀
08 불안한	09 반바지	10 결정하다
11 투구	12 언젠가	13 먼지, 때
14 (부정문에서) ~도	15 경기장	16 (야구의) 루, 베이스
17 타자	18 국제적인	19 결정하다
20 잇다	21 애완동물	22 원정 팀
23 (good의 비교급) 더 좋은, 더 나은		24 티켓
25 경기, 성냥	26 순서, 명령	27 그 뒤에, 그런 다음
28 휴가	29 의미하다	30 천둥
31 과거	32 암벽 등반	
33 (특정 스포츠 팀을) 응원하다, 지원하다		34 ~을 몹시 기대하다
35 A와 B 사이에	36 ~을 기다리다	37 ~의 열렬한 팬이다
38 서둘러 ~하다	39 ~을 기대하다	40 일주일에 두 번
41 ~에 신나다, ~에 들뜨다		42 ~로 돌아오다
43 서둘러		

단어 TEST Step 2   p.41

01 hide	02 either	03 ticket
04 vacation	05 stadium	06 base
07 rule	08 visit	09 batter
10 match	11 order	
12 determine, decide		13 pitch
14 rock climbing	15 mean	16 thunder
17 crack	18 anxious	19 competition
20 fit	21 pet	22 visiting team
23 shorts	24 past	25 forget
26 International	27 miss	28 sometime
29 dirt	30 get	31 better
32 support	33 then	
34 be about to 동사원형		
35 between A and B		36 hurry up
37 be a big fan of	38 can't wait to 동사원형	
39 twice a week	40 in a hurry	41 be excited about
42 look forward to (동)명사		43 wait for

단어 TEST Step 3   p.42

1 hide, 감추다, 숨기다   2 anxious, 불안한   3 fit, 맞다

4 home team, 홈팀   5 past, 과거   6 pitch, 투구

7 international, 국제적인   8 base, (야구의) 루, 베이스
9 determine, 결정하다   10 visiting team, 원정 팀
11 competition, 대회   12 order, 순서   13 thunder, 천둥
14 either, (부정문에서) ~도   15 crack, 찢어지는 듯한[날카로운] 소리   16 stadium, 경기장

Listen & Speak 1 A

Which sport, or / more, twice a week

Listen & Speak 1 B

1 are, doing / I'm looking at / checked, Which country, to visit, or / to visit, like to
2 I'm thinking, getting, have / What do, think, Which, better for, or / Why don't you come to, play with, can decide

Listen & Speak 2 A

Did / can't wait to watch

Listen & Speak 2 B

1 want to see / When did / bought it for me, come to my house / course, can't wait to see
2 Don't forget that, rock climbing / worry, won't forget / excited about, I can't wait
3 hear about / about, lives in / came back, wants to see / can't wait to see

Real-Life Zone A

such a worry / have to, before, between, and, starts / Which team, support, or / to miss, either / Hurry up, left / Maybe, sometime / about going to, home game together / can eat fried chicken while watching, sounds, I can't wait

Wrap Up

which sport do you like, or / How about / big fan of / soccer match, between, Have, heard about / already have, I'm going to see, can't wait / fantastic

Listen & Speak 1 A

M: Which sport do you like? Soccer or basketball?
G: I like soccer more. I play soccer twice a week.

Listen & Speak 1 B

1 G: What are you doing?
  B: I'm looking at a world map.
  G: You checked two countries. Which country would you like to visit first? The U.S. or Mexico?
  B: I want to visit the U.S. I'd like to see a basketball game there.
2 G: I'm thinking about getting a pet. Do you have a pet?
  B: Yes, I do. I have a dog and a cat.
  G: What do you think? Which pet is better for me? A cat or a dog?
  B: Why don't you come to my house someday and play with my pets? Then you can decide.

Listen & Speak 2 A

G: Did you get the tickets?
B: Yes! I can't wait to watch the game.

Listen & Speak 2 B

1 G: Do you want to see my new mountain bike?
  B: Sure. When did you get it?
  G: Yesterday my father bought it for me. Can you come to my house this afternoon?
  B: Of course. I can't wait to see it.
2 B: Don't forget that we're going rock climbing this weekend!
  G: Don't worry. I won't forget.
  B: I'm excited about going. I can't wait.
3 G: Did you hear about Jisu?
  B: What about her? She lives in Canada.
  G: She came back to Korea last month. She wants to see you.
  B: Oh, I can't wait to see her.

Real-Life Zone A

B1: Jiho, why are you in such a hurry?
B2: Hi, Alex! I have to be home before 6:00. The game between the Thunders and the Cobras starts at 6:00.
B1: Oh, are you a baseball fan? Which team do you support? The Cobras or the Thunders?
B2: The Cobras.
B1: Me, too! I don't want to miss the game either.
B2: Hurry up! We only have thirty minutes left.
B1: Okay. Maybe we can watch a game together sometime.
B2: That's a great idea! How about going to the next Cobras home game together?
B1: Okay. They have a game next Saturday. We can eat fried chicken while watching the game!
B2: That sounds great. I can't wait!

Wrap Up

B: Jimin, which sport do you like? Soccer or table tennis?
G: I love table tennis. How about you, Yunho?
B: I like soccer. I'm a big fan of James Hood. He's a

great soccer player.

G: Oh, really? There's a soccer match this weekend between Korea and Turkey. Have you heard about it?

B: Of course. I already have a ticket. I'm going to see the game on Saturday. I can't wait.

G: That's fantastic.

본문 TEST Step 1　　　　　　　　p.47~48

01 Day, Baseball Stadium

02 and, have,game　　　　　03 is at, stadium

04 your first, isn't it

05 excited, can't wait for　　　06 are coming out

07 Which team　08 Over, behind third

09 wearing, because, visiting

10 always wear, dark　　　11 that, rule

12 Home, bright, visiting, dark　13 Why, that

14 There, interesting, about

15 past, wash, every

16 wearing, hide, dirt　　　17 was, good idea

18 warming up　19 your favorite　20 Number 77

21 What does, mean

22 choose, they like　　　23 know what

24 determined by, batting order　25 there, no, with

26 is about to　　27 looks anxious

28 favorite, at bat

29 has hit, runs already

30 hits, more, be, season

31 batter misses several　　32 has, full count

33 waiting for, pitch　　　34 RUN, HOME

35 Crack, flies fast　　　　36 is going, gone

본문 TEST Step 2　　　　　　　　p.49~50

01 A Day, Baseball Stadium

02 have a game　03 is at, baseball stadium

04 your first time, isn't it

05 excited, can't wait for, to start　06 are coming out

07 Which team　08 Over there, behind third base

09 are wearing, because, visiting team

10 visiting team, wear a dark color 11 rule

12 have bright uniforms, dark uniforms

13 Why　　　　　14 There, an interesting story

15 In the past, wash their uniforms after every game

16 started wearing, to hide the dirt

17 a good idea

18 are warming up

---

19 your favorite player　　　20 Number

21 What does, number mean

22 choose, they like　　　23 You know what

24 were determined by the players' batting order

25 there were no, with　　　26 is about to

27 looks anxious　28 Your favorite, at bat

29 has hit　　　30 hits one more, this season

31 misses several balls

32 has a full count

33 waiting for, next pitch　　34 HOME RUN

35 Crack, flies fast　　　　36 is going, gone

본문 TEST Step 3　　　　　　　　p.51~52

1 야구 경기장에서의 하루

2 오늘 천둥 대 코브라 게임이 있다.

3 지훈이네 가족은 야구 경기장에 있다.

4 지훈: 지안아, 네가 야구 경기장에 온 건 이번이 처음이야, 그렇지 않니?

5 지안: 응, 나 아주 흥분돼. 나는 경기가 빨리 시작했으면 좋겠어.

6 아빠: 봐, 선수들이 지금 나오고 있어!

7 지안: 어떤 팀이 천둥이야?

8 지훈: 저기, 3루 뒤

9 그들은 원정 팀이기 때문에 어두운 회색 유니폼을 입고 있어.

10 지안: 원정 팀은 항상 어두운 색을 입어?

11 지훈: 응, 그게 규칙이야.

12 홈팀은 밝은 유니폼을 입고 원정팀은 어두운 유니폼을 입어.

13 지안: 왜?

14 엄마: 그것에 대한 흥미로운 이야기가 있단다.

15 과거에는 원정 팀이 매 경기 후 유니폼을 세탁할 수가 없었어.

16 그래서 그들은 때를 숨기기 위해 어두운 색을 입기 시작했지.

17 지안: 하하하! 좋은 생각이었네요!

18 선수들이 몸을 풀고 있다.

19 지안: 가장 좋아하는 선수가 누구야?

20 지훈: 77번.

21 지안: 그 숫자는 무엇을 의미해?

22 지훈: 음... 선수들이 원하는 번호를 선택해.

23 아빠: 그거 알아?

24 과거에는 번호가 선수들의 타순에 의해 결정되었단다.

25 지훈: 77번 선수가 없었다는 뜻이네요!

26 이제 지훈이의 가장 좋아하는 선수가 막 공을 치려고 한다.

27 지훈이는 불안해 보인다.

28 지안: 오빠가 가장 좋아하는 선수가 타석에 서네.

29 지훈: 응. 그는 올해 이미 21개의 홈런을 쳤어.

30 그가 오늘 하나를 더 치면, 그는 이번 시즌 홈런 리더가 될 거야.

31 타자는 여러 개의 공을 놓친다.

32 이제 그는 풀카운트가 되었다.

33 그는 다음 투구를 기다리고 있다.

34 지훈: 홈런! 홈런!

35 땅! 공은 빠르게 날아간다.

36 그것은 가고, 가고, 가고, 사라져 버렸다!

31 The batter misses several balls.

32 Now he has a full count.

33 He is waiting for the next pitch.

34 Jihun: HOME RUN! HOME RUN!

35 Crack! The ball flies fast.

36 It is going, going, going, gone!

1 A Day at the Baseball Stadium

2 Today the Thunders and the Cobras have a game.

3 Jihun's family is at the baseball stadium.

4 Jihun: Jian, this is your first time to come to the baseball stadium, isn't it?

5 Jian: Yes, I'm so excited. I can't wait for the game to start.

6 Dad: Look, the players are coming out now!

7 Jian: Which team is the Thunders?

8 Jihun: Over there, behind third base.

9 They are wearing dark gray uniforms because they are the visiting team.

10 Jian: Does the visiting team always wear a dark color?

11 Jihun: Yes, that's the rule.

12 Home teams have bright uniforms and visiting teams have dark uniforms.

13 Jian: Why is that?

14 Mom: There is an interesting story about that.

15 In the past, visiting teams could not wash their uniforms after every game.

16 So they started wearing dark colors to hide the dirt.

17 Jian: Hahaha! That was a good idea!

18 The players are warming up.

19 Jian: Who's your favorite player?

20 Jihun: Number 77.

21 Jian: What does the number mean?

22 Jihun: Hmm.... Players choose a number they like.

23 Dad: You know what?

24 In the past, the numbers were determined by the players' batting order.

25 Jian: That means there were no players with number 77!

26 Now, Jihun's favorite player is about to bat.

27 Jihun looks anxious.

28 Jian: Your favorite player is at bat.

29 Jihun: Yes. He has hit 21 home runs already this year.

30 If he hits one more today, he will be the home run leader this season.

Real-Life Zone B

1. Which sport, like, or

2. going to, with, this weekend, can't wait

Writing Workshop

1. Marathon Runner

2. Born, August

3. Nationality

4. was known as, international sports competitions

5. preparing to run, found out, did not fit, decided to run, without shoes

6. felt pain during, as the winner

7. one of, wasn't he

Wrap Up

1. Middle School Sports Day

2. will be held, on Wednesday, June

3. will be various, such as

4. wil also, table tennis

5. sounds like, doesn't it

Real-Life Zone B

1. A: Which sport do you like? Basketball or soccer?

2. B: I like basketball. I'm going to play it with my friends this weekend. I can't wait.

Writing Workshop

1. Abebe Bikila Marathon Runner

2. Born : August 7, 1932

3. Nationality: Ethiopia

4. Speciality: He was known as a marathon winner at the Rome and Tokyo international sports competitions.

5. When he was preparing to run the marathon in Rome, he found out that his shoes did not fit well, so he decided to run the race without shoes .

6. He felt pain during the race, but he finished the race as the winner.

7. He was one of the greatest runners in the world, wasn't he?

1. Sarang Middle School Sports Day
2. Sarang Middle School Sports Day will be held on the school playing field on Wednesday, June 15.
3. There will be various games such as baseball and soccer.
4. There wil also be table tennis.
5. It sounds like fun, doesn't it?

적중 100

영어 기출 문제집

정답 및 해설

시사 | 송미정